BIOTECHNOLOGY OF WASTE TREATMENT AND EXPLOITATION

BIOTECHNOLOGY OF WASTE TREATMENT AND EXPLOITATION

J. M. SIDWICK
Ashact Ltd, Great Missenden, Bucks

and

R. S. HOLDOM, B.Sc., Ph.D.
University of Manchester Institute of Science and Technology

ELLIS HORWOOD LIMITED
Publishers · Chichester

Halsted Press: a division of
JOHN WILEY & SONS
New York · Chichester · Brisbane · Toronto

First published in 1987 by
ELLIS HORWOOD LIMITED
Market Cross House, Cooper Street,
Chichester, West Sussex, PO19 1EB, England
The publisher's colophon is reproduced from James Gillison's drawing of the ancient Market Cross, Chichester.

Distributors:
Australia and New Zealand:
JACARANDA WILEY LIMITED
GPO Box 859, Brisbane, Queensland 4001, Australia
Canada:
JOHN WILEY & SONS CANADA LIMITED
22 Worcester Road, Rexdale, Ontario, Canada
Europe and Africa:
JOHN WILEY & SONS LIMITED
Baffins Lane, Chichester, West Sussex, England
North and South America and the rest of the world:
Halsted Press: a division of
JOHN WILEY & SONS
605 Third Avenue, New York, NY 10158, USA

British Library Cataloguing in Publication Data
Sidwick, J. M.
Biotechnology of waste treatment and exploitation. —
(Water and wastewater technology)
1. Sewage — Purification
I. Title II. Holdom, R. S. III. Series
628.3 TD745

Library of Congress CIP data available

ISBN 0–85312–917–7 (Ellis Horwood Limited)
ISBN 0–470–21031–1 (Halsted Press)

Phototypeset in Times by Ellis Horwood Limited
Printed and bound in Great Britain by Richard Clay Ltd., Chichester, W. Sussex

Table of contents

Foreword

by
Dr Theo Mann,
Chairman, Working Party on Environmental Biotechnology of the European Federation of Biotechnology

Biotechnology is today an area of high technology. It is also an area that is probably more multi-disciplinary than most because it has its foundations in a number of disciplines. These include biology, microbiology, genetics, chemistry and chemical engineering. But this was not always so.

Historically, biotechnology was an art rather than a science. This is exemplified by the old fermentation industries of, for example, the manufacture of wine, beer and sauerkraut. The techniques of manufacture were well known and reproducible but the mechanisms were not. But then the two scientific fields of microbiology and biochemistry, associated with great names such as Koch, Fleming, Florey, Pasteur and Chaine, developed rapidly. Today many, if not all, of the essential elements of the metabolic processes that take place in micro-organisms are well understood. And chemical engineers have been successful in applying the knowledge by developing and optimizing processes to give high yields in short periods of time and hence in relatively small reactors.

Modern biotechnological processes are commonly perceived as being associated with the synthesis of specific products such as antibiotics. It may not always be understood that the conversion of potentially polluting substances to forms harmless to the environment falls within the same definition. Thus, environmental biotechnology is concerned with the protection of the environment—water, land and air.

Wastewater treatment is a good example of the thesis that biotechnology started as an art rather than as a science. It was not until 1907 that Dunbar recognized that micro-organisms played an important part in the biological degradation and mineralization of the organic compounds found in wastewater. But, long before that time, natural processes such as those used on sewage farms and, later in contact beds and then in trickling filters, were well known and widely used. The activated-sludge process was only developed in 1912, in England.

The current high level of understanding of the mechanisms applied to wastewater treatment has resulted from the collaboration of microbiologists, biochemists, sanitary engineers and chemical engineers. This collaboration has led to the construction of many technically advanced and highly successful sewage-treatment plants. These plants generally use aerobic processes for the degradation and mineralization of the organic compounds in the sewage and anaerobic processes for the stabilization and mineralization of sludges, although, and conversely, anaerobic systems are also used for liquid wastewater treatment, particularly for the treatment of strong organic industrial wastewaters, and sludges are stabilized aerobically.

Whilst much is known about treatment processes there is a need for more research in the future if a full understanding of some of the processes is to be gained to permit the application of some advanced processes. Two examples of problems still to be solved are:

- How can biological degradation be controlled so that potentially polluting materials are not just mineralized but are also used to synthesize valuable by-products?
- Which is the time-determining step for the biological conversion of compounds — transport through the cell wall or membrane, or the actual metabolic process in the cell?

There is much scope for better trans-national co-operation in such research and in the transfer of technology to its users. Also, there needs to be more sharing of experience in pilot and large-scale applications of biotechnology, particularly in solving environmental problems which usually do not respect national boundary lines. There is a relatively new European organization trying to improve the situation on all these fronts.

The European Federation of Biotechnology was established some eight years ago. It is a forum for the interchange of information and for liaison generally in the field of biotechnology in Europe. The Federation has, as one of its aims, the setting up of ad hoc working parties to study particular topics or areas relevant to its interests. In 1981 a Working Party on Environmental Biotechnology was formed. By the end of 1986 it had met nine times. One of its main objectives is to collect together information to help answer outstanding questions in environmental biotechnology, to evaluate it and to identify new questions that might arise as time passes.

This book is also an attempt by the Working Party to disseminate knowledge on environmental biotechnology to a broad readership. It is sponsored by the Working Party and many of the chapters are written by Working Party members. As chairman of the Working Party I am pleased to commend it to all those working in the field of environmental biotechnology, not only in Europe but also more internationally.

Theo Mann,
Chairman,
Working Party on Environmental Biotechnology,
European Federation of Biotechnology

Introduction

J. M. Sidwick and **R. S. Holdom**

Biotechnology is by definition a multidisciplinary subject. However, as one of the many branches of biotechnology, Environmental Biotechnology (EBT) is perhaps unique in the number of different professions which have become involved during its long history, which goes back many years before the subject became known by the modern title of EBT. Civil Engineers, Chemical Engineers, Microbiologists, Chemists, Sanitation Engineers and even Mechanical Engineers can all evidence their contributions to the foundation technologies including municipal and industrial effluent treatment, water purification, composting and biogas fermentations. This professional diversity has created unusual difficulties of communication, which to a large extent have been a barrier to more rapid and effective technology transfer in this field [1]. Thus it is not easy for water treatment engineers to stay abreast of recent advances in molecular biology and to begin the planning of a new generation of process plant based on genetically engineered microbes. Equally it is not easy for molecular biologists to target their skills towards solving mass transfer or downstream processing problems which engineers describe more by mathematical formulae than conventional language.

This book is an attempt to bridge some of the communication gaps. Each author has tried to present the current state-of-the-art in his specialised field in a way that can be understood by the relatively non-specialist reader. At the same time, through smaller print sections in the text and extensive references, the authors have provided a level of detail to interest the more advanced readers. The Chapter on the applications of molecular biology particularly highlights the attempt to present complex subject matter in a somewhat prophetic style to stimulate greater interest and, hopefully, the earlier uptake of research advances in genetic manipulation towards better solutions to our environmental problems. No single author could claim technical competence in all the topics covered. Also no single country could claim that it leads the field in all areas of technology represented. This book is therefore multi-authored by experts from a range of countries in Europe.

One chapter describes significant advances being made in Developing Countries where different climates, economic and social factors have influenced the choice of technologies used.

It is noteworthy that the title of the book includes the word 'Exploitation'. Whilst waste treatment relates mainly to the traditional community service role of EBT, waste exploitation on the other hand, promotes the idea that EBT could be transformed from a resource-consuming service activity to a resource-conserving or producing industry. In such a scenario there will need to be more emphasis on the business opportunities for conversion of wastes into useful products or for by-product recovery, with financial profit in mind. Many of the developments described in this book could satisfy the profit motive given a better strategic framework by legislators who, perhaps more than in any other area of biotechnology, can make a great contribution to the creation of the long term market stability needed in this field. Investment in research and technology transfer would then be more assured.

In 1983 the European Commission's FAST programme (Forecasting and Assessment in Science & Technology) funded a Workshop Study of the future prospects for EBT and the report [1] predicts that ".....we may see the new style EBT making real contributions to economic development, energy and resource conservation, and employment, while continuing the vital function of environmental protection. These goals will only be realised in practice if we start from a foundation of technologies which are judged to be feasible now or in the near future, given the right research and development. The ultimate output from investment in this more strategic R & D should be a wider choice of good, robust processes available to those will be making the industrial, financial and political decisions in the future". This book represents a description of both the foundation technologies and the current research directions from which tomorrow's innovations will spring. The scale and trans-national characteristics of environmental problems are a real challenge to our capacity for cooperation and good communication within the scientific disciplines which can help solve the problems. Hopefully this book will appeal to a good cross section of scientists, engineers and even to those administrators whose decisions may affect resources or the general business climate allowing EBT to flourish.

REFERENCE

[1] Holdom, R. S., Sidwick, J. M. and Wheatley, A. D. (1983). Environmental Biotechnology: Future Prospects. Vol. 1. Published as Occasional Paper No. 50, Summary Report and Recommendations from the Versailles Workshop, 6–8 October 1982, by FAST, DG XIII, Commission of the European Communities, 200 Rue de la Loi, B-1049, Brussels.

1

Environmental biotechnology in Europe: Community activities

M. P. Ferranti
Commission of the European Community, Brussels

1.1 INTRODUCTION

Biological treatment of organic waste is an old and well-established technology which has long furnished many products and services and contributed to conservation through recycling of materials for different final uses.

The effective treatment of waste is an important process, especially in the highly industrialized and populous countries of Europe, where waste disposal has become a problem as a consequence of intensive farming, the development of agro-industry, and the growth of urban centres. A breakdown of organic waste produced in Europe is given in Table 1.1 and Fig. 1.1.

Any change in the composition of waste, which often includes polluting materials like heavy metals or toxic chemicals, may make necessary the development of new, more efficient treatment processes in respect of conversion rates and separation of undesirable components. Biotechnology, because of the selectivity of its processes, can play a substantial role in solving the environmental problems caused by waste.

1.2 COMMUNITY ACTIVITIES ON WASTE TREATMENT

Within the framework of the Community Action Programme on the Environment the European Community has defined a waste-management policy consisting of a set of actions to be taken at Community level to prevent environmental pollution from waste.

The general aims of the Programme are:

(1) to reduce the quantity of non-recoverable waste and to prevent it arising;
(2) to recover, recycle and reuse waste for raw materials and energy;
(3) to manage non-recoverable waste and dispose of it in a harmless manner.

Table 1.1 — Biomass Wastes in EC member states (excluding Ireland and Greece) [1].

	Wood (forestry)	Bark production	Wood processing	Wood crop	Straw cereal	Leaves beet	Leaves veg.	Manure	Food wastes	MSW SP	Micel-laneous	Total
(1) Gross ODM (Mt/a)	29.22	3.52	9.54	5.47	105.33	9.89	12.2	78.89	M 1.02 W 2.10 S 5.19	33.48 SP 10	4.17	309.10
(2) WC (%)	Range 37–18	Range 40–80	14	18	18 60	83	50	90	M 20 W 94 S 6–40	25 SP 6	95	–
(3) Availability factor (%)	35	100	0	10	30	28	50	16	M 0 W 20 S 70	72 6	78	34
(4) Available ODM (Mt/a) Line (1) × Line (3)	10.2	3.52	0	0.55	33.44	2.74	6.1	12.28	W 0.41 S 3.63	24.34 SP 0.57	3.26	101.04
(5) Mt_{OE}/a	4.82	1.12	–	0.24	13.71	0.75	1.71	4.57	S 0.73	8.75 SP 0.20	1.14	37.74

WC, water content. ODM, organic dry material. Mt_{OE}/a, million tons oil equivalent per year. M, molasses. W, whey. S, slop, drugs, skins. MSW, municipal solid waste. SP, separated paper.

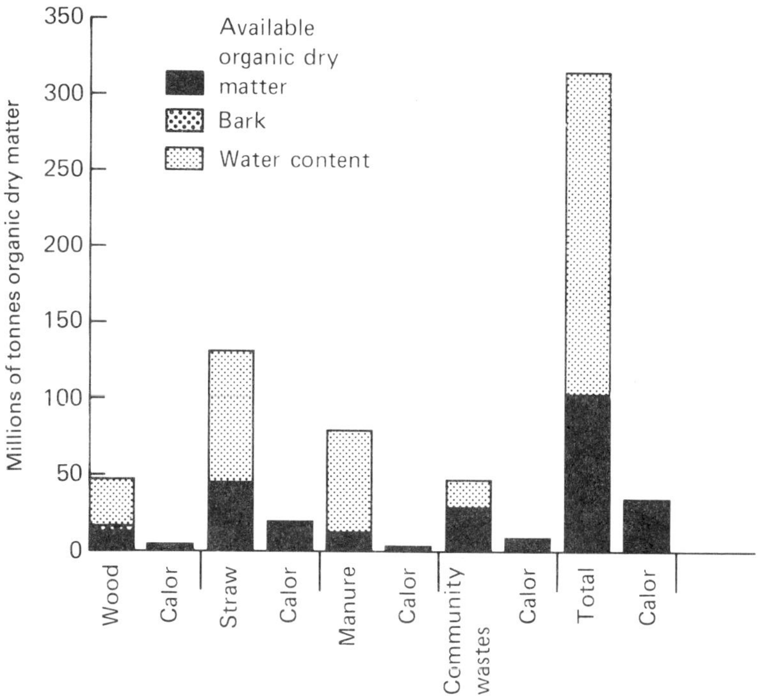

Fig. 1.1 — Biomass wastes in the EC member states (excluding Ireland and Greece) [1]. Calor: calorific value as millions of tonnes oil equivalent per year.

This policy is the responsibility of the Directorate General for Environment and is based mainly on regulations dealing with different aspects of waste management and with specific types of waste. Common procedures and, where necessary, regulations are of fundamental importance to the satisfactory development of an internal common market by preserving the environment and at the same time enhancing the quality of life in the Community.

Research results are an essential input to legislation and help to identify the possibilities and the limits of the various procedures proposed for waste management. Research is the responsibility of the Directorate General for Science, Research and Development where biological treatment of waste is the subject of a number of R&D programmes in different fields. This reflects the multi-disciplinary nature and complexity of environmental biotechnology.

The Community R&D programmes dealing with biotechnology in waste treatment are:

(1) Recycling of waste: research area on fermentation and hydrolysis.
(2) Energy from biomass: use of waste to produce energy.
(3) Environment:
   - biological treatment of water pollutants; use of sludges in agriculture;
   - methods for assessing the toxicity of waste of human beings and other animals.

(4) Biotechnology Action Programme:
   - basic research on development and evaluation of bioreactors for depollution and detoxification;
   - evaluation of toxicological effects and biological activity of molecules.
(5) Funding of demonstration projects on:
   - 'energy from waste'; responsibility of Directorate General for Energy.

The Community research actions are carried out by:

- contract research, i.e. funding up to 50 per cent of the total cost of projects selected for priority areas of an R&D programme;
- concerted or co-ordinated actions, i.e. the Community co-ordinates activities funded at national level, promotes complementary experiments and disseminates findings and information.

The Community research actions have the advantage, when compared with the activities of other international organizations dealing with waste problems, of being able to intervene with funding on priority areas defined and agreed as a result of a comprehensive discussion among experts and authorities in the member states.

Furthermore, by means of projects carried out in collaboration between two or more member states, and also between industry and research institutions, 'trans-frontier cross-fertilization' is promoted and an attempt is made to establish a Community of Science and Technology.

During the past five years, by means of regularly organized contractors' meetings, international conferences and working parties on subjects worthy of common action, developments in the field of waste treatment were followed closely within the framework of the Community R&D programmes.

In the following sections the conclusions drawn and the recommendations made for future work in the three main fields of organic waste treatment are outlined.

1.3 ANAEROBIC DIGESTION (BIOMETHANATION)

A considerable research effort was dedicated to this field: about 30 contracts were signed in the framework of the recycling and energy from biomass programmes. At present a major effort is being undertaken at demonstration level. The Directorate General for Energy is financing about 50 demonstration projects on biomethanation.

A survey on the state of the art in Europe on biogas plant [2] was requested by the Commission (see also Table 1.2). In this survey 564 biogas plants were listed and classified according to the type of digested feedstock; 27 representative plants were described. In general anaerobic digestion is a widespread technology. However, a series of outstanding problems was identified during the activities in the past programme, which are outlined below.

Further applications of this technique for the detoxification and deodorization of domestic and agricultural refuse and troublesome wastewaters need to be explored.

One of the fundamental aspects of biomethanation is interspecies hydrogen transfer. Very little is yet known about the role of 'obligate proton-reducing bacteria'

Table 1.2 — Geographical distribution of full- and pilot-scale biogas plants in the European Community and in Switzerland according to the type of waste treated [2].

Country	Type of waste				
	Agricultural	Energy crops	Domestic residues (landfills)	Industrial	Total
	Full- + pilot-scale	Pilot-scale	Full- + pilot-scale	Full- + pilot-scale	Full- + pilot-scale
Belgium	21 + 4			6 + 4	27 + 8
Denmark	22 + 1			3 + 3	25 + 4
FRG	75		10	12	97
France	62 + 12		2 + 3	10 + 5	74 + 20
Greece	3 + 1			1	4 + 1
Ireland	2 + 3			1 + 3	3 + 6
Italy	58 + 5	1	1	11 + 2	70 + 8
Netherlands	21 + 1		3 + 8	22 + 1	46 + 10
UK	12 + 9		7 + 2	3 + 2	22 + 13
Switzerland	102 + 6				102 + 6
Total	378 + 42	1	23 + 13	69 + 20	470 + 76

or acetogenic bacteria, and virtually nothing is known about their biology. The importance of micro-nutrients should be assessed, as well as the way in which inhibitions develop and act. High-rate biomethanation will be improved if a better knowledge of the ecology of mixed cultures can be obtained.

It is important to develop new processes which allow the treatment of waste outside the usual range of concentration — either very dilute or very concentrated — while maintaining good performance. The development of continuous high-rate biomethanation processes based on either dry processes or two-stage processes is important for the treatment of solid substrates. Separation of competing reaction stages needs to be researched. Conditions for using mixed substrates need to be better defined, as well as the conditions under which it is possible to switch from one substrate to another. The separation of the liquid containing the useful metabolites from residual solids has to be improved.

There is a need for a comparative evaluation of long-term reliability of equipment of different design in order to eliminate bottlenecks in the construction and operation of digesters. This applies in particular to completely mixed conventional farm digesters. The experience of the water industries may be of assistance in overcoming problems of unreliability.

It will also be necessary to develop a way of monitoring the stability and reliability of digesters. This could be achieved by developing models with a view to the automated operation of biomethanation processes.

Liquid–solid separation devices are important for both purposes: for composting the solids and possibly also for further treatment of the liquid phase. Cheap reliable separators need to be developed for small low-technology installations (farms) or for more sophisticated large digesters.

The economics of biomethanation are still unclear. Co-ordinated monitoring of digesters, with systems analysis, would given a clearer view of the profitability of biomethanation units.

Chapter 6 describes in more detail the recent progress on the microbiological and biochemical fronts.

1.4 FERMENTATION AND HYDROLYSIS

Cellulosic and ligno-cellulosic materials can find an appropriate use for production of key organic chemicals via fermentation-based technologies as an alternative to conventional production from petrochemicals. However, a major barrier to immediate increased use of biomass from waste is the fact that there is no proven economical conversion process. Chapter 10, which includes a detailed account of the chemistry of ligno-cellulosic materials, further details the problems and the opportunities. At present, biological degradation of the three major wood components — lignin, cellulose and hemicellulose — is a very dynamic field of R&D where some progress is being reported from the best laboratories.

The economic production of chemicals from renewable resources requires an integrated biochemical, chemical and microbiological approach. Research on this field is carried out in various community R&D programmes.

The utilization of lignins from new processes for the fractionation and refining of biomass should be improved in such as way as to take advantage of their macromolecular structure and their reactivity immediately after isolation, i.e. in their polymeric forms.

Since biological processes are more selective than the equivalent chemical processes, they make it possible to obtain products for specific uses, although yields are still not very high and reaction rates are slow.

Performance chemicals, with a low market volume and a high price, should preferably be obtained by means of enzymatic processes. Such processes are particularly suited to the manufacture of highly specific and special compounds such as stereoisomers, biodegradable compounds and food substitutes/additives where biocompatibility is vital.

Fundamental research should be continued in an effort to achieve a better understanding of reactions and reaction mechanisms. Much remains to be studied on the potential available in nature for micro-organisms to attack selectively different kinds of organic molecules. Isolation and screening of new strains of micro-organisms will provide an inexhaustible source of possibilities for the biodegradation or organic material.

1.5 COMPOSTING

Composting is a very important way of recycling organic matter, particularly nitrogenous materials for use as fertilizer.

The activities in the first Recycling Programme provided a fuller understanding of organic wastes as regards both quality and quantity.

An assessment of their potential for use should be made as a function of various compost specifications and quality, market requirements and economics. From this the potential for compost production could be worked out, taking into account local and national problems such as specific waste substrates or demand.

Heavy metal content is an important problem as regards compost made from urban waste. Methods should be developed to improve the quality of urban compost by removing mineral components (glass) or heavy metals.

The engineering aspect of composting is apparently well developed since many plants produce compost. However, it is noticeable that the compost produced is not always of good quality and many problems remain to be solved. This topic is considered in more depth in Chapter 13.

1.6 ECONOMIC FACTORS

At the present time, considerable emphasis is put upon avoiding pollution created by waste and protecting the environment. It would, however, be a fundamental mistake to seek a panacea that is a single technological answer to the waste problem. The combination of both aerobic and anaerobic processes can be used for waste treatment. The criteria on which to base the complementary use of these processes need to be developed. Guidelines will have to be worked out based on these criteria, the characteristics of the waste to be treated, the aims of the treatment, the scale of the operation and overall economics. Changes in priorities depend very much on the arrival of new knowledge and developments in the field. Economics of processing wastes is an important factor in promotion and development of the possible technologies. However, reliable economic estimates are difficult to obtain in many cases. Gieseler [1] has provided useful indicators in relation to the production of chemical raw materials from biomass by different processes; these are summarized in Table 1.3. Meanwhile legislation is likely to remain the primary motivating factor in the wider adoption of existing technologies, followed by cost of processing as the incentive to improve these processes and to search for new ones.

REFERENCES

[1] Gieseler, G. (1985). *Evaluation of the Potential of Organic Residues in the EC with regard to Availability and Conversion to Basic Chemicals*, study committed to Dornier-System in the framework of the EC Recycling Programme, July.

[2] Demuynck, M., Nyns, E. J. and Palz, W. (1984). *Biogas Plants in Europe*, Solar Energy R&D in the EC, series E, Vol. 6, D. Reidel, EUR 9096.

[3] Kovaly, K. A.. *Biomass Process Handbook*, Technical Insights Inc., PO Box 1304, Fort Lee, New Jersey.

[4] Reitter, F. J. and Reichert, M. *Verwertung von Biomasse*, Verlag C. F. Müller, Karlsruhe.

[5] Fathi-Afshar, S. and Rudd, D. F. (1980). *Biomass Ethanol as a Chemical Feedstock in the United States*, Biotechnology and Bioengineering Vol. XXII, pp. 677–679.

[6] Jülich, KFA (1983). *Bereitstellung und Verwertung van Lignocellulosen*, Workshop, Jülich 21–22 Nov.

[7] Moller, A. (1982). Straw mix: a system for utilisation of straw and molasses as feed. *UNEP Industry and Env.*, **5** (2).

Table 1.3 — Chemical raw materials from biomass: economy of production, 1984 [1].

Process (Yield)	Raw material	Product By-product	Capacity (t/a)	Production costs ECU/t (base case)	Cost/price relation f^* value	Remarks [Ref.]
Methanization	Municipal solid waste on landfill	Methane	1860–11 200	76	0.24–0.47	[3]
Oxidation (0.88)	Dextrose	Ca gluconate	5 000	2139	0.4	[3]
Alkaline oxidation (0.0625)	Ligno-sulphonate	Vanillin	500	9678	0.54	[3]
Acid hydrolysis (biol. 0.39)	Deciduous wood	Glucose Xylose	22 500 7 000	200 1000	–	Two-step, continuous [4]
Fermentation (0.484)	Glucose (biol.)	Ethanol	10 900	509	0.67	Solid-bed [4]
Hydrolysis (0.4)	Molasses	Citric acid	10 000	1685	0.75	[3]
Fermentation (0.45)	Molasses	Lactic acid	1500	1959	0.75	[3]
Distillation (0.29)	Wood	Charcoal Acetic acid Methanol	7500 900 315	138	0.75	Relation to wood [3]
Acid hydrolysis + fermentation (0.19)	Coniferous wood	Ethanol Furfural	30 000 1 950	699–856	0.9–1.13	France, FRG [3]
Fermentation	Whey supplemented with	Yeast	3 300 12 850	613–684	1	Pollution control [5]
Prehydrolysis by steam (DDE)	Straw	Roughage Glue (50% component)	21 000 2 340	250–293	1	[6]

Digestion (mix)	Straw	Roughage	2 700	97	1.07	[7]
Dehydration (0.58)	Xylose (biol.)	Furfural	4 070	2000	1.1	[4]
Prehydroloysis by acid and steam	Straw	Roughage for ruminants (breeding)	5 000			[8]
(+ drying + pelleting)				110 (165)	1.1 (1.65)	
Fermentation (0.22)	Molasses	Ethanol	32 000	880	1.16	[3]
Hydration (0.95)	Dextrose	Sorbitol	6 000	1117	1.21	[3]
Enzymatic hydrolysis + fermentation 0.24	Cellulosic	Ethanol	145 000	948	1.25	[3]
Acid hydrolysis (0.4)	Wood	Glucose	20 000	400	1.26	[3]
Acid hydrolysis + fermentation (0.14)	Deciduous wood	Ethanol Furfural	26 500 1 850	963–1048	1.27–1.38	France, FRG [9]
Hydrolysis + dehydration (0.096)	Bagasse	Furfural Acetic acid Formic acid	5 000 3 000 350	2396	1.3	[3]
Fermentation (0.18)	Molasses	Acetone/butanol Acetone Ethanol	10 000/6 000 3 000 1 000	1419	1.63	[3]
Gasification/synt. (0.4)	Wood	Methanol	33 000 (66 000)	450 (355)	1.9 (1.5)	[9, 1]
Gasification (0.7)	Mun.s.waste	Gas CO/H_2 = 1.65	50 000	145	2–4	Zero cost [3]
Methanization (0.018)	Manure	Methane (60%) CO_2 (40%)	1 350 (as 100% CH_4)	461	1.5–2.1 (1)	[3], [1] if high-credit fertilizer by-product

ECU: European Currency Unit. Rates of exchange vary according to current international exchange rates. One ECU is approximately £0.68, DM 2.11, FFr 6.87 or Lire 1454.

[8] Gieseler, G., Rauschenberger, H. and Wagner, B. (1983). *Clean Production Technologies, Mexico*, Vol. 3, Pulp and Paper Industry.
[9] Staneff, Th. *et al.* (1983). *Systemanalytische Untersuchung zur Nutzung nachwachsender Rohstoffe*, BML.

2

Process intensification

M. Henze
Department of Environmental Engineering, Technical University of Denmark

2.1 INTRODUCTION

To intensify biological waste-treatment processes means to increase the specific rate of conversion. The basic aim of increasing the specific conversion rate is to make the process more profitable.

There are two means of intensifying biotechnological processes: one is to increase the conversion rate per unit mass of biomass, organisms and enzymes; the other is to increase the volumetric conversion rate. Together, these two means are powerful tools for making biotechnology profitable and competitive.

Within limits of the characteristics of the microbial species in question, a temperature increase raises the biochemical conversion rate and an excess of key nutrients usually ensures maximum growth rate. Retention or recycle of biomass in a reactor also increases the overall process rate and various techniques have been developed to achieve this.

The general approaches which can be applied to intensify biotechnological processes for waste treatment and exploitation are covered in this chapter. The basic kinetics and rate expressions are described more fully in Chapter 4. Table 2.1

Table 2.1 — Specific rates.

Type of specific rate	Symbol	Dimension	Typical unit
Growth rate	u	T^{-1}	d^{-1}
Volumetric reaction rate	r_v	$M\,T^{-1}\,L^{-3}$	kg COD m^{-3} d^{-1}
Mass reaction rate	r_x	$M_i\,T^{-1}\,M_x^{-1}$	kg COD kg^{-1} VS d^{-1}

indicates the specific conversion rates which are relevant in waste-treatment processes. The ultimate goal can be the production of biomass or some compound, when the substrate is often in excess and not limiting. Process intensification is important here in order to get as high a production as possible per volume of reactor. Another situation can be the conversion of waste materials where low-concentration substrates are limiting. Some waste-treatment processes, like biomethanation, may have both these ultimate goals. Here the production of methane, simultaneously with the reduction of waste strength, may turn the engineer schizophrenic, because he may want a high volumetric specific methane production, but at the same time a reduction of the waste strength to low values. This illustrates that in many cases high specific rates are not necessarily applicable. Fig. 2.1 shows the two basic situations

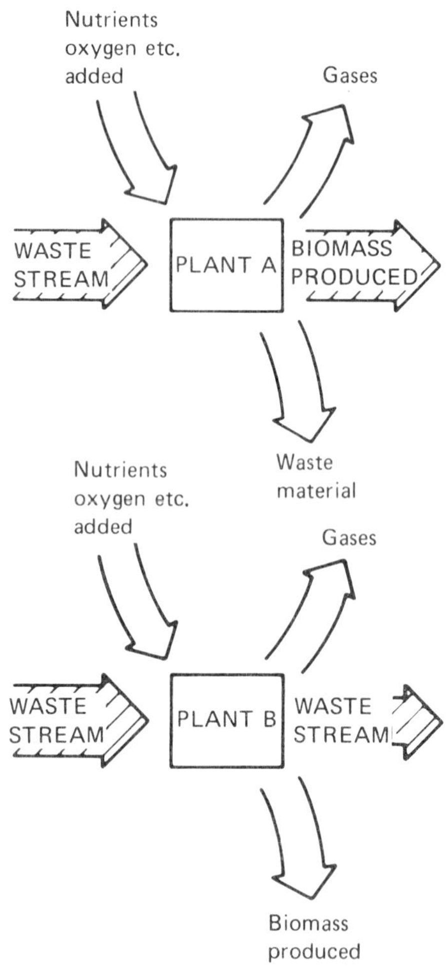

Fig. 2.1 — The two different plant approaches. The ultimate goal can be the production of valuable material (biomass, SCP, etc.) as in plant A or the reduction of the waste stream (wastewater treatment, composting, etc.) as in plant B.

when limitations to process intensification may often be found. Plant B is a good example because of the restrictions imposed upon the treated waste stream in terms both of amounts and of composition.

2.2 PHYSICAL REACTOR DESIGN

The physical design of the reactor and the method of its operation play significant roles with respect to the overall reaction rate. The various means for process intensification are listed in Table 2.2. They are discussed below. A method which

Table 2.2 — Effect of various physical means for process intensification.

Method	Possible changes in	
	Mass reaction rate, r_x	Volumetric reaction rate, r_v
Hydraulic regime (plug flow)	None or increase	None or increase
Batch operation	None or increase	None or increase
Aeration, mixing for ideal mix	Increase or decrease	Increase or decrease
Aeration, increased gas transfer	Increase	Increase
Mixing for ideal mix	Increase or decrease	Increase or decrease
Mixing to increase mass transfer	Increase	Increase
Recycle of biomass	None or decrease	Increase
Carrier for biomass	None or decrease	Increase
Temperature	Increase	Increase

increases mass reaction rate inherently also increases the volumetric reaction rate. The opposite is not the case, as methods which increase biomass concentration in a reactor do not influence the mass reaction rate, at least not positively.

The hydraulic regime is important for the mass reaction rate in processes which are not of zero order with respect to the substrate. Most waste-treatment processes operate at low substrate concentrations where the reaction order is half, first or of the Monod type (Table 2.3). For such reactions a plug-flow reactor is advantageous from

Table 2.3— Various reaction orders in waste-treatment processes

Reactor order	Rate expression
Zero	$rx = k0$
Half	$rx = k\frac{1}{2}C^{\frac{1}{2}}$
First	$rx = k1C$
Monod	$r_x = k_m\, C/(C+K_C)$

a mass reaction rate point of view. In chemical engineering, or waste-treatment engineering, plug-flow reactors are not common because of problems with operation and control of these reactor types, especially when external supplies of substrates (like oxygen) are needed. If very low effluent concentrations are required then an ideal mixed-flow pattern often means a major restriction in reaction rate. This can be partly overcome by a series of ideally mixed reactors (cascade-type reactor) where the reaction rate is gradually reduced in each step (Fig. 2.2).

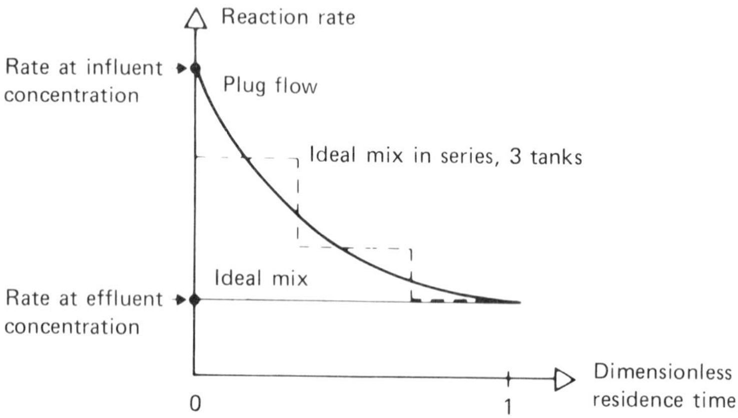

Fig. 2.2 — Reaction rates for various reactor flow regimes. To obtain identical effluent concentrations, different residence time is needed in the three reactors. The residence time increases from the plug-flow reactor via the ideal mix in series reactor to the ideal-mix reactor.

Batch operation of reactors is used for many industrial applications. The chemical and biological phenomena occurring in the reactor are identical to those of a plug-flow reactor; this means that there are problems with control and the environmental changes in the system.

Increased gas transfer will often increase the reaction rate. In wastewater-treatment processes, oxygen mass transfer is often the limiting factor in the overall reaction rate (Fig. 2.3). An adequate oxygen supply is a key factor in many biotechnological processes [2,3] and this provides good opportunities for astute equipment manufacturers. But, as shown in Table 2.4, basically only a few factors can be changed.

Efficient mixing might increase mass transfer and the effective volume of a reactor, thereby increasing the overall reaction rate. It can, at the same time, decrease the basic reaction rates by reducing the substrate concentration. Zero-order reactions will not be influenced by the reduced substrate concentration in the reactor. This is shown in Fig. 2.4.

Recycle of biomass will increase the volumetric reaction rate. At the same time there will be a decrease in the mass reaction rate if mass transfer limitations are increased owing to the higher biomass concentration. Recycle of biomass can be

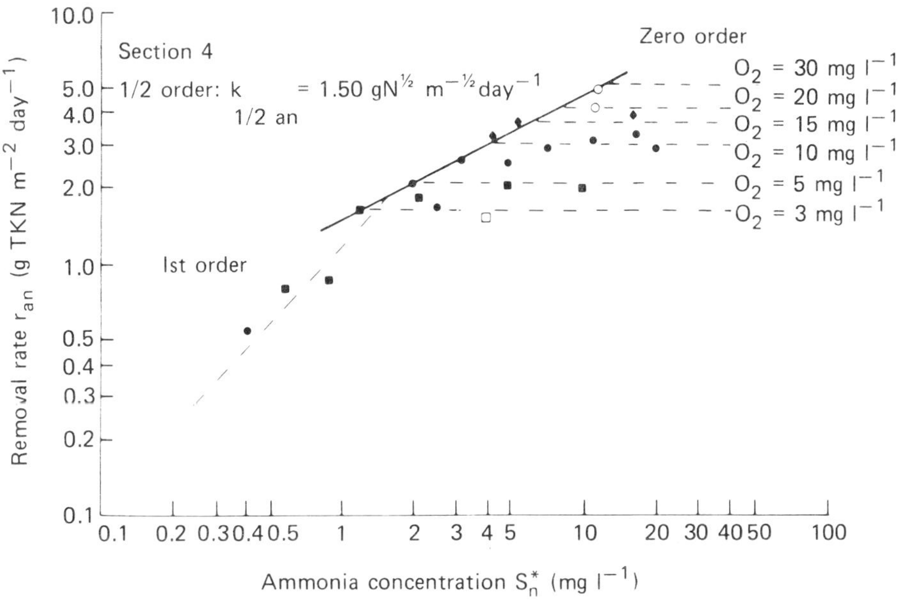

Fig. 2.3 — Nitrification rate v. effluent NH_3–N oxygen concentrations: □ 0–3; ■ 4–6; ● 7–10; ◆ 10–20; ○ >20 mg 1−1; --- theoretical lines. The figure demonstrates that increased bulk liquid oxygen concentrations increases the maximum removal rate obtainable (horizontal lines with zero-order reaction). From Ref [1], courtesy of Pergamon Press.

Table 2.4 — factors able to increase oxygen mass transfer.

Factor	Example
Increase saturation concentration	(a) Increase total pressure (b) Increase oxygen partial pressure (use of pure oxygen or chemical oxygen carriers)
Increase concentration gradient	(a) Increase mixing (b) Decrease diffusion distance
Increase area of gas–liquid increase	(a) Use small bubbles (b) Use high turbulence (to avoid coalescence)
Increase diffusion coefficient	(a) Increase temperature
Internal oxygen production	(a) Electrolytic (b) Photosynthetic
Use of oxygen 'substitutes'	(a) Hydrogen peroxide

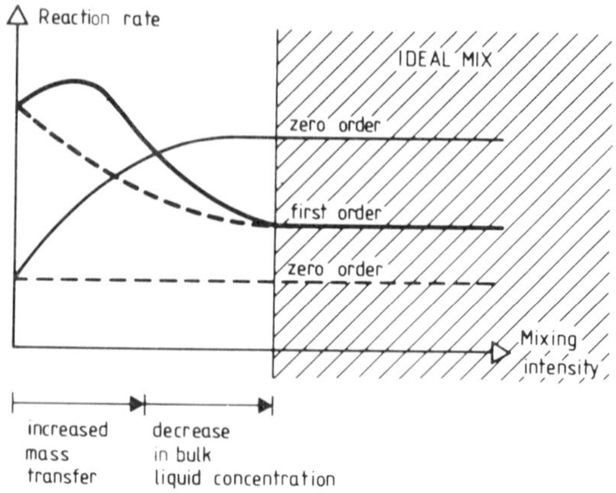

Fig. 2.4 — Mixing can also decrease reaction rate, as shown for the first-order reaction. For zero-order reactions it might increase reaction rate also. Dotted lines show situations where no mass transfer limitation occurs. In this case mixing will not influence the zero-order reaction rate and will decrease the first-order reaction rate at all intensities.

important where slow-growing organisms are used, in order to separate hydraulic and biomass retention time within the system.

Biomass-support media have a similar effect to recycle. They separate hydraulic and biomass retention times. Biomass adhering to the surface of a carrier material is also protected from washout under extreme hydraulic conditions. But the most interesting feature of biomass-support media is that the biomass growing on a surface can have a very high density and this can result in very high biomass concentrations within such systems. These high biomass densities can also be created without a carrier; an example is the pelletization achieved in anaerobic and anoxic waste-water-treatment systems. The pellets are spherical shells of micro-organisms (Fig. 2.5).

2.3 ENVIRONMENTAL FACTORS

Environmental factors have a major influence upon reaction rates for both biological and chemical reactions. Among the many factors are:

- temperature
- pH
- nutrients
- toxic substances
- moisture.

The typical temperature dependency of a biological process is shown in Fig. 2.6. An exponential increase in reaction rate is observed up to the optimum temperature, which can be a range (e.g. 30–40°C). This is shown in Fig. 2.6. Above this temperature range the reaction rate rapidly decreases. The exponential parts of the

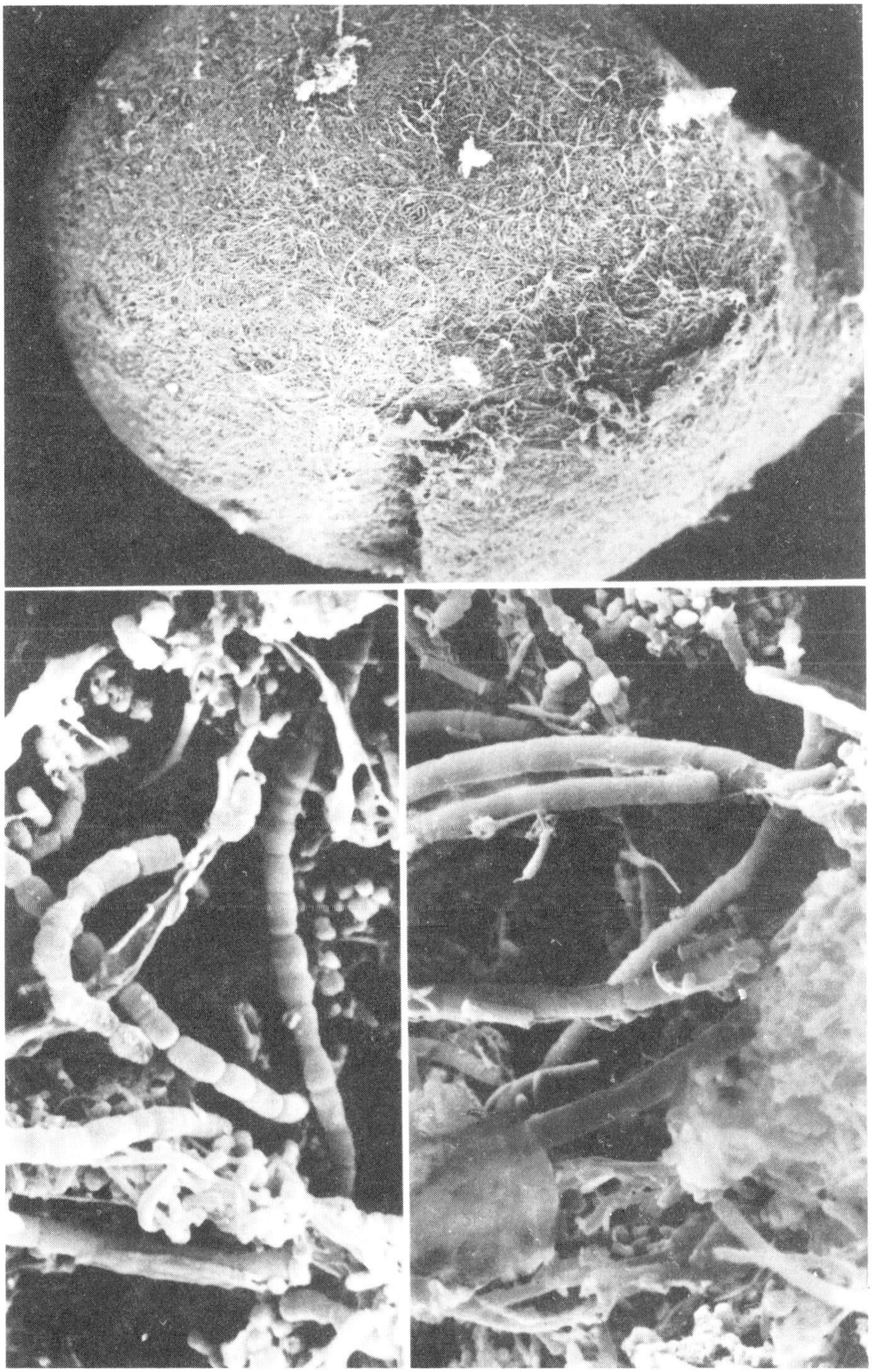

Fig. 2.5 — Pelletization of anaerobic cultures. Brewery waste. Top picture (SEM, 200×) shows pellet, bottom pictures (SEM, 9000× and 6000×) shows details of pellet structure. Courtesy of M. S. Switzenbaum.

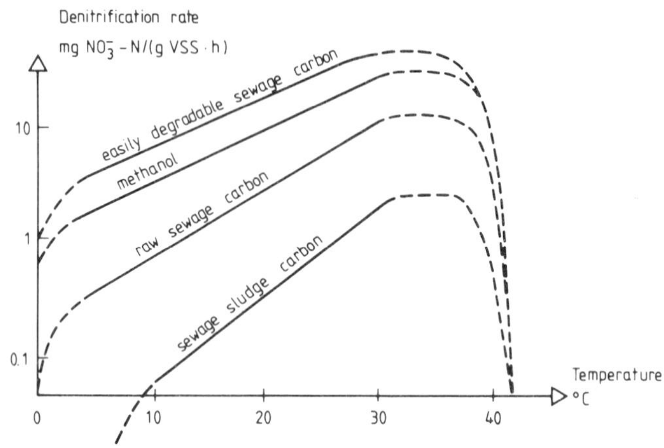

Fig. 2.6 — Denitrification rate as a function of temperature and carbon source. Based on Refs [4,5].

curves shown in Fig. 2.6 can be depicted by several mathematical equations: two are shown in Table 2.5.

The temperature dependency shown in Fig. 2.6 is typical for a pure culture, or for a homogeneous, mixed culture of bacteria. If population changes are possible, then temperature dependencies, as shown in Fig. 2.7, can be obtained. In this case a change from mesophilic bacteria to thermophilic bacteria occurs at around 45°C.

Abrupt temperature variations will decrease the overall reaction rate. An instant temperature drop of 10°C will stop bacterial metabolism, but after one or two hours the activity will be restored. This effect can be used for separation purposes in gas-producing processes (biomethanation, denitrification, etc.) where the gas production often inhibits sedimentation processes.

pH has a strong effect upon all biological and many chemical reactions. The variation in activity as a function of pH is similar to that of temperature, i.e. a bell-shaped curve with an optimum range covering 1–2 pH units. In many biotechnological processes the basic substrate is well buffered, which limits the pH variations observed. Fig. 2.8 shows the pH dependency of composting for a pH range of 6.5–8.5; Fig. 2.9 shows the pH dependency of biological nitrification.

The level of nutrients influences biological reaction rates. Nutrient requirements vary from process to process. Nitrogen and phosphorus are always essential, as are many others, such as sulphur, potassium and various metals. One should always consider whether a biotechnological process has an optimum concentration of nutrients. The addition of small amounts of nutrients can result in considerable intensification of processes. Table 2.6 illustrates the need for nitrogen and phosphorus in various biological processes.

Toxic substances that may be present in the raw wastewater can reduce biological activity considerably. Two groups of toxic substances dominate: organic compounds and metals. Organic compounds, even when toxic, may be degraded biologically, whilst metals might change their state of oxidation, or move from the soluble to the insoluble phase, or *vice versa*. The actual state of the metals is important as the toxicity is related to the metal activity and not to the total concentration of the metal.

Table 2.5 — Temperature dependency expressions

Arrhenius equation for rate constant:
$k = A_0 e^{-E/RT}$
van't Hoff equation:
$k_{T1} = k_{T2} e^{k(T1-T2)}$

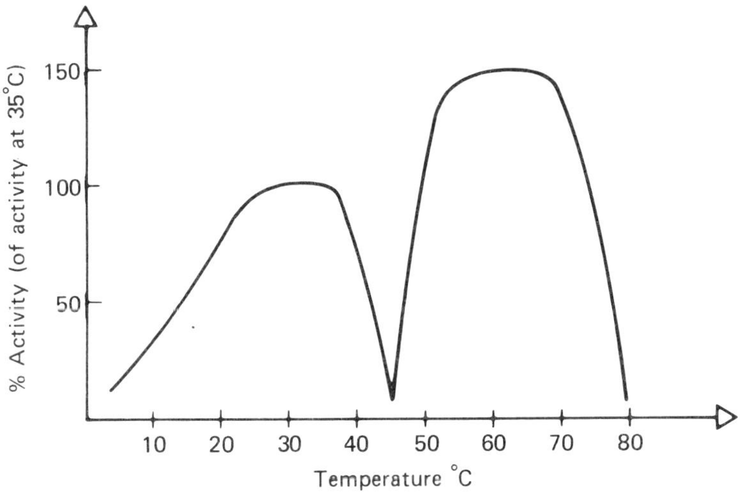

Fig. 2.7 — Activity of anaerobic processes as a function of temperature. After Ref. [6].

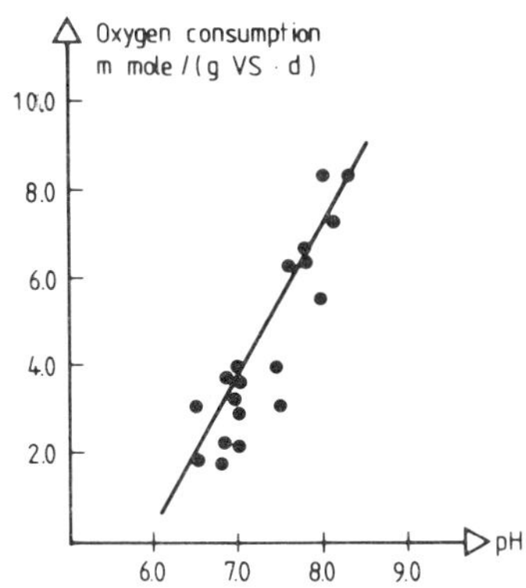

Fig. 2.8 — Effect of pH on composting. Data from Ref. [7].

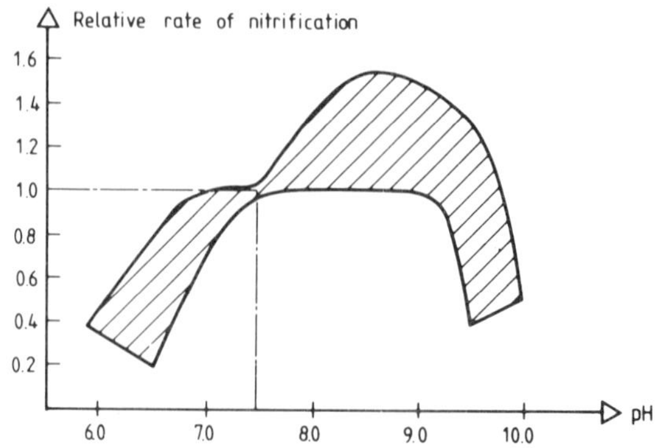

Fig. 2.9 — Effect of pH on biological nitrification of wastewater. Based on data from Ref. [8].

Table 2.6 — C/P and C/N ratios (w/w) for various biotechnology processes.

Process	C/P	C/N	Ref.
Activated sludge[a]	60–80	12–16	[10]
Trickling filters	80–100	16–20	–
Anaerobic wastewater treatment[b]	125–150	15–25	[6]
Composting	75–150	30–35	[9]

[a] Assuming C = 0.6BOD.
[b] Assuming C = 0.4COD.

Moisture must be present in adequate amounts for biological processes to proceed. For all liquid wastes or liquid-based processes this is not a problem. But for more or less dry processes, like composting, the moisture content is important. This is shown in Fig. 2.10 for solid waste disposal.

2.4 BIOLOGY

Process intensification can be achieved by changing the biology within the process. The biology of resident species is primarily a function of the raw materials used or treated. However, plant layout and operation are engineering factors which also influence the biology.

Flocculation is an important process in many solid–liquid separations, for example biological wastewater treatment and single-cell protein production. Micro-organisms capable of flocculation are selected in these processes, either actively, as

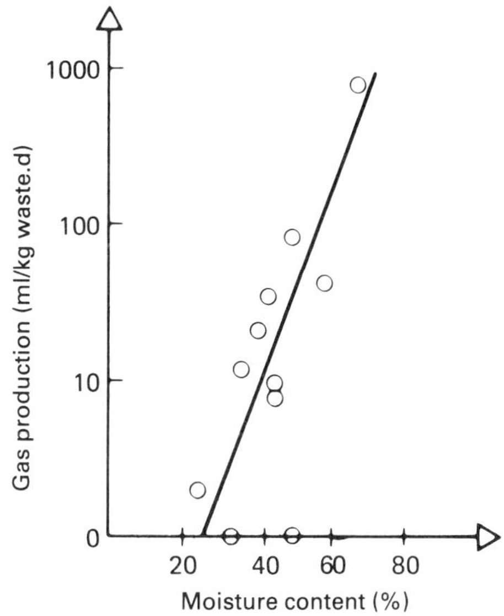

Fig. 2.10 — Moisture content v. gas production for solid waste. Data from Ref. [11].

in the selection of a given micro-organism for SCP production, or 'passively', as done in biological wastewater treatment by the activated sludge process. The theories for flocculation of micro-organisms are not well documented at present.

Surface attachment is important in fixed film processes like trickling filters, fluidized filters, anaerobic filters (which can be of any type), and rotating disks. Chapter 5 deals with 'artificial' cell immobilization techniques in more detail. 'Natural' immobilization occurs in those micro-organisms showing a general tendency to adhere to surfaces. Experience demonstrates that almost any type of surface will suffice: rock, sand, plastic, mussel shells, wood, carbon. Attachment is based on the excretion of microbial polymers which form a sticky or slimy matrix in which the micro-organisms are embedded. The main problem in achieving attachment seems to be that freely suspended micro-organisms can produce enzymes which dissolve the matrix [12]. The concentration of suspended micro-organisms should thus be kept low. This can be ensured through hydraulic wash-out of such organisms, especially important during the start-up of 'attached film' processes. When the biofilm is established the susceptibility to suspended micro-organisms seems to be smaller.

The possibilities for the use of more efficient micro-organisms (or enzymes) are:

- adaptation
- selection
- genetic manipulation (Ch. 8)
- the use of pure cultures, and
- the use of immobilized enzymes or whole cells (Ch. 6).

2.5 CONCLUSIONS

The intensification of biological waste-treatment processes offers many possibilities. Several factors will influence the overall reaction rates which can be obtained. Proper design of the reactors, based on detailed knowledge, is important for optimizing the processes. Increase in biomass concentration can result in mass transfer limitations which are not always recognized. Such limitations can be reduced by mixing, increased oxygen gas transfer, etc.

Environmental factors, such as temperature and pH, will have a significant impact upon reaction rates and should thus be optimized where possible.

SYMBOLS

A_0	temperature frequency factor
C	concentration
E	activation energy
k	reaction rate constant (subscript 0, $\frac{1}{2}$, 1, etc., indicates order of reaction)
k_m	reaction rate constant (Monod kinetics)
K_C	half saturation constant (Monod kinetics)
L	length
M	mass (as dimension)
r_v	reaction rate per unit volume
r_x	reaction rate per unit mass
R	gas constant
S_n	concentration of ammonia
T	temperature
VS	volatile solids
k	temperature constant
u	specific growth rate

REFERENCES

[1] Gönec, I. E. and Harremoës, P. (1985). *Water Res.*, **19**, 1119.

[2] Zlokarnik, M. (1978). *Advances in Biochemical Engineering*, **8**, 133.

[3] Mattiason, B. (ed.) (1983). *Immobilised cells and organelles*, Vol. II. CRC Press, Inc., Boca Raton, Florida, USA.

[4] Henze, M. and Bundgard, E. (1982). *GWF, Wasser/Abwasser*, **123**, 240.

[5] Henze Christensen, M. and Harremoës, P. (1977) *Prog. Wat. Tech.*, **8**, 509.

[6] Henze, M. and Harremoës, P. (1983). *Wat. Sci. Tech.*, **15**, 1.

[7] Jeris, J. S. and Regan, R. W. (1973). *Compost Science*, **14**, 16.

[8] Sutton, P. M. and Jank, B. E. (1976). *Conf. Proc. Res. Program Abat. Munic, Pollut. Provis. Can. -Ont. Agreement Great Lakes Qual.*, Publ. No. 3, 206.

[9] Gray, K. R., Sherman, K. and Biddlestone, A. J. (1971). *Process Biochemistry*, October, 22.

[10] Wastewater treatment plant design (1980). American Society of Civil Engineers, Manuals and reports on engineering practice — No. 36, New York.

[11] Rees, J. F. (1980). *Journ. Chem. Techn. Biotechn.*, **30**, 161.

[12] Heijnen, J. J. (1984). *Biological industrial waste-water treatment minimizing biomass. Production and maximizing biomass concentration.* Delft University Press.

3

Immobilized whole-cell biocatalysts

K. P. Flint,
Department of Biological Sciences, University of Warwick, Coventry

3.1 INTRODUCTION

Immobilization of microbial cells represents the transfer of the cells from a free state to a state in which they are confined or localized in a certain defined region of space with the retention of catalytic activity and, if possible, with the retention of viability so that the cells can be used repeatedly or continuously [1–3]. Various gel compounds and other materials are commonly used to entrap the cell without the loss of enzymatic activity and, indeed, in most cases without the loss of viability. Natural 'biofilms' also qualify as immobilized cultures and often depend on polysaccharide gel excretions for entrapment. This topic is described in more detail later (Sections 3.1.2 and 3.5). These preparations can carry out multi-enzyme reactions as easily as free cells, but, by virtue of being immobilized, they are present in a much higher initial biomass concentration and consequently reaction or processing times are much faster than with free cells (see Section 3.3). Compartmentalization of cells within a gel matrix means that cell density in solid phase is very high, with loadings $>10^{10}$ cells per millilitre of gel not uncommon [1,4], [1], a very attractive feature for environmental applications where large volumes of dilute solutions are being treated. Immobilization is one example of 'process intensification'; this is discussed from a process engineer's point of view in Ch. 5. Physiological and biochemical aspects are considered in this chapter. However, before applications to environmental problems (Section 3.5) can be appreciated it is first necessary to illustrate the main problems associated with immobilization and how they have been tackled, by reference to non-environmental work.

The efficiency of the biocatalyst produced by immobilization is influenced not only by the physiological state of the cell prior to immobilization but also by the method of immobilization used. Harsh conditions of immobilization result in a greater loss in cell viability and enzymatic activity as a general rule, but only trial and error experiments with different immobilization conditions can reveal the effects on cellular functions. Cells grown under different conditions are known to produce different cell wall or cell membrane materials, and these can affect the functional or reactive groups on the cell surface which are available for immobilization. These cells would also have altered metabolic functions.

Once immobilized the major problem, particularly for gel-immobilized preparations, is the transport of reactants into the gel. This is limited by the double-diffusion gradient which builds up: one into the gel matrix and the second from the gel to the cell. As a consequence of this diffusion barrier the cells in a gel matrix can be faced with a multitude of localized micro-environments with differences in pH, oxygen concentration and substrate/production concentrations. This can have far-reaching effects on cell viability and reactivity and produces a very heterogeneous population. These effects can be deleterious, leading to cell lysis or loss of enzyme activity, but optimization of reaction conditions usually reduces cell lysis to a minimum. The retention of cell viability is a fringe benefit of cell immobilization as viability is very often not essential for enzyme activity. In many cases cells are treated with permeabilizing reagents which kill them but at the same time make the diffusion resistance lower. Viability can be beneficial in that periodic introduction of a growth medium can lead to increase in enzyme activity and hence increase the reusability of a biocatalyst. However, viable cells respire and undergo multiplication and both functions can cause disruption of the gel matrix and contamination of the product. The retention of viability on immobilization is important in the cases were fungal spores are used (Section 3.2.1.4) or for ethanol production using fixed yeasts (Section 3.3).

Commercially the major advantage that immobilized cells have over free cells is that they can be repeatedly reused. Free cells have to be separated from the reaction mixture by centrifugation or filtration — both expensive processes — and can generally only be used once or twice before enzyme activity decays. Immobilized preparations can be stabilized such that half-lives for enzyme activity in excess of a year are not uncommon [4,5].

3.1.1 Factors affecting the choice between use of immobilized cells or immobilized enzymes

The use of immobilized enzymes as biocatalysts is discussed in Chapter 4. Whether to use cells or enzymes as the biocatalyst is a question which is very much dependent upon the process involved. In comparison with immobilized enzymes, cells do seem to have some advantages (Table 3.1). The chief advantage must be the savings made by not having to purify enzymes. Enzyme purification is an expensive and time-consuming operation, and any process using an enzyme function which can be replaced by a whole cell should become more economic. The retention of cofactors within cells is an obvious attraction. Although there are procedures available for the co-immobilization of enzymes and their cofactors, these are not as efficient or as cheap as using a whole cell where cofactors are synthesized as a matter or course. Although it is possible to immobilize together all the enzymes of a multi-enzyme reaction complex it is highly inefficient in terms of yield. Inside a cell, all the enzymes involved in a reaction are arranged in a logical fashion such that the product of one enzyme becomes the substrate for another enzyme. It is not possible to order enzymes in this way during immobilization and hence multi-enzyme reactions are

Table 3.1 — Advantages and disadvantages of using immobilized whole cells.

Advantages	Disadvantages
(1) Easy to carry out multi-enzyme reactions	(1) Diffusion leading to slow reaction rates
(2) No need to co-immobilize cofactors	(2) Cell lysis leading to contamination of product and loss of activity
(3) No expensive enzyme purification needed	(3) Side reactions giving unwanted products
(4) Increased stability as enzymes in natural environment	

best carried out by immobilized cells. At the same time these reaction complexes seem to be more stable because the enzymes are operating within their natural environment, often associated with the cell membrane.

The major problem in the use of the whole cell is the restricted diffusion of reactants. Whole cells tend to be immobilized in gels rather than fixed to surfaces and this creates a double-diffusion gradient for product and substrates. The diffusion barriers are across the gel–liquid interface into the depth of the gel and across the cell-membrane barrier. It is usual for immobilized cells to become congregated at the surface of the gel beads and, because of diffusion problems the cells in the depth of the gel tend to be starved of nutrients and oxygen. These cells may retain their viability and, upon the death of the cells at the surface, become active again as substrate reaches them. This can give very long half-lives for the retention of enzyme activity and is a characteristic of immobilized preparations. The diffusion barriers cannot easily be overcome. However, as outer layer cells die and the outer layers of gel begin to disintegrate, active cells from the inner layers become, in effect, the new outer layers where diffusion problems are minimal. The use of a more open pore structure in the gel would lead to increased leakage and the permeabilizing of cells leads to loss of viability and loss of cofactors by leakage.

Cell autolysis can be a problem in reactions in which the product or substrate is toxic to the cell, particularly if the product is slow to diffuse away. Adequate mixing can overcome this to some extent. Autolysis, although often initially compensated for by activity deep in the gel, eventually shows as a loss of activity. The major problem caused by autolysis is contamination of the product by intracellular constituents. In most applications these impurities have to be removed before a product can be considered for use.

It is usual to operate immobilized systems in a way which prevents or minimizes cell autolysis by supplying enough nutrients to allow cells to satisfy their maintenance requirement without undergoing cell division or lysis. By using strains which have been genetically manipulated to over-produce the required enzyme or product it is usually possible to operate an immobilized system such that the majority of supplied energy is being used to produce the required product rather than side products. It is always the case when using immobilized cells, with their multitude of intact metabolic pathways, that some undesirable side reactions will take place. This can cause the gels to disrupt if carbon dioxide is produced in large amounts by repairing cells, and the key to many successful processes is to keep the cells viable or in a resting state without excess gas production. The maintenance of cells in a resting state ensures that cofactors and other essential enzymes are continuously regenerated, but it does limit the use of such preparations to those enzymes which are constitutively produced, i.e. always present in the cell. However, cells can be genetically manipulated to convert inducible enzymes into constitutive ones by alteration of the regulatory mechanism of the cell; thereby reducing the need for prior induction of enzymes which, in a commercial reactor, could take up to 24 hours to accomplish.

There are many cases when the use of immobilized cells is impractical and the only viable alternative in these cases is the use of immobilized enzymes. In the case of enzymes which are purely extracellular, e.g. alkaline phosphatase of *Escherichia coli,* immobilization of cells results in little or no enzyme activity unless the enzyme can be fixed to the cell surface by glutaraldehyde or some other covalent bonding method. However, this rather defeats the object of cell immobilization and usually causes death of the cell. It is therefore more usual to use cell-free immobilized enzyme preparations when the enzyme is produced extracellularly.

Some enzymes act only on high molecular weight substrates such as proteins, cellulose and other complex polysaccharides or lipids, and the rate of diffusion of these substrates is too slow to make immobilized cell preparations economic. It is therefore more feasible to employ enzyme preparations in this case. Some enzymes are not of microbial origin, e.g. proteolytic enzymes like trypsin and papain are derived from mammalian cells. It is impossible or impracticable to immobilize such cells: only the extracted enzymes can be immobilized.

The use of co-immobilized preparations of cells and enzymes can be used to overcome some of the diffusion problems encountered with high molecular weight substrates. Co-immobilized preparations of yeast and cellulolytic enzymes enable yeast to produce alcohol directly from cellulose wastes, without the acid or heat pretreatment necessary at present. Such is the versatility of these immobilization systems that virtually any combination of cell or enzymes, or even organelle, can be co-immobilized to extend the range of reactions which can be carried out by micro-organisms.

3.1.2 Industrial scale-up of processes using immobilized cells

There are two aspects which require constant consideration: firstly the nature of the support material to be used, and secondly the organisms themselves. Both affect process-design decisions.

3.1.2.1 Support materials

If large-scale usage is intended then the support material must be widely available at low cost, especially for the production of low-value chemicals. It is impractical to consider using a highly modified synthetic substance which, although more efficient as a support than natural materials, costs many times as much. Industry shows much more interest in using wood shavings than in using modified polyacrylamide or modified purified celluloses. The size and shape of the immobilized biocatalyst can also be a problem in scaling up from the laboratory to an industrial process.

Polyacrylamide beads, k-carrageenan beads, cellulose fibres and alginate pellets have all been used successfully in industrial processes [4,6–8], but most surface-bound cells or enzymes have not progressed beyond limited pilot-plant studies because of the cost of covalent bonding. Although gels have been successfully used, there is still a lot of knowledge to be gained about the mechanical properties of the gels. Compaction of the beads and channelling of stream flows is a major problem and many workers have tried to model the effects of physical pressures on the beads [9]. By far the biggest problem is simple physical abrasion, which causes tears and leaks in the bead structure. This can be exasperated by growth of micro-organisms within the gel causing weakening and disruption by gas production within the matrix [10,11].

3.1.2.2 Process design

Any successful immobilization procedure must be simple, effective and above all retain a high proportion of the activity. Immobilization techniques which cause a loss of 50 per cent or more of activity are useless, as are techniques which cannot be carried out quickly and in bulk.

Figs 3.1 and 3.2 illustrate two typical processes using gel-immobilized cells.

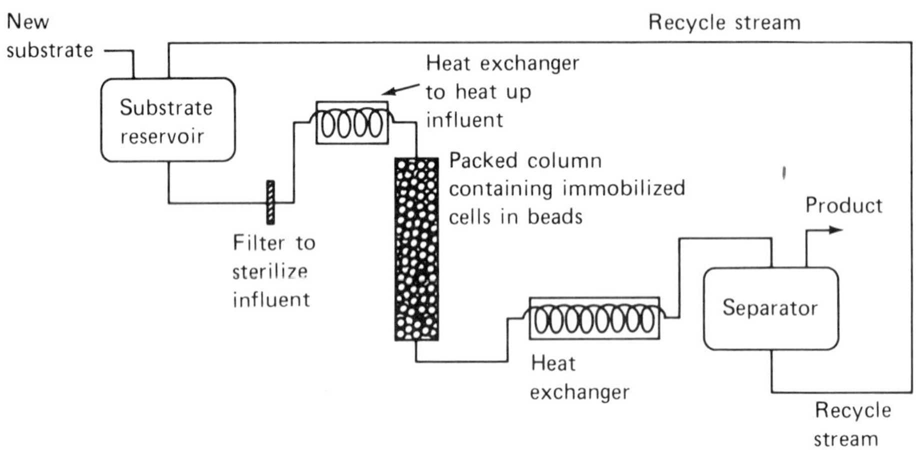

Fig. 3.1 — Reactor design (1). A schematic diagram for the production of a simple product using gel-immobilized cells in a packed-column reactor. The product should be easily removed from the fluid stream, e.g. by distillation, and residual nutrients may then be recycled to save on costs. This system would suffer from oxygen limitation as it would not prove possible to aerate the system very vigorously owing to the packing in the column.

Reactor design needs to be simple, preferably drawing on existing technology, and moreover the nutritional needs of the cells must be simple and cheaply available. Organisms able to grow on wastes have an advantage over those requiring complex growth factors and those able to utilize sunlight for energy have even more of an advantage.

Products must be extracellular, produced in high concentration with a high

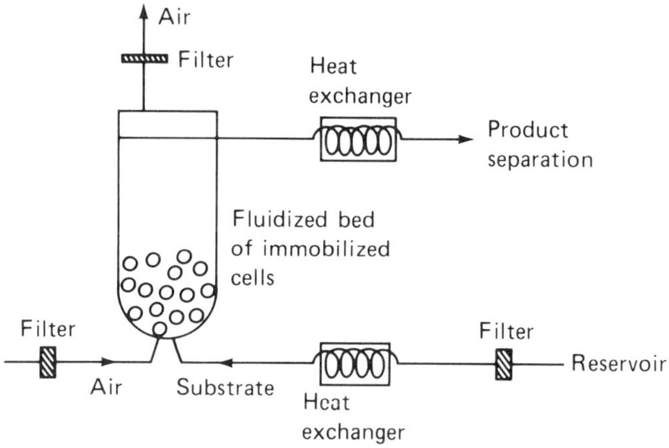

Fig. 3.2 — Reactor design (2). A fluidized-bed bioreactor, in which the gel-immobilized cells are continously agitated by filter-sterilized air injected at the base through a sparge mechanism. The key to successful operation is to aerate sufficiently to prevent anaerobiosis or oxygen limitation but not to allow cells to block the product overflow.

efficiency and, most important, easily separable from the bulk phase. If a complex growth medium is used then the product has to be removed and purified by affinity chromatography, monoclonal antibody or some other purification process. Compounds not naturally produced as extracellular materials could not previously be made by immobilized cell techniques because extraction of the products would necessitate destruction of the matrix and the cells. Fortunately genetic manipulation techniques can now be used to persuade cells to export intracellular products, and commercial interest in immobilized cell technology is increasing as a result.

Finally, and probably most important, the system needs to be stable so that the catalyst can be reused for a long period of time. The more durable the support and the longer the enzyme activity is retained the more chance there is that a process will become economic. In Chapter 4 there is an analysis of the costs of producing a product using free or immobilized enzymes which can be extrapolated to the use of cells.

3.2 IMMOBILIZED MICROBIAL CELLS AS BIOCATALYSTS IN INDUSTRY

A wide diversity of bulk and speciality chemicals can be produced by immobilized whole-cell biocatalysts and examples are listed later (Tables 3.2 and 3.6). As yet few are in commercial use but the main reason for not introducing this new technology is the cost of changeover from the existing petrochemical base, particularly with oil prices currently being artificially low. There are many advantages to be gained from continuing to investigate the future uses of these biocatalysts with the view to utilizing waste products or common natural products to produce chemicals so that, when oil supplies become scarcer or more expensive, there is an alternative technology available to replace the petrochemical-based one.

Although micro-organisms have been used for the production of foodstuffs for at least 4000 years, their use for the production of chemicals dates only from the early years of this century. During the First World War Britain and Germany were faced with the problem of obtaining acetone for cordite and glycerol for dynamite. Both used microbial production methods, but after the war the rise of the petrochemical industry saw the use of these methods decline.

Many multinational conglomerates, like Shell, ICI and duPont, have taken a stake in the future development of biotechnology. They have been tempted by the possibility of using micro-organisms to manufacture chemicals essential to the developed world's economy. At present much of the world's chemical industry relies on oil and gas as the raw material. In the US alone over $35 thousand million worth of petrochemicals were manufactured from this diminishing resource in 1983. The increased cost of oil over recent years has also been a catalyst for the development of alternative processes. Many chemicals which are at present derived from petroleum raw materials can be made from waste materials or plentiful natural renewable raw material using micro-organisms, either free or immobilized. Further biotechnological developments in the near future will lead to increased yields and decreased costs and hopefully make microbial-derived products economically competitive with conventionally derived products.

At the present time most of the work involving immobilized micro-organisms is purely of academic interest, but there are a few processes within the chemical industry producing fine or speciality chemicals on a large scale, notably the Japanese processes for the production of L-aspartate and L-malate (see also Table 3.2). Many other processes, especially those involved with the biotransformation of steroids, are approaching pilot-plant scale [12].

3.2.1 Speciality chemicals

Speciality chemicals are defined as those selling for more than $1 per pound, and they have many uses in the medical, research and food industries. Many speciality chemicals, like vitamins, amino acids, enzymes and lipids, are already produced by micro-organisms and are readily amenable to genetic manipulation to increase yields. Most of these chemicals are at present commercially produced from a petrochemical base and require a huge energy input from their production. The use of micro-organisms to produce economically competitive chemicals requires: (a) the development of suitable strains, i.e. the construction of new microbial species or the modification of the biochemical pathways in existing species [13]; (b) the development of new production methods using these strains [14]; (c) the development of immobilized preparations.

Table 3.2 shows the range of speciality chemicals which have been produced commercially or in the laboratory using immobilized cells. Viable, dead or non-growing cells have been used, almost invariably entrapped in a gel matrix. Viable cells are actively growing cells, dead cells have been chemically or physically killed to prevent growth without loss of cell activity, and non-growing cells are in a resting phase but can grow when suitable conditions prevail. Although the processes described below are rarely done for environmental reasons they do illustrate the state of the art in immobilized whole-cell technology. Many of the fermentation substrates are found in wastewaters or can be derived from waste materials which may become more attractive as alternative raw materials become scarce or too costly.

Table 3.2 — Speciality chemicals produced using immobilized whole cells as biocatalysts.

Product	Micro-organism	Immobilization method	Cell nature	Ref.
Amino acids L-alanine	*Pseudomonas dachunae*	Entrapped in k-carrageenan	Treated/non-viable	[15]
L-aspartate	*Escherichia coli*	Entrapped in polyacrylamide	Treated/non-viable	[6]
	E. coli	Entrapped in k-carrageenan	Treated/non-viable	[16]
L-arginine	*Serratia marcescens*	Entrapped in k-carrageenan	Treated/Non-viable	[17]
N-carbamyl-D-amino acids	*Bacillus* sp.	Entrapped in polyacrylamide	Resting	[18]
L-citrulline	*Pseudomonas putida*	Entrapped in polyacrylamide	Treated/non-viable	[19]
	Streptococcus faecalis	Entrapped in polyacrylamide	Treated/non-viable	[20]
L-glutamine	*Brevibacterium flavum*	Entrapped in collagen	Viable	[21]
	Corynebacterium glutamicium	Entrapped in polyacrylamide	Viable	[22]
L-glutamate	*Brevibacterium flavum*	Entrapped in agar	Treated/non-viable	[23]
L-isoleucine	*S. marcescens*	Entrapped in k-carrageenan	Viable	[24]
L-methionine	*Aspergillus ochraceus*	Cross-linked mycelial pellet	Viable	[25]
L-tryosine	*Erwinia herbicole*	Entrapped in collagen	Treated/non-viable	[26]
	Escherichia intermedia	Entrapped in polyacrylamide	Treated	[27]
L-tryptophan	*E. coli*	Entrapped in polyacrylamide	Resting	[28]
Acetyl coenzyme	*Brevibacterium ammoniagenes*	Entrapped in polyacrylamide	Treated	[29]
	B. ammoniagenes and *Saccharomyces cerevisiae*	Entrapped in polyacrylamide	Treated	[29]
Andenosine arabinoside	*Enterobacter aerogenes*	Entrapped in photocross-linkable resin prepolymer	Treated	[30]
Adenosine triphosphate	Yeast	Entrapped in photocross-linkable resin prepolymer	Treated	[31]
	S. cerevisiae	Micro-encapsulated with ethyl cellulose	Treated	[29]
	Mastigocladius laminosus	Entrapped in calcium alginate	Resting	[32]
CDP-choline	*Hansenula jadinii*	Entrapped in photo-crosslinkable resin prepolymer	Treated	[33]
	S. cerevisiae	Micro-encapsulated with ethyl cellulose	Treated	[29]
Chorismic acid	*E. aerogenes*	Entrapped in polyacrylamide	Viable	[34]
L-DOPA	*Erwinia herbicola*	Entrapped in calcium alginate	Treated	[35]

Product	Micro-organism	Immobilization method	Cell nature	Ref.
Glucose-6-phosphate	*Achromobacterium butyri*	Entrapped in polyacrylamide	Treated	[36]
Glucose-6-phosphate and glucose-1-phosphate	*Escherichia freundii*	Entrapped in polyacrylamide	Treated	[37]
Glutathinone	*S. cerevisiae*	Entrapped in polyacrylamide	Treated/resting	
	E. coli and *S. cerevisiae*	Entrapped in polyacrylamide	Resting	[39]
		Entrapped in k-carrageenan	Resting	[40]
2-keto-L-gulonic acid	*Gluconobacter melagenus* and *Pseudomonas* sp.	Entrapped in polyacrylamide gel	Treated/resting	[20]
Ketoses	*Acetobacter suboxydans*	Entrapped in polyacrylamide	Resting	[41]
L-malate	*B. ammoniagenes*	Entrapped in polyacrylamide	Treated	[6]
	Pichia membranae faciers	Entrapped in polyacrylamide	Treated	[42]
	B. ammoniagenes and *Brevibacterium flavum*	Entrapped in k-carrageenan	Treated	[43]
	B. flavum	Entrapped in polyacrylamide	Treated	[44]
L-menthol	*Rhodotorula minuta*	Entrapped in photocross-linkable resin prepolymer	Treated	[45]
NDAP	*B. ammoniagenes*	Entrapped by radiation copolymerization	Resting	[46]
	Achromobacter aceris	Entrapped in polyacrylamide	Treated	[47]
	B. ammoniagenes	Entrapped in polyacrylamide	Treated	[48]
	S. cerevisiae and *B. ammoniagenes*	Entrapped in polyacrylamide	Treated	[49]
		Micro-encapsulated in cellulose acetate–butyrate	Treated	[49]
Ornithine and putrescine	*Streptococcus faecalis*	Entrapped in polyacrylamide	Resting	[20]
Saturated and 2-*R*−-hydroxy fatty acids	*Proteus mirabilis*	Cross-linked to gelatin	Resting	[50]
	Clostridium sp.	Cross-linked to gelatin	Resting	[50]
L-sorbosone	*G. melanogenus*	Entrapped in polyacrylamide	Treated	[20]
Urocanic acid	*Achromobacter liquidum*	Entrapped in polyacrylamide	Treated	[6]
	Micrococcus luteus	Bonded to carbodiimide-activated carboxymethyl cellulose	Treated	[51]

3.2.1.1 Amino acids

These are used primarily as additives to human and animal foodstuffs and also in medicine for therapeutic purposes and in research. In 1982 sales of amino acids approached 455 000 tonnes per annum, with a predicted annual growth rate of 10 per cent for the rest of this decade [52]. Almost 75 per cent of total production is based in Japan, although the United States, through developments by Japanese companies, are hoping to catch up by the end of the 1980s [53].

Table 3.3 shows the most commonly used amino acids and the micro-organisms

Table 3.3 — Amino acid production by immobilized cells.

Amino acid	Use	Tonnes/year produced by micro-organisms	Micro-organisms
D,L-Alanine	Flavouring Food additive	150–200	*Pseudomonas dachunae* *Corynebacterium gelatinosum*
L-Arginine	Infusion Therapeutic	200–300	*Corynebacterium glutamicum* *Brevibacterium flavum*
L-Aspartate	Sugar substitute Aspartame Therapeutic	500–1000	*E. coli*
L-Glutamine	Therapeutic	300	*C. glutamicum*
L-Glutamate	Food additive (MSG)	200 000	*C. glutamicum*
L-Histidine	Therapeutic	100–200	*C. glutamicum* *B. flavum*
L-Isoleucine	Infusion	10–50	*Serratia marcescens* *B. flavum*
L-Lysine	Food additive	15 000–20 000	*C. glutamicum*
L-Methionine	Food additive	500–1000	*Aspergillus ochraceus*
L-Phenylalanine	Sugar substitute Aspartame	500–1000	*C. glutamicum* *B. flavum*
L-Proline	Infusion	10–50	*C. glutamicum* *B. flavum*
L-Serine	Cosmetic	10–50	*Corynebacterium glycinophilum*
L-Threonine	Food additive	50–100	*B. flavum*
L-Tryptophan	Food additive	1500–1000	*E. coli* *B. flavum*
L-Valine	Infusion	50–100	*C. glutamicum* *Bacillus lactofermentum*

Adapted from Refs [12, 25, 58].

which are, or could be, used to produce them. Only two groups have been extensively studied: the *corynebacteria* and *Escherichia*. Both have been genetically modified to over-produce the required amino acids, mostly by gene duplication or by modification of the regulatory mechanisms [54]. Methionine is the only commonly used amino acid which is not at present produced by micro-organisms on a commercial scale.

The production of L-aspartate using immobilized *E. coli* was the first commercial use of immobilized whole cells to produce a speciality chemical, and it also illustrates the increase in production which can be achieved by successive modifications to the micro-organisms and to the immobilization technique [6,55]. This process has been in operation in Japan since 1973 and has been shown to be superior to the conventional batch and continuous fermentation processes. Although the activity half-life of the original preparation was 20 days, only 19 per cent of activity was retained after immobilization in polyacrylamide. A stabilizing agent (hexamethylenediamene) and a cross-linking reagent (glutaraldehyde) were also added, which killed the cells. The use of k-carrageenan as the matrix since 1978 has led to more activity being retained [56], and the introduction of mutant strains has led to sevenfold higher production rates [57]. Immobilization of the new organism led to a half-life of 126 days, with 49 per cent retention of activity upon immobilization in the industrial process, and half-lives as high as 693 days in the laboratory have been reported after inhibition of intracellular proteolytic enzymes [56].

Recently it has been reported that fixation of *E. coli* to latex beads by polyazetidine linkages has resulted in the retention of 97 per cent enzyme activity, with a half-life of 611 days, and as the new medium has better engineering properties than either polyacrylamide or latex beads this could become the next alteration to the industrial process [59].

3.2.1.2 Antibiotics

Antibiotics are the most important complex of compounds manufactured by micro-biological-based processes. Over 5500 natural compounds have been described which exhibited antimicrobial activity and over 150 of these are now produced on an industrial scale using micro-organisms, directly or by the chemical modification of microbially produced products to produce novel antibiotics.

The most important novel antibiotics are those produced from 6-aminopenicillanic acid (6-APA), which is derived from penicillin G after its degradation by immobilized *E. coli* with high pencillin acylase activity [19] or from penicillin VC and immobilized spores of *Fusarium* sp. [60]. 6-APA is more amenable to chemical modification than are the penicillins, and Fig. 3.3 shows the relationship between 6-APA and the penicillins. Purified penicillin acylases have also been used for this process.

Cells of *Humicola* sp. have been used to hydrolyse rifamycin B, the natural antiobiotic product of *Nocardia mediterranei,* to rifamycin S, which is used as the starting compound for the semi-synthetic production of rifampicin. The cells were entrapped in polyacrylamide gel, defatted with acetone to improve permeability and used in a continuous process. A half-life of 8 days for enzyme activity at 40°C was reported [61].

Antibiotics themselves rather than the precursors have also been produced using immobilized cells (Table 3.4). Penicillin G used as the starting substrate for 6-APA manufacture was successfully produced by k-carrageenan-entrapped *Penicillium chrysogenum.* The production rate was constant for 9 days providing the immobilized cells were transferred to fresh medium daily. Using cells in the resting stage ensures high activity for the synthesis of secondary metabolites and regular feeding with fresh medium induces fresh enzymes. The ease with which cells can be removed from the liquid phase also allows cost savings on the final purification of the antibiotic [70].

The preparation of a mixture of penicillins and cephalosporins by immobilized enzymes user the precursor δ-(L-α-aminoadiphyl)-L-cysteinyl-D-valine [71]. Both the precursor and the enzymes are expensive and an immobilized cell preparation could also

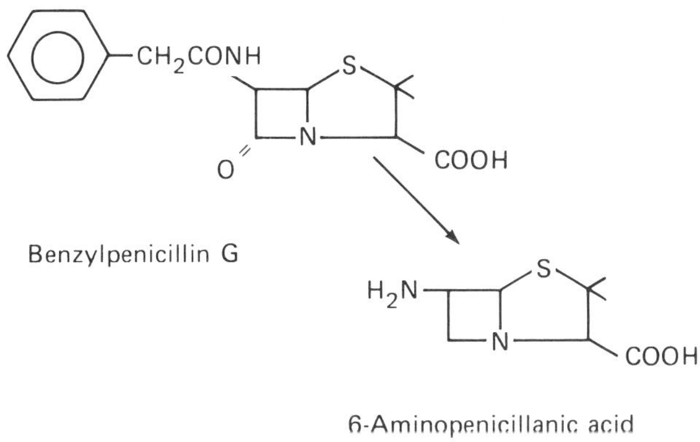

Fig. 3.3 — Sixteen or more semi-synthetic penicillins are derived by chemical modification of 6-aminopenicillanic acid. These are needed to overcome the problem of microbial resistance to natural penicillins.

Table 3.4 — Antibiotics produced by immobilized cell preparations.

Antibiotics	Micro-organism	Immobilisation technique	Ref.
Ampicillin	*Kluyvera citrophila*	Entrapped in polyacrylamide	[62]
Bacitracin	*Bacillus* sp.	Entrapped in polyacrylamide	[63]
Candicidin	*Streptomyces griseus*	Entrapped in collagen	[64, 65]
Colistin			
Cephalosporin	*Streptomyces clavuligerus*	Glutaraldehyde fixed to prepolymerized poly-acrylamide	[66]
Nikkomycin/tylosin	*Streptomyces* sp.	Entrapped in calcium alginate	[67]
Nisin	*Streptomyces lactis*	Entrapped in polyacrylamide	[68]
Patusium	*Pencillium ulticae*	Entrapped in k-carrageenan	[69]
Penicillin	*P. chrysogenum*	Entrapped in polyacrylamide	[62]
		Entrapped in k-carrageenan	[70]

be used. If the problems of cell permeability are resolved and the establishment of immobilized fungal preparations is successful then more antibiotics could be produced very cheaply using these immobilized techniques.

3.2.1.3 Steroids

Using free enzymes or cells reactions have to be carried out in an aqueous environment, as cells and enzymes are usually unstable in the organic solvents necessary for the solubilization of water-insoluble lipophilic compounds like steroids. However, immobilization does stabilize cells against the denaturing effects of organic solvents and immobilized cells have been used for the laboratory study of steroid biotransformation. The use of photocross linkable resin prepolymers as the immobilization matrix allows the construction of particles with a controlled degree of hydrophobicity, which allows the optimum conditions for the enzyme reaction to be achieved [72].

These biotransformations are extremely difficult to achieve using chemical methods, and the successful commercial preparation of steroids using micro-organisms and their associated enzymes will lead to greatly reduced production costs.

Many biotransformations, including 1,2 dehydrogenation, 20 β-reduction, 17β-reduction, 11β-hydroxylation, 11α-hydroxylation and 9α-hydroxylation, have been reported [73,74] and these are illustrated in Fig. 3.4. Table 3.5 shows the reactions which have so far been studied in immobilized cell preparation using viable, dead and resting cells. Although all these reactions require a single enzymatic step, it has proved far easier to use cells than free or immobilized enzymes, as the enzymes are more stable in their natural environment. Half-lives of up to 144 days have been reported in cells of *Arthrobacter globiformis,* providing the cells were given recovery periods during a continuous operation. Few of the cells were viable but enzyme activity was retained [73].

Some of these reactions are now nearing pilot-plant study but the amount of steroid produced is generally small owing to diffusion problems and generally low enzyme activity of the preparations. Genetic manipulation can be used to boost enzyme activity, and modifications to the solvent system could be used to overcome some of the diffusion problems [88].

3.2.2 Commodity chemicals

Commodity chemicals are defined as those which sell for less than $1 per pound, e.g. lactate, ethylene, toluene, acetic acid, ethanol, phenol. At present, all are derived from petroleum or natural gas resources and are widely used in industry as precursors for paints, plastics, polymers, etc. Approximately 8 per cent of US oil imports are used solely to produce these chemicals, and the reliance on a single feedstock has often been cited as dangerous owing to the potential disruption which could occur to the oil supply. Whilst microbial production is at present less economic, given the amount of potential feedstock such as agricultural cellulosic and starch waste materials, these processes could in future become important. Lipinsky [89] has calculated that 1 per cent of the US corn production would be enough to supply sufficient starch to produce over 1 thousand million pounds of commodity chemicals like butanol. Although use of a cash food crop would compete with food supply uses, there are large amounts of agricultural waste available. Problems, often cited to dissuade investment in microbial processes, include the seasonal nature of waste supply and its transportation (the US farm lobby would not support the siting of the chemical production facility in the heart of the US grain belt, for instance).

The basic method for the production of bulk chemicals involves the pretreatment of the wastes by a combination of biological, physical and chemical means to produce glucose and other fermentable sugars. These can then be readily converted to the required end product by micro-organisms (Fig. 3.5 illustrates some of the basic pathways involved). The use of immobilized micro-organisms would allow almost 100 per cent conversion efficiency even in dilute feedstocks, an efficiency which could

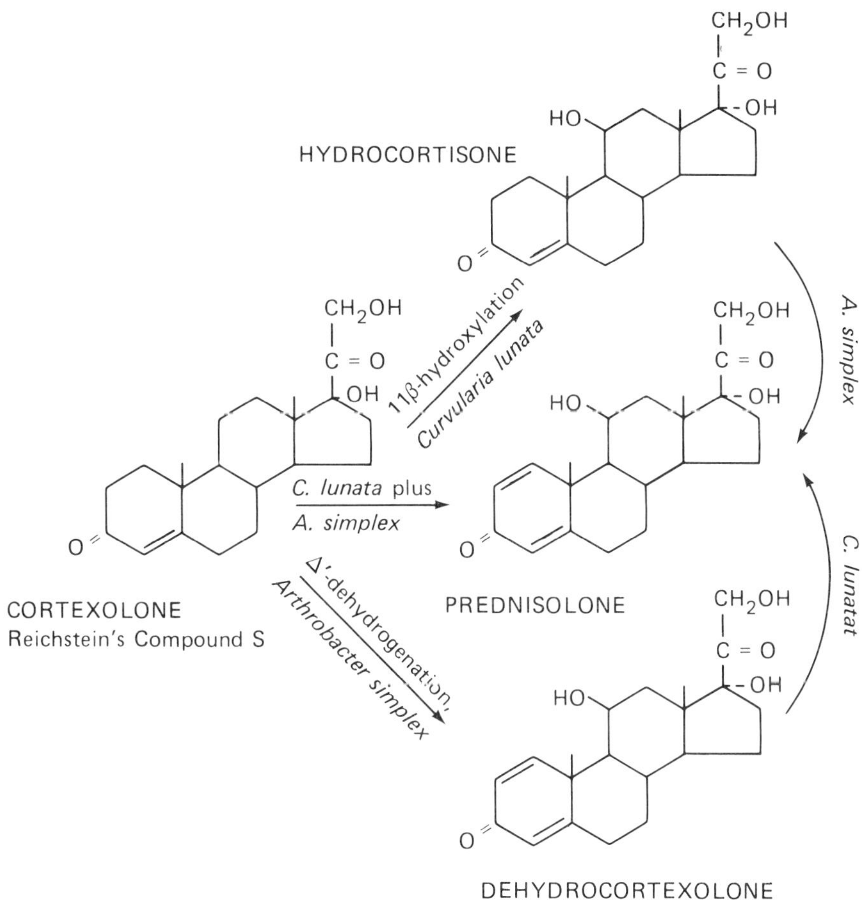

Fig. 3.4 — Transformations of steroids catalysed by bacteria. These transformations are difficult to achieve chemically and therefore the use of immobilized bacteria as the catalysts of these conversions has aroused much interest in the medical and fine chemical fields. Other possible conversions which have been investigated are Δ'-dehydrogenation of 4-androstene-3,17-dione to 1,4-androstadiene-3,17-dione; Δ'-dehydrogenation of testosterone to Δ'-dehdro-testosterone; 3β-hydroxy Δ'-steroid dehydrogenation of cholesterol to cholestone; and 17β-hydroxy steroid dehydrogenation of testosterone to 4-androstene-3,17-dione.

not be approached using free cells or chemical conversions. Some of the chemicals produced using immobilized cell preparations are shown in Table 3.6; almost all were produced from glucose as the simple starting material.

Ethanol production which has received most attention, is discussed further in Section 3.3. Few of these processes have reached commercial operation, but *Absidia regneiri* and *Mortierella vinacea* have been used for the production of galactose and sucrose from raffinose in molasses. *Actinoplanes missouriensis, Bacillus coagulans, Streptomyces olivacen* and *Streptomyces albus* have been used to produce glucose and galactose from lactose, all for use in the Japanese food and soft-drinks industry. The only other bulk chemicals which could be produced economically using cells are ethanol, *n*-butanol, isopropanol and 2,3-butanediol [113].

Table 3.5 — Biotransformation of steroids by immobilized micro-organisms.

Organism	Immobilization method	Transformation	Ref.
Arthrobacter simplex	Entrapped in photocross-linkable resin prepolymer	Hydrocortisone→prednisolone	[7]
	Entrapped in collagen	Hydrocortisone→prednisolone	[76]
	Entrapped in polyacrylamide gel or calcium alginate	Hydrocortisone→prednisolone	[77]
	Entrapped in photocross-linkable resin prepolymer	Cortexolone→prednisolone	[74]
Arthrobacter globiformis	Entrapped in polyacrylamide gel	Hydrocortisone→prednisolone	[78]
Aspergillus ochraceus and *A. simplex*	Entrapped in polyacrylamide	16-hydroxycortexolone→3-ketocortexolone	[79]
Corynebacterium sp.	Entrapped in polyacrylamide gel	4-Androstene-3,17-dione→1,4-androstadiene-3-dione	[80]
Curvularia lunata	Entrapped in polyacrylamide	Reichstein's Compound S→hydrocortisone	[20]
	Entrapped in photocross-linkable resin prepolymer	Cortexolone→prednisolone	[74]
	Entrapped in polyacrylamide or calcium alginate gel	Reichstein's Compounds S→hydrocortisone	[81]
	Entrapped in photocross-linkable resin prepolymer	Reichstein's Compound S→hydrocrotisone	[82]
Myobacterium phlei	Entrapped in polyacrylamide gel	4-Cholesten-3-(O-carboxy-methyl)-oxime→4-androstene-17-on-3-(O-carboxymethyl)-oxime	[83]
Nocardia rhodocrous	Entrapped in photocross-linkable resin prepolymer	4-Androstene-3,17-dione→1,4-androstadiene-3,17-dione	[84]
	Entrapped in photocross-linkable resin prepolymer	3-Hydroxy-5-steroids→3-keto-4-steroids	[45]
	Entrapped in urethane prepolymer	Testosterone→dehydrotestosterone	[85]
Pseudomonas testosteroni	Entrapped in polyacrylamide gel	Reichstein's Compound S→1-dehydro-Reichstein's Compound S	[86]
Rhizopus nigricans	Entrapped in agar	Progesterone→11-hydroxyprogesterone	[87]

Butanol production using micro-organisms has been practised since 1861 using *Clostridium acetobutylicum* and *Clostridium beijerinckii* growing anaerobically on starch. A mixture of acetone, butanol and ethanol is produced in proportions dependent upon the operational conditions. The continuous removal of the products from the dilute feedstream is essential as they are toxic to the cells at high concentrations. The use of immobilized cells allows easy separation of the bulk phase and the cells such that the products can be removed by vacuum distillation from the liquid in a separate reactor vessel. Immobilized cell systems to produce butanol allow a high initial cell density to be used, giving fast conversion rates for minimum energy input, and have proved to be very stable under normal operating conditions [93].

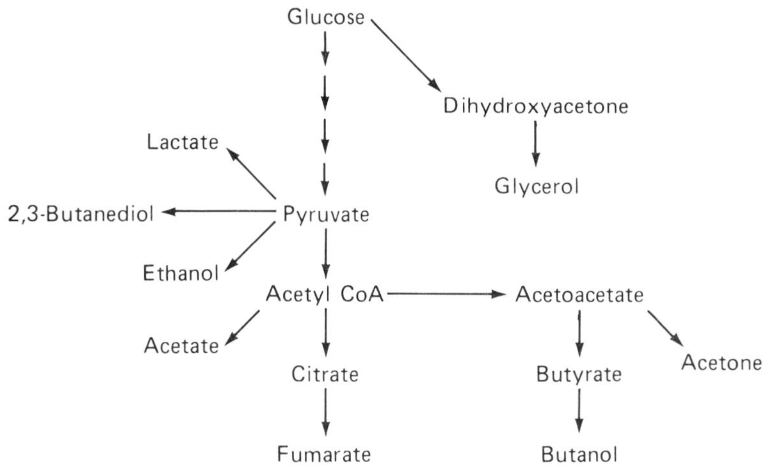

Fig. 3.5 — This represents a small fraction of the bulk chemicals which can be produced by micro-organisms from a simple starting precursor, in this case glucose. Glucose itself can be produced in quantity from waste carbohydrates like starch and cellulose by the action of micro-organisms. Whilst no one strain of micro-organism can carry out all of these conversions, careful screening of strains allows selection of the most proficient. The major problem is not finding suitable micro-organisms but finding a suitable cheap substrate.

3.3 THE PRODUCTION OF ETHANOL BY IMMOBILIZED WHOLE-CELL BIOCATALYSTS

Ethanol is a bulk chemical which is as important as a constituent of drink and as a fuel as it is as a versatile chemical.

The production of fuel alcohol is one of the fastest growing biotechnological applications. Brazil initiated their 'gasohol' programme in 1973, turning excess sugar-cane and sugar-cane waste (bagasse) into ethanol to be used in combination with petrol as a fuel for powering cars. Other projects aimed at replacing petroleum with alcohol derived mainly from agricultural wastes are underway in the US, EC and many Third World countries with no natural oil resources but plenty of farm wastes.

The key to a successful alcohol industry is the supply of a suitable, cheap raw material. The Brazilian programme relies on sugar-cane and the US on corn, both more valuable as food crops than as the raw material for alcohol production. The search is on for a plentiful, preferably renewable and continously available supply of biomass. Trees, grasses and crops have been examined but all contain much lower sugar content than sugar-cane, although they do have a lot of sugars bound up in long-chain polysaccharide polymers like starch and cellulose. The development of a cheap method of converting these to fermentable sugar solutions is vital to the economic production of fuel alcohol, as 50 per cent of the total production cost has been estimated to be the cost of converting the raw material into a liquid fermentation substrate [114].

One of the more plentiful natural polymers is starch, α-1,4-linked glucopyranose units. Starch is a carbohydrate reserve material found in large quantities in tubers and roots, such as cassava and potato. It is easily hydrolysed by chemical means and hence has been preferred to cellulose as a raw material. There are two pre-fermentation steps in the preparation of a fermentable sugar solution: (i) the gelatinization of starch under

Table 3.6 — Bulk chemicals produced using immobilized whole cells

Product	Organism	Immobilization method	Cell nature	Ref.
Acetic acid	*Acetobacter aceti*	Fixed to titanium hydroxide	Viable	[90]
	A. aceti	Entrapped in k-carrageenan	Viable	[91]
2,3-Butanediol	*Enterobacter aerogenes*	Entrapped in k-carrageenan	Viable	[92]
Butanol and isopropanol	*Clostridium beijerinki*	Entrapped in calcium alginate	Treated	[93]
Citric acid	*Aspergillus niger*	Entrapped in calcium alginate	Viable	[94]
Dihydroxyace-tone	*Acetobacter xylenum*	Entrapped in polyacrylamide	Resting	[95]
	Gluconobacter oxydans	Entrapped in calcium alginate	Resting	[96]
Ethanol	*Saccharomyces carlsbergensis*	Entrapped in k-carrageenan	Viable	[9]
	Saccharomyces cerevisiae	Entrapped in calcium alginate	Resting	[98]
		Fixed to Raschig rings	Viable	[99]
		Entrapped in k-carrageenan	Viable	[24]
		Entrapped in calcium alginate	Viable	[100]
		Absorbed on Carrier A	Viable	[101]
	Zymomonas mobilis	Entrapped in calcium alginate	Viable	[102]
Epoxyalkanes	*Pseudomonas oleovorans*	Entrapped in k-carrageenan	Treated	[103]
Ethylene oxide	*Mycobacterium* sp.	Entrapped in calcium	Treated	[104]
Fructose	*Actinoplanes missouriensis*	Entrapped in cellulose fibres	Treated	[105]
	Streptomyces phaeochromo-genes	Radiation polymerization of 2-hydroxyethyl methacrylate	Treated	[106]
	Kluyveromyces fragilis	Cross-linked by glutaraldehyde	Treated	[107]
Gluconic acid	*Gluconobacter oxydans*	Fixed on nylon	Viable	[108]
	G. oxydans	Entrapped in calcium alginatc	Viable	[109]
Glucose and galactose	*Lactobacillus bulgaricus, E. coli and Kluyveromyces lactis*	Entrapped in polyacrylamide	Treated	[110]
Isomaltulose	*Erwinia rhapontica*	Entrapped in calcium alginate	Resting	[111]
Lactic acid	*Lactobacillus delbruckii*	Entrapped in calcium alginate	Viable	[112]

acid conditions; and (ii) the saccharification by amylolytic enzymes. Numerous yeast strains can be used to produce alcohol from the sugars (Table 3.6 lists some of those which have been immobilized). A single-step operation to produce ethanol directly from starch using the amylolytic yeast *Saccharomyces diasticus* has recently met with success [115]. Free cells and immobilized cells (fixed to polyurethane foam cubes) produced similar yields of ethanol, about 70 g/l, with a conversion rate of about 75 per cent. The immobilized cells produced alcohol faster owing to the higher biomass present initially. The reaction was limited by α-amylase activity of the yeasts and the reaction rate could be increased using α-amylase enzymes or by inclusion of an immobilized mutant of the fungus *Endomycopsis fibuligera*.

The production of ethanol from starch-based raw materials is simple compared to the treatment that cellulosic materials such as straw require. All woody materials require extensive acid hydrolysis, usually at high temperatures, before the sugars can be fermented. The genetic manipulation of yeasts by the insertion of cellulase genes to allow them to ulitize wastes directly has been postulated. The creation of novel strains which could produce ethanol directly from cellulosic waste plant materials would be highly beneficial, but diffusion limitation would have to be overcome.

The use of yeasts to produce ethanol is one of the major growth areas in biotechnology. A definitive study of which method is most economically viable and which is the most economical feedstock is needed. The only published comparison of different production methods using the same immobilized preparations has shown that operating conditions for production using stirred-tank reactors and packed-bed columns containing *S. cerevisiae* in alginate gels are very different. Productivity in both systems was high but activity was lost as cells were killed by localized high ethanol concentrations. Recovery periods allowed activity to increase and although enzymes were repressed by high glucose concentration this situation is unlikely to be met in practice [116].

S. cerevisiae has been used in many immobilized forms to produce ethanol. Karkare *et al.* [117] have used a fluidized bed with k-carrageenan-immobilized *S. cerevisiae* to produce ethanol from a glucose feed. Prolonged use led to rupture of the gel due to growth of the yeast, and although productivity was twenty times higher than using free cells the presence of yeast cells in the effluent stream renders this system unsatisfactory. The most difficult problem with a fluidized-bed reactor is to ensure mixing without the use of air or vigorous stirring which could damage the particles. *S. cerevisiae* covalently bonded to cellulose gauze [118], to glass [119] or to wood chips [120], all produce ethanol at high concentrations, but cells can be released into the stream as the biomass increases.

Organisms other than yeasts can also produce ethanol from sugar solutions [121]. One of the most studied organisms is *Zymomonas mobilis*. This organism produces alcohol three to four times faster than *S. cerevisiae* strains and is also capable of producing 96 per cent of the theoretical amount compared to the 75 per cent for yeasts [122]. Conditions need to be maintained strictly anaerobic. The rate-limiting step in *Z. mobilis* hydrolysis is α-amylase activity and the reaction rate can be increased by co-immobilization of enzyme [116]. The development of new strains by genetic manipulation in order to extend the range of sugars which can be fermented, to increase productivity and to produce better flocculation characteristics, has been investigated [123, 124]. *Z. mobilis* has been used immobilized in alginate [102] in k-carrageenan (125) and fixed in towers [126]. The use of these systems with high ethanol-tolerant strains would allow total utilization of substrate in a short time with little or no production of biomass. *Z. mobilis* is widely regarded as being the organism of choice for future fermentations to produce ethanol [121].

Feedstocks other than glucose solutions have been evaluated. One of the more common sugars produced by acid hydrolysis of lignocellulosic materials from woods is xylose. This can be fermented by *Pachysolen tannophilus* or *Candida tropicalis* [127]. Although production rate, using calcium alginate immobilized preparations in column reactors was less than could be expected in theory, alterations to the operating conditions should overcome this problem. The use of mixed cultures of yeast to grow on the variety of sugars produced by acid or alkaline pretreatment of hardwoods and waste woods would also be advantageous. *P. tannophilus* has also been shown to be resistant to sulphite and hence it could be used to produce ethanol from the waste liquor from the softwood-processing industry as well as from the hydrolysis products of hardwoods [128]. Recently bacteria, mainly *Clostridium saccharolyticum,* have also been grown on xyloses obtained from the hemicellulose content of grasses, but production is slow and productivity low compared with using yeasts [129,130].

Another potentially valuable feedstock is whey; the annual production is 3.5 thousand million pounds, of which more than 1 thousand million pounds is thrown away. Whey is rich in lactose, which can be hydrolysed to galactose and glucose or fermented directly by *Kluyveromyces lactis* or *K. fragilis,* which have β-galactosidase activity, in a free or immobilized from [110, 131, 132]. The reaction rate is limited by β-galactosidase activity of these strains and the rate of alcohol production can be increased by the co-immobilization of enzyme from *E. coli* or *Lactobacillus bulgarius*.

Ethanol is widely used as a drink in the form of beer, wine, mead or spirits. The conventional beer-brewing process requires the yeast to produce alcohol whilst growing in a fermentation vessel. Subsequent removal of the yeast is necessary before the drink can be consumed. The total time for this process is 4–5 days and energy is expended in removing the excess yeast by centrifugation or filtration. An alternative method of brewing has been proposed in recent years, in which a high density of yeast is immobilized in a column reactor fed with the fermentable wort. The high biomass present in this process allows complete fermentation to occur in 24 hours, and there are few yeast cells present in the finished product [133]. The major problem using *Saccharomyces uvarum* in calcium alginate gel was the control of dissolved oxygen (DO) levels induced by mixing. DO in excess of 0.04 g/l produced a high diacetyl concentration which causes an off flavour in the beer. It has also been reported that continuous production results in a high α-amino nitrogen content in the beer, again resulting in a change in taste of the finished product [134]. An alternative process using *S. carlsbergensis* or *S. cerevisiae* fixed to Raschig rings has been proposed [135]. Both processes produce beer in a much shorter time period and are in use in Japan and the US for the commercial production of beer. Recently mead has also be produced by *S. cerevisiae* immobilized in calcium alginate gel with a honey feedstock [136].

Many plant species, e.g. Jerusalem artichoke, store sugars as fructans or inulins (β12,1-linked fructofuranose units). The production of ethanol from these sugars requires the use of organisms with high inulase activity like *Kluveromyces fragilis, Kluyveromyces marxianus, Candida pseudotropicalis* or *Debaromyces phaffi.* All have been immobilized as active preparations to DEAE cellulose [107]. The ethanol produced in this way can be converted to other chemicals like butanol, acetone and lactic acid using further micro-organisms [137]. Jerusalem artichokes have also been used as a source of high-fructose syrups which have better sweetener properties than sucrose or D-glucose and also acts as a preservative. It is widely used in the food and soft-drink industry [138].

3.4 IMMOBILIZED CELLS FOR ENERGY GENERATION

As reserves of fossil fuels become depleted an alternative source of energy is being sought. This source should be plentiful and replenishible, and natural resources like the sun, and waste materials like agricultural wastes, will become more important as sources of fuels. The use of immobilized biocatalysts to produce fuel ethanol has already been discussed (Section 3.3) and here the production of fuel gases like hydrogen and methane and the direct production of electricity in a biological fuel cell is discussed.

3.4.1 Hydrogen production

Hydrogen is considered to be a clean fuel because burning hydrogen produces only water vapour, which replenishes one of the raw materials used to produce hydrogen. Hydrogen generation can occur via the biologically catalysed biophotolysis of water by bacteria and algae, via photosynthetic bacteria, or via the fermentation of waste materials by anaerobic micro-organisms. This last method is currently the least efficient and least important, as the generation of methane from these same wastes is not only cheaper and more efficient but methane is also a more energy-rich fuel gas. A feasibility study using the fermentation of domestic wastes and wastewaters from the chemical and wood-pulp industry is under way [139]. By using mixed cultures rather than pure cultures it is hoped that systems producing hydrogen from a wide range of substrates can be developed. Some members of these mixed communities will possess cellulolytic or amylolytic activity, so that hydrogen can be produced in a single step from cellulosic and starch wastes. Further genetic manipulations of photosynthetic bacteria like *Rhodopseudomonas capsulata* will produce single species able to produce hydrogen from wastes [140,141]. The use of these strains immobilized in k-carrageenan [141] in agar [142], or in alginate [143] to produce hydrogen has already been investigated. The most obvious advantage of immobilization is the use of a high biomass such that rapid utilization of wastes is possible even in dilute streams without consequent wash-out of the cells. The use of immobilized cells for biophotolysis does pose the problem of light penetration. Long, thin reactors have to be used to prevent, or reduce, light limitation problems [144]. Removal of suspended solids from waste streams is also essential to increase light penetration. Using photosynthetic bacteria, high yields of hydrogen have been achieved with *R. capsulata* growing on malate and *R. palustis* growing on wastes from a sugar refinery, whey and straw paper-mill effluent [145,146].

Bacteria other than photosynthetic bacteria have been used to produce hydrogen from organic wastes. However, there is little reduction in BOD during this process, which is necessary before a waste can be discharged. Unless the production of hydrogen is coupled to an existing plant already reducing BOD the costs could become uneconomic. The best yields have been obtained with *Clostridium butyricum,* and alteration of supports and operating conditions could increase the yields further. However, it is unlikely that the production of hydrogen from organic wastes will ever replace methane production [147].

The production of hydrogen from water using biophotolysis is seen as the ultimate method of energy generation as it is clean, uses an infinite energy source (the sun) and a renewable raw material (water). However, liquid hydrogen is not an ideal product as it is expensive and dangerous to handle if it needs to be transported any distance [148,149].

Hydrogen production has been demonstrated using a range of immobilized whole-cell preparations and immobilized organelles (mostly chloroplasts) including processes where the substrates are present in wastewaters or are known to be common pollutants (Table 3.7). Perhaps the most interesting production method is the biophotolysis of water using cyanobacteria, micro-algae or photosynthetic bacteria. This makes use of a reversible hydrogenase enzyme which functions coupled to an electron carrier like ferredoxin or flavodoxin. This is extremely sensitive to oxygen, but many algal enzymes can be reactivated by a period of anaerobic conditions [156]. The stability problems and hypersensitivity to oxygen have tended to push interest in hydrogen generation by biophotolysis into the background but immobilization can aid stability, particularly if alginate is used. Alginate has proved most useful as it can carry a high cell loading without loss of mechanical stability [143]. Better yields are obtained by incorporating purified hydrogenase enzymes into the immobilized system [157] or by including chloroplasts in the system [147]. For the biophotolysis of water to become economically viable much more research is needed into the mechanics of hydrogen production and into the genetic control so that manipulations can be carried out to improve productivity.

3.4.2 Methane production

Methane production is very efficiently carried out by free micro-organisms in anaerobic digesters. Methane production from wastes by a mixed community immobilized in agar and an alginate-immobilized preparation of *Methanosarcin barkeri* has been demonstrated. It is unlikely that these methods will replace the conventional process [158,159]. However, anaerobic biofilm reactors are increasingly popular particularly in Sweden and Holland; this technology is fully described in Chapter 6.

3.4.3 Fuel cells

Hydrogen-producing bacteria can also be used in biological fuel cells where, rather than gas generation being important, the electrons are used to produce an electric current. Almost all fuel-cell experiments have used *Mastigocladus laminosus* [154], *Anabena* sp. [150] or bacteria like *Rhodopseudomonas rubrum* [160] or *Clostridium butyricum* [142]. In all these cases a small current was produced over a considerable period of time from light, energy and water, and an organic waste. Fig. 3.6 illustrates the basic fuel-cell configuration.

Using highly active microbial species maximizes the potential of the indirect fuel cell, and the selection of a mixed culture, rather than pure culture, would allow a range of substrates to be utilized. Most fuel cells of this type use free cells but recently *E. coli* immobilized to a surface has been used to produce an electric current via thionine as an electron transfer intermediary and lactose waste as a substrate [161]. This 20-ml cell gave 0.4 mW of power continuously for two weeks. The whole-organism fuel cell has advantages over the enzyme-based fuel cells [162,163], but the need for completely anaerobic conditions reduces the types of organisms which can be used in the cell.

There are basically two types of fuel cell: the indirect fuel cell, involving the microbial production of an electro-active substance like hydrogen and its subsequent oxidation at the anode of a conventional fuel cell [164]; and the direct fuel cell, which involves the direct transfer of electrons from a biological reaction to the electrode through an electron transfer intermediary. Although simpler in design the direct fuel cell is

Table 3.7 — The production of hydrogen using immobilized whole cells.

Organism	Nature	Immobilisation method	Substrate	Ref.
Anabena sp.	Resting	Entrapped in agar	Water	[150]
Anabena cylindrica	Resting	Absorbed on glass beads	Water	[151]
Chlorella vulgaris and *Clostridium butyricum*	Resting	Entrapped in agar	Water	[150]
Clostridium butyricum	Resting	Entrapped in polyacrylamide gel	Glucose	[20]
	Resting	Entrapped in agar	Wastewater	[152]
	Resting	Entrapped in polyacrylamide gel	Wastewater	[147]
Klebsiella pneumoniae and *Rhodopseudomonas rubrum*	Resting	Entrapped in agar	Glucose	[153]
Mastigocladus laminosus	Resting	Entrapped in calcium alginate	Water	
	Resting	Entrapped in PVA film	Water	[154]
Rhodopseudomonas capsulata	Resting	Entrapped in alginate	Malate	[155]
	Resting	Entrapped in k-carrageenan	Lactate and glutamate	[141]
R. rubrum	Resting	Entrapped in agar	Malate	[145]

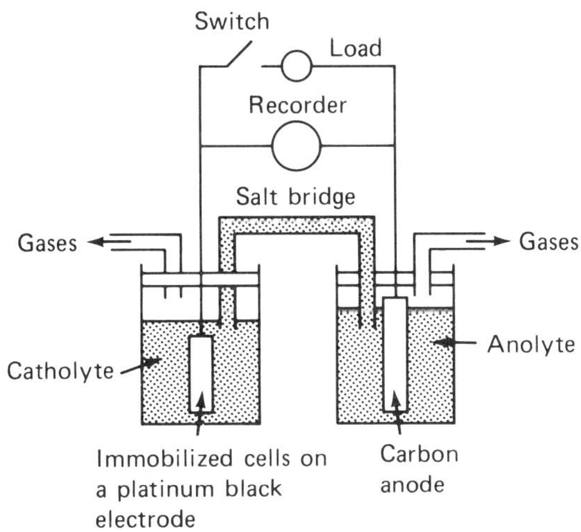

Fig. 3.6 — A schematic representation of a fuel cell using immobilized cells. The substrate necessary for the reaction would be in the catholyte.

hampered by the larger size of the protein molecules involved, and as they have to be in direct contact with the electrode surface, this limits the size and therefore the output of a cell.

Much more research is needed before fuel cells or hydrogen can be used to produce commercial quantities of power. Particular attention needs to be paid to the anaerobes, their genetics and their physiology, because these offer the best hope of successfully producing clean power from wastes or cheap, renewable raw materials.

Although it has been estimated that about 30 years' more research is needed to produce a commercially viable system, it is worth noting that in only six years the stability of the systems employing isolated chloroplasts has increased from five minutes to more than six hours, and bacterial systems are stable for several weeks.

3.5 IMMOBILIZED WHOLE CELLS AND WASTEWATER TREATMENT

Both conventional methods of sewage treatment — trickling filters and activated sludge — involve the use of immobilized whole cells as the biocatalysts for the removal of carbonaceous and nitrogenous wastes. In trickling filters the cells are immobilized in their own polymer matrix onto a surface, usually of stone or man-made plastic, in the form of a 'biofilm'. In an activated-sludge system, cells bind to each other through physical force interactions and in a polymer matrix to form 'flocs'. The end result, in both cases, is that cells are retained *in situ* at high cell densities, even at high flow rates, so that an effective treatment of sewage is made feasible. Biotechnological developments in recent years have been directed towards the upgrading of sewage works in order to make them more efficient and to improve the metal/phosphorus removal capabilities and the rate at which novel chemicals may be degraded.

3.5.1 Immobilized cells in the biofilm

Microbial cells naturally adhere to and colonize virtually any surface immersed in an aquatic environment. The tangled mass of cells which develops at the surface is termed the biofilm. There have been numerous reviews of biofilm formation and the kinetics of substrate removal at a biofilm/liquid interface [165–167].

The understanding of the way in which a biofilm develops and the physiology of the cells in the film is fundamental to our understanding of the mechanisms to be used to upgrade sewage-treatment facilities. The replacement of the traditional stone media with plastic media results in different organisms being held in a trickling filter bed. The type and composition of the plastic media can have an effect on the organisms attaching and their metabolic activity.

The fluidized-bed method of waste treatment also uses biofilm development as its base. Here the substrate is sand with a particle diameter usually less than 0.3 mm [168]. The sand particles are contained in a vertical column with an upward flow of the waste stream. Adjustment of the flow rate allows a compromise between keeping the particles in motion without carrying over into the treated effluent. These beds have a very large surface area available for treatment, usually in excess of 3000 m^2/m^3, and the treatment of high organic wastes in a minimum of area and time is possible [168]. Unfortunately energy costs of the aerobic process are high, because air or oxygen have to be used to keep the particles in motion [169]; however, the use of anaerobic treatment of wastes with methane generation [170,171] and for dentrification [172] is under active investigation.

Their major advantage over conventional works, however, is their ability to withstand shock loadings of very high BOD wastes, e.g. from the dairy industry, where BODs in excess of 2000 mg/l are not uncommon. It has been shown that fluidized beds can treat these wastes as effectively as low-BOD wastes, with over 90 per cent BOD removal in a few hours [170,173].

3.5.2 Use of immobilized cells to remove pollutants

Immobilized cells have a major role to play in the removal of organic pollutants in effluents from industrial plants or from partially treated sewage effluents. Highly active preparations of whole cells are commercially available as Fosbac or Actizyme preparations for seeding sewage effluents to treat wastes which occur at times, e.g. lignins, lipids and phenolic wastes. A better way of treating such wastes, though, is to introduce live organisms into a works and ensure their retention. Most introduced micro-organisms are quickly washed from a sewage works owing to their inability to compete successfully with the indigenous microflora. It is therefore of more importance to manipulate genetically successful colonizers of sewage works — either those present in sewage flocs or in biofilms — than to manipulate laboratory cultures in the hope that they survive in a works. These problems are more fully discussed in Ch. 8.

Some industrial effluents need on-site treatment before discharge to the sewage system. These wastes could be treated using specifically adapted micro-organisms. For instance, Chakrabarty *et al.* [174] have constructed organisms capable of degrading most of the components of oil and, although these *Pseudomonas* spp. cannot successfully compete in a sewage works, when used in isolation they are successfully maintained in the system. Similarly, organisms have been developed which can degrade pesticides [175–177]. The possibilities for genetic manipulation towards environmental uses are explored more fully in Ch. 10. One aspect (plasmid maintenance) is particularly relevant to the use of immobilized cells and is discussed briefly below.

Table 3.8 shows some compounds whose biodegradation has been achieved using

Table 3.8 — Biodegradation using immobilized whole-cell preparations

Organism	Immobilization	Substrate	Ref.
Achromobacter guttatus	Entrapped in polyacrylamide	E-aminocaproic acid cyclic dimer	[178]
Candida tropicalis	Entrapped in polyacrylamide	Phenol	[179]
E. coli	Entrapped in k-carrageenan	Catechol	[180]
Pseudomonas sp.	Entrapped in calcium alginate	Phenol	[181]
Pseudomonas putida	Entrapped in polyacrylamide	Benzene	[182]

immobilized preparations. Some wastes can be converted to useful products, most notably methane, via anaerobic digestion or anaerobic degradation in a fluidized bed. This process, however, is unlikely to use immobilized cells. The degradation of most xenobiotic and organic polutants requires genetically constructed organisms, usually harbouring plasmids. The maintenance of the plasmid in such strains puts a substantial drain on the energy-generating capacity of the cell, such that there is a tendency to 'lose' plasmids carrying out unnecessary functions. This is particularly the case if the plasmid is large or constructed from foreign DNA, either from another micro-organism species or from mammalian or plant DNA. The stability of plasmids in gel-immobilized *E. coli* has been investigated [180]. *E. coli,* with a plasmid encoding for catechol-2,3-dioxygenase, an enzyme involved in aromatic ring cleavage and hence in the biodegradation of xenobiotic pesticides, was stable for many months in k-carrageenan, even in the absence of a selection pressure. Other authors have also shown the activity of plasmids in immobilized *Bacillus subtilis* — produced rat proinsulin at a faster rate than free cells [183]. As these immobilized cells are often non-growing there is no loss of plasmids, unlike in actively cultured cells.

3.5.3 Immobilized cells to remove inorganic pollutants

Concern over the pollution of the environment caused by toxic heavy metals, phosphate and nitrates has led to the investigation of numerous methods to remove these pollutants from effluent streams.

The biological removal of phosphorus from sewage effluent was first reported in 1967 [184] and is now known to be due to the rapid uptake of orthophosphate by the biomass present in a sewage plant under aerobic conditions. Anaerobic conditions result in the release of this phosphate back into the effluent. A number of commercial phosphorus-removal processes are available in the US. The A/O system has sludge recycled to the anaerobic phase where phosphate is released [185]. In the aerobic phase phosphate is rapidly taken up and the settled sludge, rich in phosphate, can be used as a fertilizer. The phosphate-free effluent can be safely discharged. Other variants of this basic technique incorporate an additional nitrogen-removal phase [186,187] or a chemical precipitation step for phosphate removal as a chemical [188].

The removal of phosphorus is an energy-dependent process leading to the accumulation of polyphosphates in the cells [189]. It is believed that the major species involved are *Acinetobacter lwoffi* and *A. calcoaceticus* [190] however, as they form a very small component of the total biomass in a sewage works this role is open to question [191].

At present, this process uses free cells but for efficient operation it is dependent upon the rapid settlement of biomass and its removal from the system before the onset of anaerobic conditions and release of bound phosphate. Immobilized cells could be used to remove phosphate and are more readily removed from the system. If *A. calcoaceticus* or *A. lwoffi* are major organisms involved, immobilization of these species at high density would allow rapid removal of even high concentrations of phosphate. The use of non-growing cells should allow the diversion of more energy to the energy-dependent uptake process and simultaneously reduce the need for an organic carbonaceous source to be present. The system as it stands requires the phosphorus to be present in a stream with BOD which fuels the uptake process; hence this removal system will not function at industrial sites where, although phosphate may be abundant, organic material is not.

The removal of metals from wastewaters is not only of environmental importance to prevent gross pollution problems but can also be of economic importance. Most metals are removed by electroplating methods or chemical precipitation, but these are inefficient for dilute streams such as could be encountered at a sewage works. Recent work using a polyacrylamide gel-immobilized preparation of a *Citrobacter* sp. has shown that metals, at least divalent cations, can be removed at high efficiency from dilute metal streams [192,193]. The metals tested include cadmium, copper and uranium and their removal is dependent upon the pre-growth conditions, which induce an alkaline phsophatase enzyme, and the metal solution. Metals are removed as metal–phosphate complexes produced in the gel by the action of the phosphatase enzyme on an organic phosphate, β-glycerophosphate. The removal is limited only by the capacity of the gel before it becomes physically blocked. The metal can be stripped from the gel by running acid through the column or by washing the gel pieces in acid solution, and the gel can be reused. Cadmium could be removed from a liquid containing 200 μg/ml and concentrated to a density of 2.5 g/0.5 g of cells over a period of several weeks; 95–96 per cent removal efficiency of both cadmium [192] and uranium [193] was achieved. At present no other immobilized cell preparations have been used for the removal of metals, although the use of fungal hyphae and algal mats has been documented in the past [194]. *Zooloea ramigera,* which produces copious amounts of extracellular polymer, has also been used to accumulate heavy metals [195]. The metal cations simply bind to negatively charged groups on the cell surface and can easily be recovered by altering conditions which release the metal and recharge the organisms. This process again did not use immobilized cells, but providing the polysaccharide matrix remains intact on immobilization there is no reason to suppose that immobilized cells could not perform the same function as the free cells more efficiently. Methods involving simple absorption are better than those relying on intracellular accumulation of the metals, since the latter are energy-dependent and can be changed by changes in physicochemical conditions in the flow.

3.6 IMMOBILIZED WHOLE CELLS IN BIOSENSORS

Biosensors are likely to play an increasing role in the detection and analysis of small concentrations of pollutants. Since the sensors are often based on whole-cell preparations immobilized behind a protective membrane, they are briefly described here.

Enzymes have been used for the development of enzyme electrodes for the assay of a wide range of compounds because of their high specificity and high sensitivity. Many reviews are available describing the use and construction of these biosensors [196–198]. Microbial cells can also be utilized in these systems as they are equally good biocatalysts. The advantages and disadvantages of biosensors based on whole cells are detailed in Table 3.9.

Several types of sensor are described in the literature, and most are based on the use of the oxygen electrode or other ion-specific electrode as the detector. Table 3.10 lists the range of compounds which can be detected using a whole-cell-based sensor. Almost all the compounds are utilized as substrates by the organisms, causing a change in dissolved oxygen or other ion around an electrode. This change is measured and gives a good quantitative assessment of the substrate concentration.

Microbial sensors are probably more adaptable than enzyme electrodes, as their specificity for a particular substrate can be changed by altering growth conditions and they are more able to carry out multi-enzyme reactions. As an example of the versatility of microbial sensors. *Trichosporon brassicae* immobilized on a porous acetylcellulosic membrane was attached to an oxygen electrode. At pH 6 ethanol could be detected at concentrations up to 22 p.p.m. over 2100 assays [199,200], but at pH 4.75 the assay was specific for acetic acid [201]. BOD sensors based on *Clostridium butyricum*; in a type of fuel cell and *Trichosporon cutaneum* in an oxygen electrode have been developed to replace the traditional 5-day BOD test [202]. The sensor was linear up to 20 mg/l BOD with dilution required for the more concentrated effluents and influents. Results were obtained in 10 minutes and correlated well with 5-day BOD results for water from food-processing plants, a slaughterhouse and an alcohol-producing plant.

Table 3.9 — The advantages and disadvantages of using immobilized whole cells in biosensors.

Advantages	Disadvantages
(1) More adaptable as can be switched from one substrate to another	(1) Diffusion limitation lowers sensitivity compared to enzyme electrodes
(2) Regeneration of own cofactors	(2) Slower response, again due to diffusion barrier
(3) More stable	(3) Less specific as can respond to a wide range of substrates
(4) Cheaper as no expensive purification of enzymes required	(4) More susceptible to change in physicochemical conditions.
(5) Activity can be regenerated by regrowth	

An interesting electrode able to detect mutagens in water samples has been reported [147]. The sensor is based on two electrodes: one with a recombination-deficient *Bacillus subtilis* (rec^-) and the other with a wild-type *B. subtiis* (rec^+). Cells were immobilized by simple entrapment between porous cellulose acetate membranes around an oxygen electrode and used to measure the change in respiration rate of both organisms in the presence of mutagens. The rec^- *B. subtilis* was inhibited within one hour by 1.6 p.p.m. of the recognized mutagens mitomycin and captan. Other inhibitors like cyanide and antibiotics affected both the rec^- and the rec^+ strains identically; hence mutagens could be distinguished by their specific action on the rec^- strain.

Virtually all microbial sensors have so far been used for the detection of specific substances which are usually substrates for a single enzyme system or are detected because they are readily metabolized with the consumption of oxygen. It has recently been suggested that such sensors could also be used for the detection of specific pollutants in aquatic environments [230]. Here the principle would be to measure the degree of inhibition of an enzyme reaction caused by toxic substances such as pesticides, heavy metals and organic compounds which could cause problems in drinking-water purification plants or sewage-treatment plants. The chief problem with this possible application is that typical pollutants are present usually in sub-p.p.m. concentrations and are not inhibitory to immobilized cells or enzymes at these low concentrations.

3.7 THE USE OF IMMOBILIZED PLANT CELLS FOR INDUSTRIAL PURPOSES

With the advances over the last decade in our understanding of the techniques for the immobilization of microbial cells and the effects of such immobilization on modification and retention of cellular activity, attention is now being focussed on the use of

Table 3.10 — Chemicals assayed using microbial sensors.

Substance	Organism	Detection method	Ref.
Acetic acid	*Trichosporon brassicae*	Oxygen electrode	[201]
Ammonia	*Nitrosomonas europea*	Oxygen electrode	[203]
Arginine	*Streptococcus faecium*	Ammonia electrode	[204]
Aspartame	*Bacillus subtilis*	Oxygen electrode	[205]
Aspartate	*Bacterium cadaveris*	Ammonia electrode	[206]
BOD	*Clostridium butyricum*	Biofuel cell	[202]
Cephalosporin	*Citrobacter freundii*	pH electrode	[207]
Cholesterol	*Nocardia erythropolis*	Oxygen electrode	[208]
Cysteine	*Proteus morganii*	Sulphide electrode	[209]
Ethanol	*T. brassicae*	Oxygen electrode	[199]
Formic acid	*Cutyricum*	Biofuel cell	[142]
Gentamycin	*E. coli*	Oxygen electrode	[206]
Glucose	*Pseudomonas fluorescens*	Oxygen electrode	[210]
Glutamic acid	*E. coli*	Carbon dioxide electrode	[211]
Glutamine	*Sarcina flava*	Ammonia electrode	[212]
Histidine	*Pseudomonas* sp.	Ammonia electrode	[213]
Methane	*Methylomonas flagellata*	Oxygen electrode	[214]
Methanol	Unidentified	Oxygen electrode	[199]
Mutagens	*B. subtilis*	Oxygen electrode	[147]
NAD	*E. coli*	Ammonia electrode	[215]
Nicotinic acid	*Lactobacillus arabinosus*	pH electrode	[216]
Nystatin	*Saccharommyces cervisiae*	Oxygen electrode	[210]
Phenol	*T. cutaneum*	Oxygen electrode	[217]
Phenylalanine	*Leuconostoc mesenteroides*	Oxygen electrode	[218]
Phosphate	*Chromatium* sp.	Hydrogen current	[219]
Serine	*Clostridium acidiurici*	Ammonia electrode	[220]
Steroids	*Nocardia opaca*	Oxygen electrode	[221]
Streptomycin	*E. coli*	Carbon dioxide electrode	[222]
Sugars	*Brevibacterium lactofermentum*	Oxygen electrode	[223]
Sulphide	*Chromatium* sp.	Hydrogen current	[224]
Tetracycline	*E. coli*	Carbon dioxide electrode	[225]
Vitamins	*S. cerevisiae*	Oxygen electrode	[226]
	Lactobacillus fermentii	Oxygen electrode	[227]
Nitrate	*Azotobacter vinelandii*	Ammonia electrode	[228]
Nitroacetic acid	*Pseudomonas* sp.	Ammonia electrode	[229]

cells isolated from higher organisms, particularly plants. Although whole plants (e.g. water hyacinth) and algae have been used in pollution abatement and treatment of industrial wastewaters, the use of plant-cell tissue cultures has generally been confined to low-volume, high-cost production formation. Plants are noted for their metabolic versatility and are an important source of natural products, like steroids, alkaloids and other medicinal compounds (Table 3.11). The harnessing of this biosynthetic capacity into commercially viable processes has led to numerous advances in the use of cell tissue culture suspensions to produce chemicals and more recently in the use of immobilized cell preparations to produce the chemicals under more advantageous conditions [231–233]. These advances are briefly reviewed to illustrate the principles of cultivation, which are likely to apply equally well to environmental applications in the future.

Fig. 3.7 shows the steps necessary for the successful immobilization of plant cells.

Table 3.11 — The most commonly used secondary plant metabolites.

	Source	Use
Atropine	*Atropa belladonna*	Anticholinergic
Codeine	*Papaver somniferum*	Analgesic
Colchicine	*Colchicum autumnale*	Anti-gout
Digitoxin	*Digitalis purpurea*	Cardiovascular
Digoxin	*Digitalis lanata*	Cardiatonic
Emetine	*Uragoga ipecacuanha*	Amoebicide
Hyoscyamine	*Hyoscyamus niger*	Anticholinergic
Jasmine	*Jasminum* spp.	Perfume
Morphine	*Papaver somniferum*	Analgesic
Pilocarpine	*Pilocarpus jaborandi*	Cholinergic
Pyrethrin	*Chrysanthemum cinerariaefolium*	Insecticide
Quinidine	*Cinchona ledgeriana*	Antimalarial
Quinine	*Cinchona ledgeriana*	Antimalerial, bittering agent
Reserpine	*Rauwolfia serpentia*	Antrihypertensive
Scopolamine	*Datura stramonium*	Anticholinergic
Sennoside A and B	*Cassia angustifolia*	Cathartic
Steroids (from disogenin)	*Dioscorea deltoidea*	Antifertility
Thaumatin	*Thaumatococcus danielli*	Sweetener
Tubocurarine	*Chondrodendron tomentosum*	Muscle relaxant
Vincristine	*Catharanthus roseus*	Antileukaemic

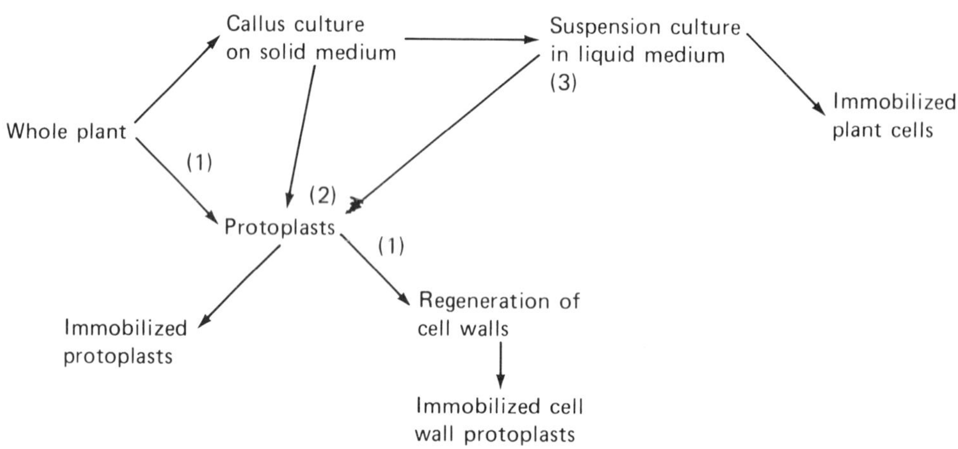

Fig. 3.7 — Scheme for the production of plant cells. (1) Enzyme treatment necessary. (2) Suitable for genetic manipulation. (3) Suitable for mutagenesis.

Fig. 3.8 shows how these immobilized preparations can be built into an industry able to produce large quantities of the desired products at an economically viable price. The key step for the industrial use of plant cells is the production of stable protoplasts, as these are more amenable to genetic manipulation than the intact plant cells. Genetic manipulation will enable new biosynthetic capabilities to be introduced. Alternatively, capabilities may be modified, either to increase product formation by alterations to the regulatory system, or by the removal of unnecessary side reactions.

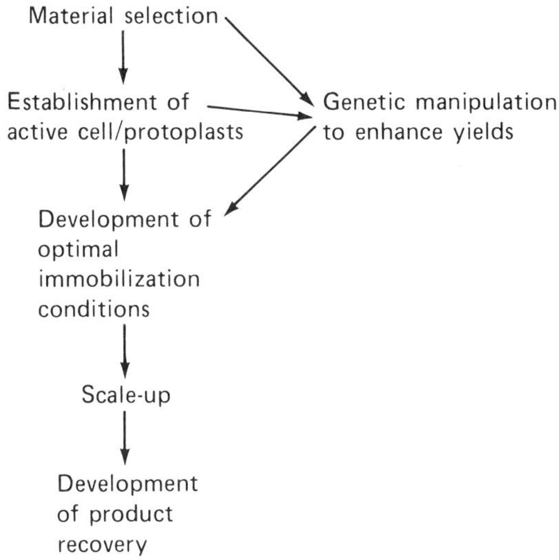

Fig. 3.8 — Framework for the successful development of plant cell biotechnology.

3.7.1 Industrial applications

From a biotechnological view the major importance of plant cells is their ability to carry out the synthesis of fine chemicals from either added precursors or *de novo* from simple precursors, and their ability to carry out simple biotransformations of preformed products, either prepared from harvested materials or chemically synthesized.

3.7.1.1 Synthesis from added precursors

Synthesis of novel compounds from added precursors is a type of multi-step transformation. However, these experiments or applications require detailed knowledge of biosynthetic pathways and the regulation of these pathways in plants.

The indole alkaloid, ajmalicine, was produced from added tryptamine and secologenin y alginate-entrapped *Catharanthus roseus* as shown in Fig. 3.9 [235]. The *C. roseus* beads were held in a column reactor and product was removed from a continuously circulating stream by chloroform extraction of the lipophilic materials. The chloroform also permeabilized the cells, allowing more product to diffuse from the cell vacuoles, but eventually led to cell death.

Other successful applications include the production of capsicum from phenylalanine by *Capsicum frutescens* cells [236] and the production of quinoline alkaloids from 4-hydroxy-2-quinoline by *Ruta gravolens* cells [237].

3.7.1.2 De novo synthesis

The synthesis of complex secondary products from simple precursors requires that the cells be highly active and metabolically intact. The use of cells to produce complex chemicals from simple materials is the keystone to the biotechnological

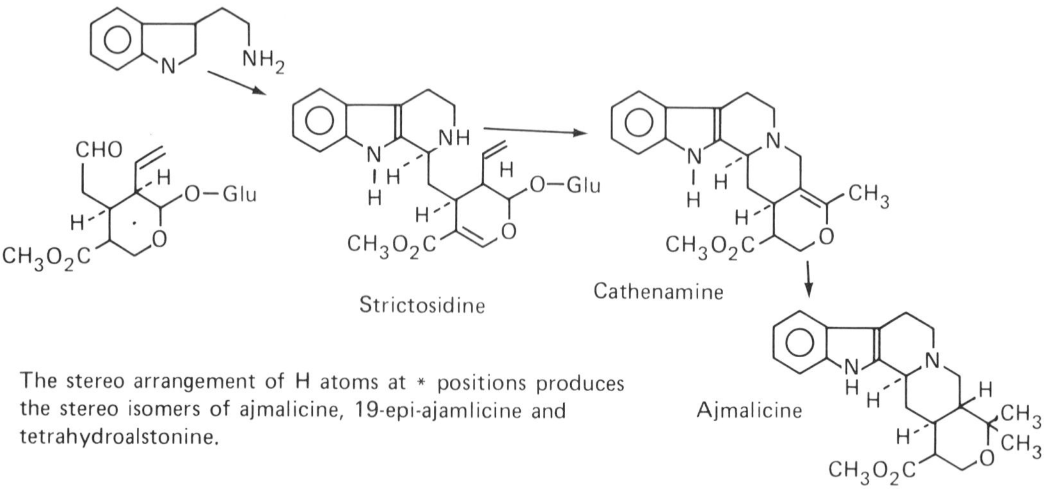

Fig. 3.9 — The synthesis of ajmalicine from simple precursors. The stereo arrangement of H atoms at * positions produces the stereoisomers of ajmalicine, 19-*epi*-ajmalicine and tetrahydroalstonine.

development of plant-cell techniques and much more useful than the biotransformations described above (Section 3.7.1.1). The key to success is to obtain high-yielding cell lines for immobilization. Plant-cell regulatory systems are poorly understood and, unlike the case with microbial cells where genetic manipulation and mutation is well understood, selection for high-yielding strains is very much a trial and error process [238]. The screening of thousands of specimens will ultimately yield a strain which over-produces a desired product, and subsequent culturing will yield more advanced cultures.

High anthraquinone-producing strains of *Morinda citrifolia* have been established and immobilized in calcium alginate gels [239,240]. The immobilized cells showed an increased production of secondary metabolites, probably due to the creation of micro-environments within the gel matrix more favourable to the production of secondary metabolites.

Further methods to increase yield have been investigated, including the use of fixed resting-phase cells [241], two-stage fermenters with free cells [242], oxygen tension [243] and changing nutrient supply [244].

3.7.1.3 *Biotransformations*

The production of valuable products by biotransformations from cheap precursors which cannot be transformed effectively by chemical or microbial means is a rapidly expanding field, reviewed by Reinhard and Alfermann [245].

Important biotransformations include those of phenolic compounds by *Datura ferox* and *Agrostemma githago;* of anilines by *Nictotiana tabacum;* of coumarins and alkaloids by *C. roseus* and of terpenoids by *Cannabis sativa.* The biotransformation of cardenolides is of special importance as the glycoside products have many uses in medicine, particularly for the treatment of heart disease. *Digitalis lanata* is the natural source of digoxin and digitoxin, but only the former is widely used. Stockpiles of digitoxin can be converted to digoxin cheaply using hydroxylation at the C-12 position, a reaction which the whole cell is unable to perform. Some representative transformations are shown in Fig. 3.10; others include acetylation or demethylation.

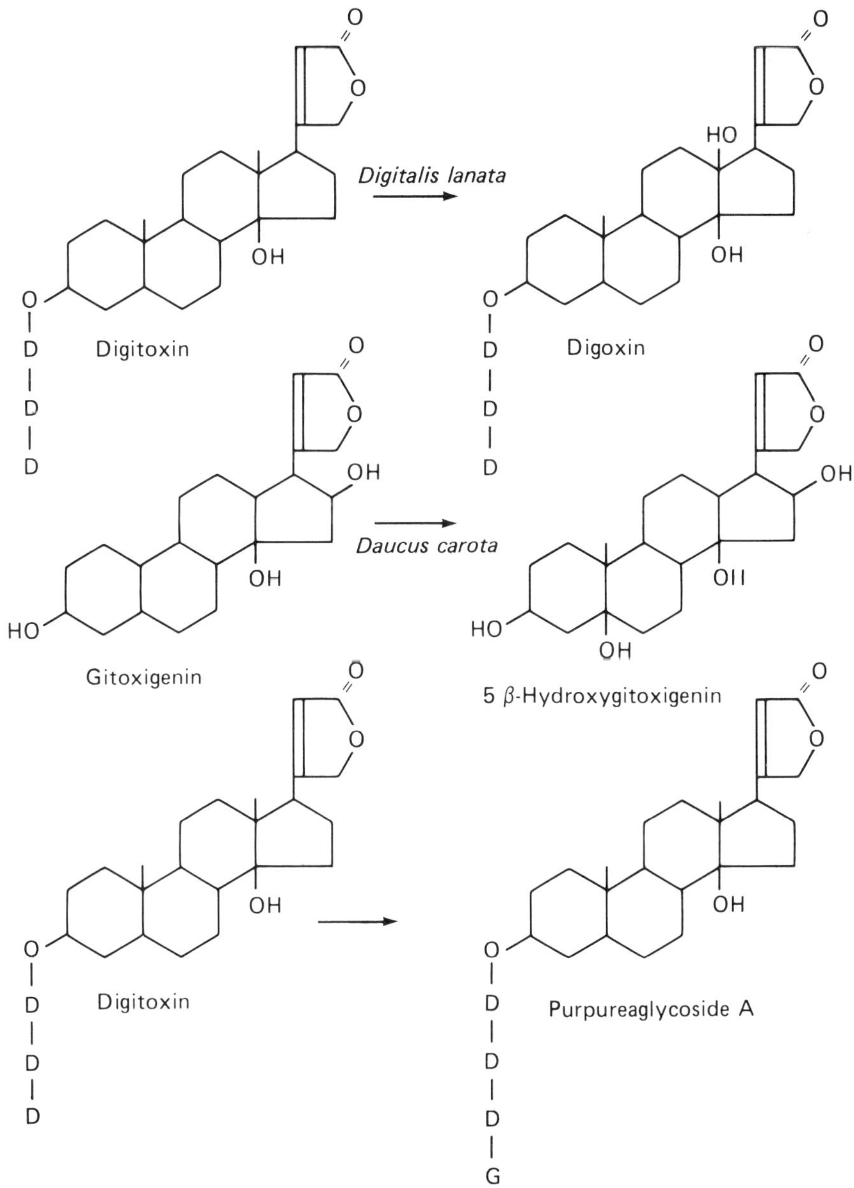

Fig. 3.10 — Biotransformation of glycosides and glycones by plant cells.

Table 3.12 shows the performance data of some alginate-entrapped plant-cell preparations carrying out batch or continuous biotransformations. The strain of *D. lanata* used had a high 12-hydroxylation capacity [246] and was stable until bead disruption occurred owing to cell growth within the matrix.

3.7.2 Future prospects

At present there are few established commercially viable processes which employ plant cells. This is hardly surprising given our lack of understanding of the biosynthesis of secondary plant metabolites. One of the major constraints holding back the development of immobilized microbial cell-production systems is the need to compete successfully with established processes using free cells. However, with immobilized plant cells there are no competing free-cell processes in commercial use. These processes have to prove themselves viable compared to the cost of harvesting a diminishing natural resource, chemical synthesis or transformation. The major drawback with plant cells is the need to have the product secreted into the medium. Most secondary metabolites are produced in the cell and stored in vacuoles; release requires some destruction of the cell structure. This limits the continuous use of immobilized systems but the problem is not insurmountable.

3.8 CONCLUSIONS

Although few processes have as yet reached commercial application the reasons have not been due to lack of productivity, rather to lack of ability to compete with the existing chemical or biological synthetic processes. Any change to technology involving immobilized biocatalysts will obviously involve capital costs and it is these costs which have so far decided industry against making a heavy investment in this new technology.

Nevertheless there are areas where lack of existing processes makes the use of immobilized biocatalysts attractive, particularly steroid biotransformations which are difficult to achieve with chemical methods and the use of plant cells to produce secondary metabolites for which there is no conventional industry. Further refinements of immobilization techniques and the successful genetic manipulation of the strains involved will make many more processes attractive if the cost of oil as the feedstock for the petrochemical industry rises in the near future. The development of alternative feedstocks for the production of chemicals, especially wastes or readily available natural materials, will then bring immobilized biocatalysts to the fore.

Table 3.12 — Biotransformation using plant cells.

Reaction	Species	Stability	Ref.
Digitoxin → digoxin	*Digitalis lanata*	>33 d	[235]
β-Methyldigitoxin → β-methyl-digoxin	*D. lanata*	61 d	[246]
Digitoxin → purpurea glycoside A	*D. lanata*	61 d	[246]
Digitoxigenin → 5β-hydroxydigitoxigenin	*Dauca carota*	20 d	[247]
Gitoxigenin → 5β-hydroxygitoxigenin	*D. carota*	30 d	[248]

REFERENCES

[1] Klein, J. and Wagner, F. (1983). Methods for the immobilisation of microbial cells. *Applied Biochemistry and Bioengineering,* **4,** 12–51.
[2] Chibata, I. (1978). *Immobilised Enzymes: Research and Development.* Wiley, New York.
[3] Trevan, M. D. (1980). *Immobilised Enzymes.* Wiley, New York.
[4] Chibata, I. (1979) Development of enzyme engineering—application of immobilised cell system. *Kem-Kemi,* **6,** 705–714.
[5] Kokubu, T., Karube, I. and Suzuki, S. (1981). Protease production by immobilised mycelia of *Steptomyces fradiae. Biotechnology and Bioengineering,* **23,** 29–39.
[6] Chibata, I., Tosa, T. and Sato, T. (1974). Immobilised aspartase containing microbial cells: preparation and enzymatic properties. *Applied Microbiology,* **27,** 878–885.
[7] Marconi, W. (1978). Immobilised enzymes. In: *Biotechnology,* DECHEMA Monograph, Vol. 82, Verlag Chemie, Weinheim, pp. 88–141.
[8] Bungard, S. J., Reagan, R., Rogers, P. J. and Wyncoll, K. R. (1979) The use of whole cell immobilisation for the production of glucose isomerase. *ACS Symposium Series,* **106,** 139–146.
[9] Klein, J. and Kluge, M. (1981). Immobilisation of microbial cells in polyurethane matrices. *Biotechnology Letters,* **3,** 65–70.
[10] Klein, J. and Eng, H. (1979). Immobilisation of microbial cells in epoxy carrier systems. *Biotechnology Letters,* **1,** 171–176.
[11] Kolot, F. B. (1981). Microbialcarriers—strategy for selection. Part II. *Process Biochemistry,* **16,** 30–35.
[12] Neidleman, S. L. (1984). Applications of biocatalysis to biotechnology. *Biotechnology and Genetic Engineering Reviews,* **1,** 1–38.
[13] Lidstrom, M. R. (1983). Directed genetic modification of potentially useful micro-organisms. *Biotechnology and Bioengineering Symposium,* **13,** 239–244.
[14] Blanch, H. W. (1983). Engineering challenges of genetic engineering. *Biotechnology and Bioengineering Symposium,* **13,** 467–479.
[15] Yamanoto, K., Tosa, T. and Chibata, I. (1980). Continuous production of L-alanine using *Pseudomonas dacunhae* immobilised with carrageenan. *Biotechnology and Bioengineering,* **22,** 2045–2054.
[16] Sato, F., Nisida, Y., Tosa, T. and Chibata, I. (1979). Immobilisation of *Escherichia coli* cells containing asparatase activity with k-carrageenan: enzymic properties and application for L-aspartic acid production. *Biochimica et Biophysica Acta,* **570,** 179–186.
[17] Fujimura, M., Kato, J., Tosa, T. and Chibata, I. (1984). Continuous production of L-arginine using immobilised growing *Serratia marcescens* cells: effectiveness of supply of oxygen gas. *Applied Microbiology and Biotechnology,* **19,** 79–84.
[18] Yamada, H., Shimizu, S., Shimada, H., Tani, Y., Takahashi, J. and Ohashi, T. (1980). Production of D-phenylglycine related amino acids by immobilised microbial cells. *Biochimie,* **62,** 395–399.

[19] Chibata, I. and Tosa, T. (1977). Transformations of organic compounds by immobilised microbial cells. *Advances in Applied Microbiology,* **22,** 1–27.

[20] Abbott, F. J. (1977). Immobilised cells. *Annual Report on Fermentation Processes,* **1,** 205–233.

[21] Constantinides, A., Bhatia, D. and Vieth, W. R. (1981). Immobilisation of *Brevibacterium flavum* cells on collagen for the production of glutamic acid in a recycle reactor. *Biotechnology and Bioengineering,* **23,** 899–916.

[22] Slowinski, W. and Charm, S. E. (1973). Glutamic acid production with gel-entrapped *Corynebacterium glutamicum. Biotechnology and Bioengineering,* **15,** 973–979.

[23] Karube, I., Kawari, M., Matsuoka, H. and Suzuki, S. (1985). Production of L-glutamate by immobilised protoplasts. *Applied Microbiology and Biotechnology,* **22,** 270–272.

[24] Wada, M., Kato, J. and Chibata, I. (1979). A new immobilisation method for microbial cells. *European Journal of Applied Microbiology and Biotechnology,* **8,** 241–247.

[25] Hirano, K., Karube, I. and Suzuki, S. (1977). Amino-acylase pellets. *Biotechnology and Bioengineering,* **19,** 311–321.

[26] Yamada, H., Yamada, K., Kumagi, H., Hino, T. and Okamura, S. (1978). Immobilisation of β-tyrosinase cells with collagen. *Enzyme Engineering,* **3,** 57–62.

[27] Para, G. Lucciardi, P. and Baratti, J. (1985). Synthesis of L-tyrosine by immobilised *Escherichia intermedia cells. Applied Microbiology and Biotechnology,* **21,** 273–279.

[28] MarechaL, P. D. L., Calderon-Seguin, R., Vandecasteele, J. P. and Azerad, R. (1979). Synthesis of L-tryptophan by immobilised *Escherichia coli* cells. *European Journal of Applied Microbiology and Biotechnology,* **7,** 33–44.

[29] Samejima, H., Kimura, K., Ado, Y., Suzuki, Y. and Tadokoro, T. (1978). Regeneration of ATP by immobilised microbial cells and its utilisation for the synthesis of nucleotides. *Enzyme Engineering,* **4,** 237–244.

[30] Yokozeki, K., Yamanaka, S., Utagawa, T., Takinami, K., Hirose, Y., Tanaka, A., Sonomoto, K. and Fukui, S. (1982). Production of adenine arabinoside by gel-entrapped cell of *Enterobacter aerogenes* in water organic cosolvent system. *European Journal of Applied Microbiology and Biotechnology,* **14,** 225–231.

[31] Asada, M., Morimoto, K., Nakanishi, K., Matsuno, R., Tanaka, A., Kimura, A. and Kamikubo, T. (1979). Continuous ATP regeneration using immobilised yeast cells. *Agricultural and Biological Chemistry,* **43,** 1773–1774.

[32] Sawa, Y., Klanayama, K. and Ochiai, H. (1980). Photosynthetic ATP accumulation using intact blue-green algal cells. *Agricultural and Biological Chemistry,* **44,** 1967–1969.

[33] Kimura, A., Tatsutomi, Y., Matsuno, R., Tanaka, A. and Fukuda, H. (1981). Some properties of an immobilised glycolysis system of yeast in fermentative phosphorylation of nucleotides. *European Journal of Applied Microbiology and Biotechnology,* **11,** 78–80.

[34] Keller, E. and Lingens, F. (1984). Synthesis of chorismic acid by immobilised cells of *Enterobacter aerogenes* 62–1. *Applied Microbiology and Biotechnology,* **20,** 3–5.

[35] Para, G., Rifai, S. and Baratti, J. (1984). Production of L-DOPA from pyrocatechol and D/L-serine by bioconversion using immobilised *Erwinia herbicola* cells. *Biotechnology Letters,* **6,** 703–708.
[36] Murata, K., Uchida, T., Tani, K., Kato, J. and Chibata, I. (1979). Continuous production of glucose-6-phosphate by immobilised *Achromobacter butyri* cells. *European Journal of Applied Microbiology and Biotechnology,* **7,** 45–51.
[37] Saif, S. R., Tani, Y. and Ogata, K. (1975). Preparation of glucose phosphate through transphosphorylation with immobilised cells. *Journal of Fermentation Technology,* **53,** 380–385.
[38] Murata, K., Tani, K., Kato, J. and Chibata, I. (1978). Continuous production of glutathione by immobilised *Saccharomyces cerevisiae* cells. *European Journal of Applied Microbiology and Biotechnology,* **6,** 23–27.
[39] Murata, K., Tani, K., Kato, J. and Chibata, I. (1980). Continuous production of glutathione using immobilised microbial cells containing ATP generating systems. *Biochimie,* **62,** 347–352.
[40] Murata, K. and Kimura, A. (1982). Some properties of glutathione biosynthesis deficient mutants of *Eschericha coli* B. *Journal of General Microbiology,* **128,** 1047–1052.
[41] Schnarr, G. W., Szarek, W. A. and Jones, J. K. N. (1977). Preparation and activity of immobilised *Acetobacter suboxydans* cells. *Applied and Environmental Microbiology,* **33,** 732–734.
[42] Rossi, J. and Clementi, F. (1985). L-Malic acid production by polyacrylamide gel entrapped *Pichia membranaefaciens. Biotechnology Letters,* **7,** 329–334.
[43] Takata, I., Yamamoto, K. Tosa, T. and Chibata, I. (1980). Immobilisation of *Brevibacterium flavum* with carrageenan and its application for continuous production of L-malic acid. *Enzyme and Microbial Technology,* **2,** 30–36.
[44] Takata, I., Tosa, T. and Chibata, I. (1984). Stability of fumarase activity of *Brevibacterium flavum* immobilised with k-carrageenan and Chinese gallotannin. *Applied Microbiology and Biotechnology,* **19,** 85–90.
[45] Omata, T., Iwamoto, N., Kimuro, T., Tanaka, A. and Fukui, S. (1981). Stereoselective hydrolysis of dl-menthyl succinate by gel-entrapped *Rhodotorula minuta* var. *texensis* cells in organic solvent. *European Journal of Applied Microbiology and Biotechnology,* **11,** 199–204.
[46] Hayashi, T. Tanaka, Y. and Kawashima, K. (1979). Immobilisation of microbial cells containing NAD-Kinase. *Biotechnology and Bioengineering,* **21,** 1019–1030.
[47] Uchida, T., Watanabe, T., Kato, J. and Chibata, I. (1978). Continuous production of NADP by immobilised *Achromobacter aceris* cells. *Biotechnology and Bioengineering,* **20,** 255–266.
[48] Murata, K., Kato, J. and Chibata, I. (1979). Continuous production of NADP by immobilised *Brevibacterum ammoniagenes* cells. *Biotechnology and Bioengineering,* **21,** 887–895.
[49] Murata, K., Tani, K., Kato, J. and Chibata, I. (1981). Glycolytic pathway as an ATP generating system and its application to the production of glutathione and NADP. *Enzyme and Microbial Technology,* **3,** 233–242.

[50] Tischer, W., Tiemeyer, W. and Simon, H. (1980). Stereospecific hydrogenations with immobilised microbial cells or enzymes. *Biochimie,* **62,** 331–339.
[51] Jack, T. R. and Zajic, J. E. (1977). The enzymatic conversion of L-histidine to urocanic acid by whole cells of *Micrococcus luteus* immobilised on carbodimide activated carboxymethyl cellulose. *Biotechnology and Bioengineering,* **19,** 631–648.
[52] OTA Report (1984). *Commercial Biotechnology. An International Analysis,* Office of Technology Assessment, Washington, DC, OTA-BA-218, 612 pp.
[53] Layman, P. H. (1983). Capacity jumps for amino acids. *Chemistry and Engineering News,* **1983,** 18–20.
[54] Choi, Y. T. and Tribe, D. E. (1982). Continuous production of phenylalanine using an *Escherichia coli* regulatory mutant. *Biotechnology Letters,* **4,** 223–228.
[55] Tosa, T., Sato, T., Mori, T. and Chibata, I. (1974). Basic studies for continuous production of L-aspartic acid by immobilised *Escherichia coli* cells. *Applied Microbiology,* **27,** 886–889.
[56] Nishida, Y., Sato, T., Tosa, T. and Chibata, I. (1979). Immobilisation of *Escherichia coli* cells having asparatase activity with carrageenan and locust bean gum. *Enzyme and Microbial Technology,* **1,** 95–99.
[57] Umemura, I., Takamatsu, S., Sato, T., Tosa, T. and Chibata, I. (1984). Improvement of production of L-aspartic acid using immobilised microbial cells. *Applied Microbiology and Biotechnology,* **20,** 291–295.
[58] Hirose, Y. and Okada, H. (1979). Microbial production of amino acids In: Peppler, H. J. and Perlman, D. (eds) *Microbial Technology,* 2nd ed., Academic Press, New York.
[59] Wood, L. L. and Carlton, G. J. (1984). Method and compositions for preparing phenylalanine. European Patent application EP 132–999.
[60] Charles, M. (1980). Production of 6APA using immobilised *Fusarium* spp. *Abstracts of International Fermentation Symposium.*
[61] Lee, G. M., Choi, C. Y., Park, J. M. and Han, M. H. (1984). The properties of immobilised whole cell of *Humicola* spp. with rifamycin oxidase activity. *Biotechnology Letters,* **6,** 143–148.
[62] Morikawa, Y., Karube, I. and Suzuki, S. (1979). Pencillin G production by immobilised whole cells of *Pencillium chrysogenum. Biotechnology and Bioengineering,* **21,** 261–270.
[63] Morikawa, Y., Karube, I. and Suzuki, S. (1980). Continuous production of bacitracin by immobilised living whole cells of *Bacillus* spp. *Biotechnology and Bioengineering,* **22,** 1015–1023.
[64] Venkatasubramaniam, K. and Vieth, W. R. (1979). Immobilised microbial cells. *Progress in Industrial Microbiology,* **15,** 61–86.
[65] Vandamme, E. J. (1983). Peptide antibiotic production through immobilised biocatalyst technology. *Enzyme and Microbial Technology,* **5,** 403–416.
[66] Freeman, A. and Aharonowitz, Y. (1981). Immobilisation of microbial cells in crosslinked, prepolymerised linear polyacrylamide gels: ;antibiotic production by immobilised *Streptomyces clavuligerus. Biotechnology and Bioengineering,* **23,** 2747–2759.
[67] Veelken, M. and Pape, H. (1982). Production of tylosin and nikkomycin by

immobilised *Streptomyces* cells. *European Journal of Applied Microbiology and Biotechnology,* **5,** 206–210.

[68] Egorov, N. S., Baranova, I. P. and Kozlova, Y. I. (1978). Nisin production by immobilised cells of *Streptococcus lactis. Antibiotiki (Moscow),* **23,** 872–874.

[69] Deo, Y. M. and Gaucher, G. M. (1983). Semicontinuous production of the antibiotic, patulin, by immobilised cells of *Penicillium urticae. Biotechnology Letters,* **5,** 125–130.

[70] Deo, Y. M. and Gaucher, G. M. (1984). Semi continuous and continuous production of Penicillin G by *Penicillium chrysogenum* cells immobilised in k-carrageenan beads. *Biotechnology and Bioengineering,* **2,** 285–295.

[71] Jensen, S. E. and Westlake, D. W. S. (1984). Production of penicillins and cephalsosporins in an immobilised enzyme reactor. *Applied Microbiology and Biotechnology,* **20,** 155–160.

[72] Omata, T., Iida, T., Tanaka, A. and Fukui, S. (1979). Transformation of steroids by gel-entrapped *Nocardia rhodocrous* cells in organic solvent. *European Journal of Applied Microbiology and Biotechnology,* **8,** 143–155.

[73] Koshcheyenko, K. A., Turkina, M. V. and Skryabin, G. K. (1983). Immobilisation of living microbial cells and their application for steroid transformations. *Enzyme and Microbial Technology,* **5,** 14–25.

[74] Mazumder, T. K., Sonomoto, K., Tanaka, A. and Fukui, S. (1985). Sequential conversion of cortexolone to prednisolone by immobilised mycleia of *Curvularia lunata* and immobilised cells of *Arthrobacter simplex. Applied Microbiology and Biotechnology,* **21,** 154–161.

[75] Sonomoto, K., Jin, I. N., Tanaka, A. and Fukui, S. (1980). Application of urethane prepolymer to immobilisation of biocatalysts: Δ'-dehydrogenation of hydrocortisone by *Arthrobacter simplex* cells entrapped with urethane prepolymers. *Agricultural and Biological Chemistry,* **44,** 1119–1126.

[76] Constantinides, A. (1980). Steroid transformation at high substrate concentrations using immobilised *Corynebacterium simplex* cells. *Biotechnology and Bioengineering,* **22,** 119–136.

[77] Larsson, P. O., Ohlson, S. and Mosbach, K. (1976) New approach to steroid conversion using activated immbolised micro-organisms. *Nature,* **263,** 796–797.

[78] Koshcheenko, K. A., Sukhodolskaya, G. V., Tyurin, V. S. and Skryabin, G. K. (1981). Physiological, biochemical and morphological changes in immobilised cells during repeated periodical hydrocortisone transformations. *European Journal of Applied Microbiology and Biotechnology,* **12,** 161–169.

[79] Lee, B. K., Brown, W. E., Ryu, D. Y. and Thoma, R. W. (1981). Sequential 11α-hydroxylation and dehydrogenation of 16α-hydroxycortexolone. *Biotechnology and Bioengineeing,* **13,** 503–515.

[80] Sonomoto, K., Usui, N., Tanaka, A. and Fukui, S. (1983). 9α-hydroxylation of 4-androstene-3,17-dione by gel-entrapped *Corynebacterium* sp. cells. *European Journal of Applied Microbiology and Biotechnology,* **17,** 203–210.

[81] Ohlson, S., Flygare, S., Larsson, P. O. and Mosbach, K. (1980). Steroid hydroxylation using immobilised spores of *Curvularia lunata* germinated *in situ. European Journal of Applied Microbiology and Biotechnology,* **10,** 1–9.

[82] Sonomoto, K., Hoq, M. M., Tanaka, A. and Fukui, S. (1983). 11β-hydroxy-

lation of cortexolone (Reichstein's Compound S) to hydrocortisone by *Curvularia lunata* entrapped in photocrosslinked resin gels. *Applied and Environmental Microbiology,* **45,** 436–443.

[83] Atrat, P., Huller, E. and Horhold, C. (1981). Steroid transformation with immobilised micro-organisms v continuous side chain cleavage of a cholesterol derivative with immobilised *Mycobacterium phlei* cells. *European Journal of Applied Microbiology and Biotechnology,* **12,** 157–160.

[84] Yamane, T., Nakatani, H., Sada, E., Omata, T., Tanaka, A. and Fuikui, S. (1979). Steroid bioconversion in water-insoluble organic solvents: Δ'-dehydrogenation by free microbial cells and by cells entrapped in hydrophilic or lipophilic gels. *Biotechnology and Bioengineering,* **21,** 2133–2145.

[85] Fukui, S., Sonomoto, K., Itoh, N. and Tanaka, A. (1980). Several novel methods for immobilisation of enzymes, microbial cells and organelles. *Biochimie,* **62,** 381–386.

[86] Yang, H. S. and Studebaker, J. F. (1978). Continuous dehydrogenation of a steroid with immobilised microbial cells: effect of an exogenous electron acceptor. *Biotechnology and Bioengineering,* **20,** 17–25.

[87] Maddox, I. S., Dunnill, P. and Lilly, M. D. (1981). Use of immobilised cells of *Rhizopus nigricans* for the 11α-hydroxylation of progesterone. *Biotechnology and Bioengineering,* **23,** 345–354.

[88] Fukui, S. and Tanaka, A. (1982). Immobilised microbial cells. *Annual Review of Microbiology,* **36,** 145–172.

[89] Lipinsky, E. S. (1981). Chemicals from biomass: petrochemical substitution options. *Science,* **212,** 1465–1471.

[90] Kennedy, J. F. (1978). Microbial cells immobilised and living on solid supports and their application to fermentation processes. *Enzyme Engineering,* **4,** 323–328.

[91] Osuga, J., Mori, A. and Kato, J. (1984). Acetic acid production by immobilised *Acetobacter aceti* cells entrapped in a k-carrageenan gel. *Journal of Fermentation Technology,* **62,** 139–149.

[92] Chua, J. W., Erarslan, A., Kinoshita, S. and Taguchi, H. (1980). 2,3-Butanediol production by immobilised *Enterobacter aerogenes* IAM1133 with k-carrageenan. *Journal of Fermentation Technology,* **58,** 123–127.

[93] Krouwel, P. G., Groot, W. J., Kossen, N. W. F. and van der Laan, W. F. M. (1983). Continuous isopropanol butanol ethanol fermentation by immobilised *Clostridium beyerinckii* cells in a packed bed fermentor. *Enzyme and Microbial Technology,* **5,** 46–54.

[94] Eikmeier, H. and Rehm, H. J. (1984). Production of citric acid with immobilised *Aspergillus niger. Applied Microbiology and Biotechnology,* **20,** 365–370.

[95] Nabe, K., Izuo, N., Yamada, S. and Chibata, I. (1979). Conversion of glycerol to dehydroxyacetone by immobilised whole cells of *Acetobacter xylinum. Applied and Environmental Microbiology,* **38,** 1056–1060.

[96] Adlercruetz, P., Holst, O. and Mattiasson, B. (1985). Characterisation of *Gluconobacter oxydans* immobilised in calcium alginate. *Applied Microbiology and Biotechnology,* **22,** 1–7.

[97] Chibata, I. and Tosa, T. (1980). Immobilised microbial cells and their applications. *Trends in Biological Sciences,* **5,** 88–90.

[98] Kierstan, M. and Bucke, C. (1977). The immobilisation of microbial cells, subcellular organelles, and enzymes in calcium alginate gels. *Biotechnology and Bioengineering,* **19,** 387–397.

[99] Sitton, O. R. and Gaddy, J. L. (1980). Ethanol production in an immobilised cell reactor. *Biotechnology and Bioengineering,* **22,** 1735–1748.

[100] Fukushima, S. and Hanai, S. (1982). Pilot operation for continuous alcohol fermentation of molasses in an immobilised bioreactor. *Enzyme Engineering,* **6,** 347–348.

[101] Ghose, T. K. and Bandyopadhyay, K. K. (1980). Rapid ethanol fermentation in immobilised yeast cell reactor. *Biotechnology and Bioengineering,* **22,** 1489–1496.

[102] Margaritis, A. and Wallace, J. B. (1982). The use of immobilised cells of *Zymomonas* in a novel fluidised bioreactor to produce ethanol. *Biotechnology and Bioengineering Symposium,* **12,** 147–159.

[103] Habets–Crutzen, A. Q. H., Brink, L. E. S., Van Ginkel, C. G., de Bont, J. A. M. and Tramper, J. (1984). Production of epoxides from gaseous alkenes by resting cell suspensions and immobilised cells of alkene utilising bacteria. *Applied Microbiology and Biotechnology,* **20**, 245–250.

[104] deBont, J. A. M., Van Ginkel, C. G., Tramper, J. and Luyben, K. C. A. M. (1983). Ethylene oxide production by immobilised *Mycobacterium* Py1 in a gas–solid reactor. *Enzyme and Microbial Technology,* **5,** 55–60.

[105] Linko, Y. Y., Pohola, L. and Linko, P. (1977). Entrapped glucose isomerase for high frutose syrup production. *Process Biochemistry,* **12,** 14–16.

[106] Kumakura, M., Yoshida, M. and Kaetsu, I. (1979). Immobilisation of *Streptomyces phaerochromogenes* by radiation induced polymerisation of glass forming monomers. *Biotechnology and Bioengineering,* **21,** 679–688.

[107] Workman, W. E. and Day, D. F. (1984). Enzymatic hydrolysis of inulin to fructose by glutaraldehyde fixed yeast cells. *Biotechnology and Bioengineering,* **25,** 905–910.

[108] Seiskari, P., Linko, Y. Y. and Linko, P. (1985). Continuous production of gluconic acid by immobilised *Gluconobacter oxydans* cell bioreactor. *Applied Microbiology and Biotechnology,* **21** 356–360.

[109] Tramper, J., Luyben, K. C. A. M. and van den Tweel, W. J. J. (1983). Dinetic aspects of glucose oxidation by *Gluconobacter oxydans* cells immobilised in calcium alginate. *European Journal of Applied Microbiology and Biotechnology,* **17,** 13–18.

[110] Ohmiya, K., Ohashi, H., Kobayashi, T. and Shimizu, S. (1977). Hydrolysis of lactose by immobilised micro-organisms. *Applied and Environmental Microbiology,* **33,** 137–146.

[111] Cheetham, P. S. J., Imber, C. E. and Isherwood, J. (1982). The formation of isomaltulose by immobilized *Erwinia rhapontica. Nature,* **299**, 628–631.

[112] Linko, P. (1980). Immobilised biological systems for continuous fermentation. In: Linko, P. and Lavinkaris, J. (eds) *Food Process Engineering,* Vol. 2, Applied Science, London.

[113] Palsson, B. O., Fathi-Afshar, S., Rudd, D. F. and Lightfoot, E. N. (1981). Biomass as a source of chemical feedstocks: an economic evaluation. *Science,* **213,** 513–517.

[114] Faust, U., Praeue, P. and Schlingmann, M. (1983). An integral approach to power alcohol. *Process Biochemistry,* **18,** 31–37.

[115] Amin, G., Standaert, P. and Verachterl, H. (1984). Effects of metabolic inhibitors on the alcoholic ferementation by several yeasts in batch or in immobilised cell systems. *Applied Microbiology and Biotechnology,* **19,** 91–99.

[116] Lee, T. M., Ahn, J. C. and Ryu, D. D. Y. (1983). Performance of an immobilised yeast reactor system for ethanol production. *Enzyme and Microbial Technology,* **5,** 41–45.

[117] Karkare, S. B., Dean, R. C. and Venkatasubramanian, K. (1985). Continuous fermentation with fluidised slurries of immobilised micro-organisms. *Biotechnology,* **3,** 247–251.

[118] Gainer, J. L., Kirwan, D. J., Foster, J. A. and Seyhan, E. (1980). Use of absorbed and covalently bound microbes in reactors. *Biotechnology and Bioengineering Symposium,* **10,** 35–42.

[119] van Haecht, J. L., Bolipombo, M, and Rouxhet, P. G. (1985). Immobilisation of *Saccharomyces cerevisiae* by adhesion: treatment of the cells by Al ions. *Biotechnology and Bioengineering,* **27,** 217–224.

[120] Gencer, M. A. and Mutharasan, R. (1983). Ethanol fermentation in a yeast immobilised tubular fermentor. *Biotechnology and Bioengineering,* **25,** 2243–2262.

[121] Rogers, P. L., Goodman, A. E. and Heyes, R. H. (1984). *Zymomonas* ethanol fermentations, *Microbiological Sciences,* **1,** 133–136.

[122] Scott, C. D. (1983). Ethanol production in a fluidised bed bioreactor utilising flocculating *Zymomonas mobilis* with biomass recycle.

[123] Skotnicki, M. L., Warr, R. G., Goodman, A. E., Lee, K. J. and Rogers, P. L. (1983). High productivity alcohol fermentations using *Zymomonas mobilis. Biochemical Society Symposium,* **48,** 52–86.

[124] Dally, E. L., Stokes, H. W. and Eveleigh, O. E. (1984). Recombinant DNA approaches for enhancing the ethanol productivity of *Zymomonas mobilis.* In: Wise, D. L. (ed.) *Organic Chemicals from Biomass,* Addison Wesley, Reading, Mass.

[125] Grote, W. G., Lee, K. J. and Rogers, P. L. (1980). Continuous ethanol production by immobilised cells of *Zymomonas mobilis. Biotechnology Letters,* **2,** 481–486.

[126] Prince, I. and Barford, J. (1982). Tower fermentation using *Zymomonas mobilis* for ethanol production. *Biotechnology Letters,* **4,** 525–530.

[127] Jeffries, T. W. (1982). A comparison of *Candida tropicalis* and *Pachysolen tannophilus* for the conversion of xylose to ethanol. *Journal of Bacteriology,* **12,** 103–110.

[128] Neirinck, L., Maleszka, R. and Schneider, H. (1982). Alcohol production from sugar mixtures by *Pachysolen tannophilus. Biotechnology and Bioengineering Symposium,* **12,** 161–169.

[129] Detroy, R. W., Cunningham, R. L. and Herman, A. L. (1982). Fermentation of wheatstraw hemicelluloses to ethanol by *Pachysolen tannophilus*. *Biotechnology and Bioengineering Symposium*, **12**, 81–89.
[130] Asther, M. and Kahn, A. W. (1984). Conversion of cellobiose and xylose to ethanol by immobilised growing cells of *Clostridium saccharolyticum* on charcoal support. *Biotechnology Letters*, **6**, 809–812.
[131] Linko, Y. Y., Jalanka, H. and Linko, P. (1981). Ethanol production from whey with immobilised living yeast. *Biotechnology Letters*, **3**, 263–268.
[132] Marweka, S. S. and Kennedy, J. F. (1984). Ethanol production from whey permeate by immobilised and free cells of *Kluyveromyces marxianus*. *Process Biochemistry*, **19**, 79–80.
[133] Onaka, T., Nakanishi, K., Inoue, T. and Kubo, S. (1985). Beer brewing with immobilised yeast. *Biotechnology*, **3**, 467–70.
[134] Pardonova, B., Polednikova, M., Sedova, H., Kahler, M. and Ludvid, J. (1982). Biocatalyst for beer production. *Brawissenschaft*, **35**, 254–258.
[135] Kolot, F. B. (1980). New trends in yeast technology — immobilised cells. *Process Biochemistry*, **15**, 2–8.
[136] Qureshi, N. and Tamhane, D. V. (1985). The production of mead by immobilised whole cells of *Saccharomyces cerevisiae*. *Applied Microbiology and Biotechnology*, **21**, 280–281.
[137] Kosaric, N., Wieczorek, A., Buczek, L. and Kliza, S. (1984). Semi-continuous and continuous production of alcohol from Jerusalem artichokes and fodder beets by *Saccharomyces diastaticus*. *Canadian Bioenergy, R. and D. Seminar, Proceedings*, 496–498.
[138] Fleming, S. E. and Groot-Wassink, J. W. D. (1979). Preparation of high fructose syrup from the tubers of the Jerusalem artichoke *(Helianthus tuberosus)*. *CRC Critical Review of Food Science and Nutrition*, **12**, 1–28.
[139] Hallenbeck, P. C. (1983). Immobilised micro-organisms for hydrogen and ammonia production. *Enzyme and Microbial Technology*, **5**, 171–180.
[140] Macler, B. A., Pelroy, R. A. and Bassham, J. A. (1979). Hydrogen formation in nearly stoichiometric amounts from glucose by a *Rhodopseudomonas sphaeroides* mutant. *Journal of Bacteriology*, **138**, 446–452.
[141] Franconi, N. and Vignais, P. M. (1984). Hydrogen production by *Rhodopseudomonas capsulata* cells entrapped in carrageenan beads. *Biotechnology Letters*, **6**, 639–644.
[142] Matsunaga, T., Karube, I. and Suzuki, S. (1980). A specific microbial sensor for formic acid. *European Journal of Applied Microbiology*, **10**, 235–243.
[143] Paul, F. and Vignais, P. M. (1980). Photophosphorylation in bacterial chromatophores entrapped in alginate gel: improvement of the physical and biochemical properties of gel beads with barium as gel-inducing agent. *Enzyme and Microbial Technology*, **2**, 281–287.
[144] Benemann, J. R. (1979). Production of nitrogen fertilizer with nitrogen-fixing blue-green algae. *Enzyme and Microbial Technology*, **1**, 83–90.
[145] Vincenzini, M., Balloni, W., Manelli, D. and Florenzano, G. (1981). A bioreactor for continuous treatment of waste waters with immobilised cells of photosynthetic bacteria. *Experientia*, **37**, 710–712.

[146] Zurrer, H. and Bachofen, R. (1979). Hydrogen production by the photosynthetic bacterium *Rhodospirillum rubrum. Applied and Environmental Microbiology,* **37,** 789–793.
[147] Karube, I., Matsunaga, T., Nakahara, T. and Suzuki, S. (1981). Preliminary screening of mutagens with a microbial sensor. *Analytical Chemistry,* **53,** 1024–1026.
[148] Egorov, A. M., Recharshky, M. V. and Berezin, I. V. (1981). Coal derived liquid fuels provide hydrogen for fuel cell power vehicle propulsion. *Chemical Institute,* **5,** 20–26.
[149] Bockris, J. O'M. (1981). The economics of hydrogen as a fuel. *International Journal of Hydrogen Energy,* **6,** 223–241.
[150] Kayano, H., Karube, I., Matsunaga, T., Suzuki, S. and Nakayma, O. (1981). A photochemical fuel cell system using *Anabena* N7363. *European Journal of Applied Microbiology and Biotechnology,* **12,** 1–5.
[151] Lambert, G. R., Daday, A. and Smith, G. D. (1979). Hydrogen evolution from immobilised culture of the cyanobacterium *Anabena cylindrica* B629. *FEBS Letters,* **101,** 125–128.
[152] Suzuki, S., Karube, I., Matsunaga, T., Kuriyama, S., Suzuki, N., Shirogami, T. and Takamura, T. (1980). Biochemical energy conversion using immobilised whole cells of *Clostridium butyricum. Biochimie,* **62,** 353–358.
[153] Weetall, H. H., Sharma, D. P. and Detar, C. C. (1981). Photometabolic production of hydrogen from organic substrates by free and immobilised mixed cultures of *Rhodospirillum rubrum* and *Klebsiella pneumoniae. Biotechnology and Bioengineering* **23,** 60–64.
[154] Ochiai, H., Shibata, H., Sawa, Y., Katoh, T. (1980). Procedures National Academy of Sciences, USA **72,** 2442-2444. "Living electrode", as a long-lived photoconverter for biphotolysis of water.
[155] Paul, F. and Vignais, P. M. (1981). Hydrogen production by the photosynthetic bacteria, *Rhodopseudomonas capsulata,* entrapped in alginate gels. In: Palz, W., Chartier, P. and Hall, D. O. (eds) *Energy from Biomass,* Applied Science, London.
[156] Benemann, J. R. (1978). Hydrogen production by microalgae. In: Klaus, D. L. (ed.) *Energy from Biomass and Wastes,* Institute of Gas Technology, pp. 558–578.
[157] Rao, K. K. and Hall, D. O. (1979). Hydrogen production from isolated chloroplasts. In: Barber, J. (ed.) *Topics in Photosynthesis,* Vol. 3, Elsevier, Amsterdam, pp. 299–329.
[158] Karube, I., Kuriyama, S., Matsunaga, T. and Suzuki, S. (1980). Methane production from wastewaters by immobilised methanogenic bacteria. *Biotechnology and Bioengineering,* **22,** 847–857.
[159] Scherer, P. Kluge, M., Klein, J. and Sahm, H. (1981). Immobilisation of the methanogenic bacterium *Methanosarcina barkeri. Biotechnology and Bioengineering,* **23,** 1057–1065.
[160] Berk, R. S. and Canfield, J. H. (1964). Bioelectrochemical energy conversion. *Applied Microbiology,* **12,** 10–12.
[161] Roller, S. D., Mason, J. R., Bennetts, M. P., Stirling, J. L., Delaney, G. M.,

Thurston, C. R. and White, D. R. (1983). A biofuel cell for utilisation of lactose wastes. In: *BioTech 83, Proceedings of the International Conference on Commercial Application and Implications of Biotechnology,* On Line Publications, Northwood, UK.

[162] Turner, A. P. F. (1983). Applications of direct electron transfer bioelectrochemistry in sensors and fuel cells. In: *BioTech 83, Proceedings of the International Conference on Commercial Applications and Implications of Biotechnology,* On Line Publications, Northwood, UK, pp. 643–654.

[163] Aston, W. J., Scott, L. P., Higgins, I. J., Turner, A. P. F. and Hill, H. A. O. (1983). Enzyme base methanol sensor. In: *Proceedings, Bioelectrochemistry and Bioenergetics Symposium.* Allen, M. J. and Usherwood, P. R. N. (eds.), Abacus Press, Tunbridge Wells, pp. 491–498.

[164] Suzuki, S., Karube, I. and Matsunaga, T. (1979). Application of a biochemical fuel cell to waste-waters. *Biotechnology and Bioengineering Symposium,* **8,** 501–511.

[165] Characklis, W. G., Trulear, M. G., Bryers, J. D. and Zelver, N. (1982). Dynamics of biofilm processes: methods. *Water Research,* **16,** 1207–1216.

[166] Trulear, M. G. and Characklis, W. G. (1982). Dynamics of biofilm processes. *Water Pollution Control Federation Journal,* **54,** 1288–1301.

[167] Characklis, W. G. and Cooksey, K. E. (1983). Biofilms and microbial fouling. *Advances in Applied Microbiology,* **29,** 93–138.

[168] Cooper, P. F. (1981). The use of biological fluidised beds for the treatment of domestic and industrial waste waters. *Chemical Engineer,* **371,** 373–376.

[169] Forster, C. F. (1980). Hydrogen production by *Rhodopseudomonas capsulata* cell entrapped in carrageenan beads. *Environmental Technology Letters,* **6,** 639–644.

[170] Bull, M. A., Sterritt, R. M. and Lester, J. N. (1983). Response of the anaerobic fluidised bed reactor to transient changes in process parameters. *Water Research,* **17,** 1563–1568.

[171] Mosey, F. E. (1978). Anaerobic filtration: a biological treatment process for warm industrial effluents. *Water Pollution Control,* **77,** 370–378.

[172] Jeris, J. S. and Owen, R. W. (1975). Pilot scale, high rate denitrification using a granular fluidised bed. *Water Pollution Control Federation Journal,* **47,** 2043–2057.

[173] Jewell, W. J., Switzenbaum, M. S. and Morris, J. W. (1981). Municipal wastewater treatment with the anaerobic attached microbial film expanded bed process. *Water Pollution Control Federation Journal,* **53,** 482–490.

[174] Chakrabarty, A. M. (1980). Plasmids and dissimilation of synthetic environmental pollutants. In: Stuttard, C. and Rozee, K. R. (eds) *Plasmids and Transposons, Proceedings of 4th Annual Conference,* Academic Press, New York, pp. 21–30.

[175] Slater, J. H. and Godwin, D. (1980). Microbial adaptation and selection. In: Ellwood, D. C., Hedger, J. N., Latham, M. J., Lynch, J. M. and Slator, J. H. (eds) *Contemporary Microbial Ecology,* Academic Press, London, pp. 137–160.

[176] Munnecke, D. M. (1979). Chemical, physical and biological methods for the disposal and detoxification of pesticides. *Residue Review,* **70,** 1–26.

[177] Munnecke, D. M. (1980). Hydrolysis of organophosphate insecticides by an immobilised enzyme system. *Biotechnology and Bioengineering,* **21,** 2447–2461.

[178] Chibata, I. and Tosa, T. (1980). Immobilised microbial cells and their applications. *Trends in Biological Sciences,* **5,** 88–90.

[179] Klein, J., Hackel, U., Schara, P., Washausen, P., Wagner, R. and Martin, C. K. A. (1978). Polymer entrapment of microbial cells: preparation and reactivity of catalytic systems. *Enzyme Engineering,* **4,** 339–341.

[180] Dhulster, P., Barbotin, J. N. and Thomas, D. (1984). Culture and bioconversion use of plasmid harboring strain of immobilised *E. coli. Applied Microbiology and Biotechnology,* **20,** 87–93.

[181] Bettmann, H. and Rehm, H. J. (1984). Degradation of phenol by polymer entrapped micro-organisms. *Applied Microbiology and Biotechnology,* **20,** 285–290.

[182] Somerville, M. J. and Ruffell, R. (1977). Benzene degradation by bacterial cells immobilised in polyacrylamide gel. *European Journal of Applied Microbiology,* **4,** 75–85.

[183]Mosbach, K., Birnbaum, S., Hardy, K., Davies, J. and Bulow, L. (1983). Formation of proinsulin by immobilised *Bacillus subtilis. Nature,* **302,** 543–545.

[184] Vacker, D., Connell, C. H. and Wells, W. N. (1967). Phosphate removal through municipal waste water treatment at San Antonio, Texas. *Water Pollution Control Federation Journal,* **39,** 750–771.

[185] Deakyne, C. W., Patel, M. A. and Krichten, D. J. (1984). Pilot plant demonstration of biological phosphorus removal. *Water Pollution Control Federation Journal,* **56,** 867–873.

[186] Burdick, C. R., Refling, D. R. and Stensel, H. D. (1982). Advanced biological treatment to achieve nutrient removal. *Water Pollution Control Federation Journal,* **54,** 1078-1086.

[187] Barnard, J. L. (1982). The influence of nitrogen on phosphorus removal in activated sludge plants. *Water Science Technology,* **14,** 31–45.

[188] Matsch, L. C. and Drnevich, F. R. (1978). Phostrip — a biological chemical system for removing phosphorus. *Proceedings of Advanced Water/Wastewater Treatment. Biological Nutrient Removal,* 115–142.

[189] Fuhs, G. W. and Chen, M. (1975). Microbiological basis of phosphate removal in the activated sludge process for the treatment of wastewater. *Microbial Ecology,* **2,** 119–138.

[190] Deinema, M. H., Habets, L. H. A., Scholten, J., Turkstra, E. and Webers, H. A. A. M. (1980). The accumulation of polyphosphate in *Acinetobacter. FEMS Microbiology Letters,* **9,** 275–279.

[191] Brodisch, K. E. U. and Joyner, S. (1983). The role of micro-organisms other than *Acinetobacter* in biological phosphate removal in activated sludge processes. *Water Science Technology,* **15,** 117–125.

[192] Macaskie, L. E. and Dean, A. C. R. (1984). Heavy metal accumulation by immobilised cells of a *Citrobacter* species. *Biotechnology Letters,* **6,** 71–76.

[193] Macaskie, L. E. and Dean, A. G. R. (1985). Uranium accumulation by immobilised cells of *Citrobacter* species. *Biotechnology Letters,* **7,** 457–462.

[194] Nakajima, A., Horikoshi, T. and Sakaguchi, T. (1982). Recovery of uranium by immobilised micro-organisms. *European Journal of Applied Microbiology and Biotechnology,* **16,** 88–91.
[195] Norberg, A. B. (1984). Accumulation of heavy metal ions by *Zoogloea ramigera. Biotechnology and Bioengineering,* **26,** 239–246.
[196] Aston, W. J. and Turner, A. P. F. (1984). Biosensors and biofuel cells. *Biotechnology and Genetic Engineering Reviews,* **1,** 89–120.
[197] Loew, C. R. (1984). Biosensors. *Trends in Biotechnology,* **2,** 59–65.
[198] Neujhar, H. Y. (1984). Biosensors for environmental control. *Biotechnology and Genetic Engineering Reviews,* **1,** 167–186.
[199] Karube, I. and Suzuki, S. (1980). Microbial sensors for ethyl alcohol, acetic acid and ammonia. *Enzyme Engineering,* **5,** 263–265.
[200] Hikuma, M., Kubo, T., Yasuda, T., Karube, I. and Suzuki, S. (1979) Microbial electrode sensor for alcohols. *Biotechnology and Bioengineering,* **21,** 1845–1853.
[201] Hikuma, M., Kubo, T., Yasuda, T., Karube, I. and Suzuki, S. (1979). Amperometric determination of acetic acid with immobilised *Trichosporon brassicae. Analytica Chemica Acta,* **109,** 33–38.
[202] Karube, I., Matsungaga, T., Mitsuda, S. and Suzuki, S. (1977). Microbial electrode BOD sensor. *Biotechnology and Bioengineering,* **19,** 1535–1547.
[203] Hikuma, M., Kubo, T., Yasuda, T., Karube, I. and Suzuki, S. (1980). Ammonia electrode with immobilised nitrifying bacteria. *Analytical Chemistry,* **52,** 1020–1024.
[204] Rechnitz, G. A., Kobos, R. K., Reichel, S. J. and Gebauer, C. R. (1977). A bio-selective membrane electrode prepared with living bacteria cells. *Analytica Chemica Acta,* **94,** 357–365.
[205] Renneberg, R., Riedel, K. and Scheller, F. (1984). Microbial sensor for aspartame. *Applied Microbiology and Biotechnology,* **21,** 180–181.
[206] Kobos, R. K. and Rechnitz, G. A. (1977). Regenerable bacterial membrane electrode for L-aspartate. *Analytical Letters,* **10,** 717–758.
[207] Matsumoto, K., Seijo, H., Watanabe T., Karube, I., Satoh, I., and Suzuki, S. (1979). Immobilised whole cell based flow-type sensor for cephalosporn. *Analytica Chemica Acta,* **105,** 429–432.
[208] Wollenberger, U., Scheller, F. and Atrat, P. (1980) Microbial membrane electrode for determination of cholesterol. *Analytical Letters,* **13,** 825–836.
[209] Jensen, M. A. and Rechnitz, G. A. (1978). Bacterial membrane electrode for L-cysteine. *Analytica Chimica Acta,* **101,** 125–130.
[210] Karube, I., Matsunaga, T. and Suzuki, S. (1979). Microassay of nystatin with a yeast electrode. *Analytica Chimica Acta,* **109,** 39–44.
[211] Hikuma, M., Obana, H., Yasuda, T., Karube, I. and Suzuki, S. (1980). A potentiometric microbial sensor based on immobilised *Escherichia coli* for glutamic acid. *Analytica Chemica Aca,* **116,** 61–67.
[212] Rechnitz, G. A., Riechel, T. L., Kobos, R. K. and Meyerhoff, M. E. (1978). Glutamine selective electrode that uses living bacterial cells. *Science,* **199,** 440–441.
[213] Walters, R. R., Moriarty, B. E. and Buck, R. P. (1980). *Pseudomonas*

bacterial electrode for determination of L-histidine. *Analytical Chemistry,* **52,** 1680–1684.

[214] Okada, T., Karube, I. and Suzuki, S. (1981). Microbial sensor system which uses *Methylomonas* sp. for the detection of methane. *European Journal of Applied Microbiology,* **12,** 102–106.

[215] Reichel, T. L. and Rechnitz, G. A. (1978). Hybrid bacterial and enzyme sensor with NAD response. *Journal of Membrane Science,* **4,** 243–250.

[216] Matsunaga, T., Karube, I. and Suzuki, S. (1978). Rapid determination of nicotinic acid by immobilised *Lactobacillus arabinosus. Analytica Chimica Acta,* **99,** 233–239.

[217] Neujhar, H. Y. and Kjellen, K. G. (1979). Bioprobe electrode for phenol. *Biotechnology and Bioengineering,* **21,** 671–678.

[218] Karube, I., Matsunaga, T., Teraoka, N. and Suzuki, S. (1980). Microbioassay of phenylalanine in blood sera with a lactate electrode. *Analytica Chimica Acta,* **119,** 217–276.

[219] Matsunaga, R., Suzuki, T. and Tomoda, R. (1984). Photomicrobial sensors for selective determination of phosphate. *Enzyme and Micriobial Technology,* **6,** 355–358.

[220] DiPaolantonio, C. L., Arnold, M.A. and Rechnitz, C. A. (1981). Serine selective membrane probe based on immobilised anaerobic bacteria and a potentiometric ammonia gas sensor. *Analytica Chimica Acta,* **128,** 121–127.

[221] Wollenberger, U., Scheller, F. and Atrat P. (1980). Microbial membrane electrode for steroid assay. *Analytical Letters,* **13,** 825–836.

[222] Simpson, D. L. and Kobos, R. (1982). Microbiological assay of tetracycline with a potentiometric carbon dioxide gas sensor. *Analytical Letters,* **15,** 1345–1359.

[223] Hikuma, M., Obana, H., Yasuda, T., Karube, I. and Suzuki, S. (1980). Amperometric determination of total assimilable sugars in fermentation broths with the use of immobilised whole cells. *Enzyme and Microbial Technology,* **2,** 234–238.

[224] Matsunaga, T., Tomoda, R. and Matsuda, H. (1984). Photomicrobial electrode for selective determination of sulphide. *Applied Microbiology and Biotechnology,* **19,** 404–408.

[225] Simpson, D. L. and Kobos, R. K. (1983). Potentiometric microbiological assay of gentamicin, streptomycin and neomycin with a carbon dioxide gas-sensing electrode. *Analytical Chemistry,* **55,** 1974–1977.

[226] Matiasson, B., Larsson, P. O., Lindahl, L. and Sahlin, P. (1982). Vitamin analysis with use of a yeast electrode. *Enzyme and Microbial Technology,* **4,** 153–157.

[227] Matsunaga, T., Karube, I. and Suzuki, S. (1978). Electrochemical microbioassy for Vitamin B1. *Analytica Chemica Acta,* **98,** 25–30.

[228] Kobos, R. K., Rice, D. J. and Flournoy, D. S. (1979). Bacterial membrane electrode for the determination of nitrate. *Analytical Chemistry,* **51,** 1122–1125.

[229] Kobos, R. K. and Pyon, H. Y. (1981). Application of microbial cells as multistep catalysts in potentiometric biosensing electrodes. *Biotechnology and Bioengineering,* **23,** 627–633.

[230] Harrison, L. A. and Flint, K. P. (1986). The use of immobilised enzymes to detect river pollutants. In: Hopton, J. W. and Hill, E. C. (eds) *Industrial Microbiology Testing,* in press.
[231] Rosevear, A. and Lambe, C. (1985). Immobilised plant cells. *Advances in Biochemical Engineering,* **31,** 37–58.
[232] Anderson, L. A., Phillipson, J. D. and Roberts, M. F. (1985). Biosynthesis of secondary products by cell cultures of higher plants. *Advances in Biochemical Engineering and Biotechnology,* **31,** 1–36.
[233] Brodelius, P. and Mosbach, K. (1982). Immobilised plant cells. *Advances in Applied Microbiology,* **28,** 1–26.
[234] Zenk, M. H. (1978). The impact of cell culture on industry. In: Thorpe, T. A. (ed.) *Frontiers of Plant Tissue Culture 1978,* University of Calgary, Canada.
[235] Brodelius, P., Deus, B., Mosbach, K. and Zenk, M. H. (1979). Immobilised plant cells for the production and transformation of natural products. *FEBS Letters,* **103,** 93–97.
[236] Yeoman, M. M., Miedzybrodzka, M. B., Lindsey, K. and McLauchlan, W. R. (1980). The synthetic potential of cultured plant cells. In: Sala, F., Parisi, B., Cella, R. and Ciferri, O. (eds) *Plant Cell Culture:* Results and Perspectives, Elsevier, Amsterdam, pp. 327–343.
[237] Boulanger, D., Bailey, B. K. and Steck, W. (1973). Formation of edulinine and furoquinoline alkaloids from quinoline derivatives by cell suspension cultures of *Ruta graveolens. Phytochemistry,* **12,** 2399–2405.
[238] Deus, B. and Zenk, M. H. (1982). Exploitation of plant cells for the production of natural compounds. *Biotechnology and Bioengineering,* **24,** 1965–1974.
[239] Zenk, M. H., El-Shagei, H. and Schulte, U. (1975). Anthroquinone production by cell suspension cultures of *Morinda citrifolia. Planta Medica Supplement,* 79–101.
[240] Brodelius, P., Deus, B., Mosbach, K. and Zenk, M. H. (1980). The potential use of immobilised plant cells for the production and transformation of natural products. *Enzyme Engineering,* **5,** 373–381.
[241] Pareilleux, A. and Vinas, R. (1984). A study on the alkaloid production by resting cell suspensions of *Catharanthus roseus* in a continuous flow reactor. *Applied Microbiology and Biotechnology,* **19,** 316–320.
[242] Sahai, O. P. and Shuler, M. L. (1984). Multistage continuous culture to examine secondary metabolite formation in plant cells: Phenolics from *Nicotiana tabacum. Biotechnology and Bioengineering,* **26,** 27–36.
[243] Tanaka, A., Sonomoto, K., Hoq, M., Usui, N., Nomura, K. and Fukui, S. (1982). Hydroxylation of steroids by immobilised microbial cells. *Enzyme Engineering,* **6,** 131–133.
[244] Lindsey, K. and Yeoman, M. M. (1983). Novel experimental systems for studying the production of secondary metabolites by plant tissue cultures. In: Mantell, S. H. and Smith, H. (eds) *Plant Biotechnology,* Cambridge University Press, Cambridge, pp. 29–36.
[245] Reinhard, E. and Alfermann, A. W. (1980). Biotransformations by plant cell cultures. *Advances in Biochemical Engineering,* **16,** 49–83.
[246] Alfermann, A. W., Boy, H. M., Doller, P. C., Hagedorn, W., Heins, J. W.,

Wahl, J. and Reinhard, E. (1977). Biotransformation of cardiac glycosides by plant cell cultures. In: Barz, W., Reinhard, E. and Zenk, M. H. Springer Verlag, Berlin, pp 125–141.

[247] Jones, A. and Veliky, I. A. (1981). Examination of the parameters affecting the 5-hydroxylation of digitoxigenin by immobilised cells of *Daucus carota*. *European Journal of Applied Microbiology and Biotechnology,* **13,** 84–89.

[248] Veliky, I. A., Jones, A., Ozubko, R. S., Przybylska, M. and Ahmed, F. P. (1980). 5β-Hydroxygitoxigenin, a product of gitoxigerin produced by *Daucus carota* culture. *Phytochemistry,* **19,** 2111–2112.

4

Immobilized enzymes and their applications

Lesley A. Harrison
Department of Environmental Sciences, University of Newcastle upon Tyne

4.1 INTRODUCTION

4.1.1 The use of soluble enzymes in industry

The industrial use of enzymes as biocatalysts dates back to the early 1900s with the development of enzyme processes to manufacture cheese products, bread, beer and wine. Although most of these processes can also be catalysed using chemicals, there are several distinct advantages in using enzymes [1]. Enzymes are able to differentiate between chemicals with closely related structures and can catalyse reactions at relatively low temperatures (0–110°C) and in the pH range 2–14. This results in high-quality products, fewer by-products and simpler purification procedures. In addition, enzymes are non-toxic and biodegradable, and can be produced in large quantities without the need for special chemical-resistant equipment.

Both animal and plant enzymes, together with microbial enzymes, have been used in industry in the past, but today the trend is changing as animal and plant enzymes are being replaced by microbial enzymes. This is mainly owing to the ease with which microbial enzymes can be obtained but also because these enzymes are generally more stable. Furthermore, the fact that micro-organisms can be genetically engineered, by DNA recombination or mutation, to produce higher levels of the required enzyme has also favoured the use of microbial enzymes in industry. Extracellular microbial enzymes are usually selected in preference to intracellular or cell-bound enzymes, as the former are easier to isolate.

The highly purified enzyme preparations which are required for some industrial processes can be obtained by a variety of enzyme-purification procedures; other industries operate using crude enzymes. The extent to which the enzyme is purified is dependent upon the cost of purification, the stability of the enzyme and whether unwanted side reactions are likely to occur.

4.1.2 Development of immobilized enzymes

An immobilized enzyme has been defined [2] as an enzyme which is converted into a distinct phase, usually water-insoluble and often of high molecular weight, which is separate from the bulk substrate-containing phase. Alternatively, Chibata [3] described an immobilized enzyme as an enzyme which is physically defined or localized in a defined region, enabling it to be reused in a continuous process.

Probably the most important feature of an immobilized enzyme is that it is reusable and therefore more economical to use in an industrial process than a soluble enzyme. This is particularly important in industries which use expensive enzymes. Other advantages of using immobilized enzymes are that they enable industrial processes to be operated continuously and enzyme reactions can be readily controlled. Furthermore, higher product yields can be obtained and product purification is made easier as problems associated with separation of the catalyst from the product are eliminated. In addition, enzyme immobilization can result in increased enzyme stability, as the support material can provide protection from changes in pH and temperature in the surrounding environment. An example which illustrates the advantages of using an immobilized enzyme in industry is that of L-amino acid production (Fig. 4.1). Using immobilized aminoacylase, the cost of amino acid

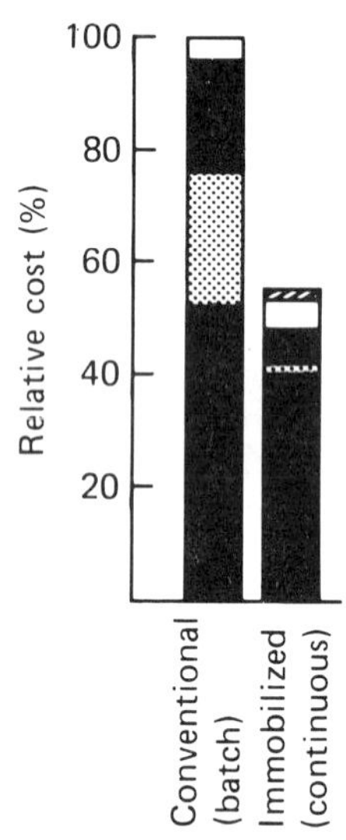

Fig. 4.1 — Comparison of relative cost for industrial production of L-amino acids (adapted from Chibata *et al.*, 1972 [88]).

production is reduced by 40% in comparison with the soluble enzyme owing to simpler product purification, increased enzyme stability, higher yields and automation of the process.

Immobilized enzymes do, however, have their drawbacks since there is the added cost of immobilizing the enzyme and possible loss of some enzyme activity during immobilization, particularly when chemical procedures are used. Furthermore, sophisticated equipment is usually required to control the process and there is an increased risk of microbial contamination owing to the greater length of time the immobilized enzyme process is in operation.

4.2 IMMOBILIZATION TECHNIQUES

The methods used to immobilize enzymes and whole cells are essentially the same and these techniques, and the principles behind them, will be considered here. As already stated, the principle of enzyme immobilization is the conversion of enzymes from a soluble state to an insoluble state, whether by the use of covalent bonding to a carrier, by entrapment in a gel or in an insoluble but carrier-free state (Fig. 4.2). For

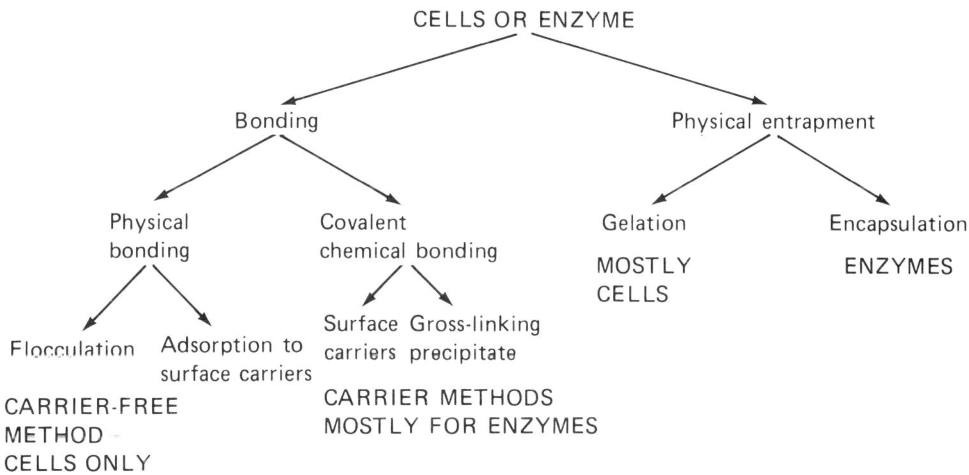

Fig. 4.2 — Techniques of enzyme/cell immobilization.

cells this principle is a little different as they cannot be defined as soluble, therefore immobilization consists of methods to cause the cells to be fixed in a particular place. Each of the immobilization methods will be described here with reference to their advantages/disadvantages for enzyme or whole-cell immobilization.

4.2.1 Surface immobilization

Various natural or synthetic materials, both organic and inorganic, have been used as carriers for immobilized enzymes and cells. This method of surface immobilization is more often used for enzymes than for cells. Carriers vary dependent upon their size, surface charge, nature of reactive groups, porosity, water retention capacity and physical strength. The degree of interaction between the surface and biocatalyst is also dependent upon the surface charge of the micro-organism, which to some extent can be altered by changing growth conditions, and on the charge on an enzyme.

Kolot [4,5] has described the properties of many carriers and assessed the strategy for the selection of a carrier suitable for immobilization and operation under a range of conditions.

4.2.1.1 Adsorption of biocatalysts onto solid supports

Probably the simplest procedure for immobilizing an enzyme or cell is to allow physical bonding to occur between functional groups of the biocatalyst and support material. This technique can be applied to a wide range of inorganic and organic support materials, e.g. ion-exchange resins, Sephadex, starch, agarose, carbon, cellulose, silica, alumina, glass and ceramics [3]. These supports can also be modified to improve the efficiency of bonding or to allow the co-immobilization of cofactors like NADH [6–8].

Ion-exchange resins, which readily adsorb proteins and are used in protein purification, have been widely used. However, they suffer greatly from the problem of enzymes and cells leaching from the support and consequent loss of activity. Adsorption is easily brought about by mixing the biocatalyst and ion-exchange resin, pouring onto a column, and eluting excess and loosely bound material. These immobilized preparations are most often used in a column-type bioreactor where they can be easily retained by filters or plugs. One of the great disadvantages of the use of ion-exchange resins is that they are not as easy to handle as some other supports like glass or ceramics, but enzymes and cells do not adsorb readily to these.

An advantage of the adsorption process over covalent attachment to other surfaces is that the adsorbed enzyme is subject to the minimum amount of distortion and, hence, there is little loss of activity. The enzyme or cell is usually adsorbed by simple physical linkages, such as ionic bonds, van der Waals' forces, hydrogen bonding or hydrophobic interactions, but all of these are greatly dependent upon the nature of the bulk phase. The influence of pH, ionic strength and support nature on adsorption have been analysed for both organic and inorganic supports [9–11]. Changes in pH, ionic strength or temperature can result in rapid desorption and hence loss of enzyme activity from the immobilized preparation. In some cases, the ease with which desorption can occur is beneficial, particularly if it is more important to retain the support material for reuse rather than the biocatalyst [12]. However, it also means that the enzyme or cell could be present in the finished product, which is unsatisfactory in many areas of the food or medical industries. Although the first commercial process using immobilized enzymes made use of aminoacylase adsorbed to DEAE–Sephadex [3] there has been little interest in using this method in more recent years.

4.2.1.2 Covalent attachment of biocatalysts to solid supports

A variety of supports have been used, at least in the laboratory, to provide a surface for the firm covalent attachment of a wide variety of enzymes and cells. These supports range from inorganic materials like porous glass, ceramics, steel, sand and metallic oxides through to organic materials like charcoal, cellulose polymers and Sephadex. Because enzymes are complex molecules they can have a multitude of reactive groups, ranging from amino and carboxyl groups to phenolic, sulphydryl and imidazole groups, and cells by their very nature also have many such surface groups. These groups can react with functional agents on the supports or on modified supports to form tight covalent bonds. Such firmly bonded enzymes or cells do not desorb under normal operating conditions. The types of surface used, or the linkage agents used, are limited only by the knowledge and expertise of the organic chemists who design them [13–15].

The most commonly used technique has been the cyanogen bromide (CNBr) activation of the organic support materials Sephadex and Sepharose, and commercial preparations of this modified support are now available [16]. The major drawback of this process and, indeed, any covalent bonding process is the loss of enzyme activity caused by covalent bonding, which affects the active site of the enzyme by direct inactivation or by steric hinderance. As covalent bonding is an uncontrolled reaction it is very difficult to predict how reactive the finished product will be and usually a trial-and-error process has to be adopted. This is not such a great problcm with wholc cclls as thc cnzymcs of concern arc usually intracellular and thus protected from inactivation, except in the rare event of the functional agent being taken up into the cell. However, covalent bonding can affect the ability of cells to take up nutrients and substrates as the functioning of permease enzymes can be affected by attachment to surfaces, particularly if micro-environments are created.

Cellulose was one of the first materials to be used as an enzyme support, but other naturally occurring polysaccharides, like starch, can also be used. Organic materials are used either in their natural form or after chemical modification to alter the nature of the covalent bonds which may be formed with the biocatalyst. This can have the effect of modifying enzyme function in some cases, and can also also affect the amount of enzyme activity retained after immobilization. Carboxymethyl cellulose is the most widely used of cellulose derivatives and this can be modified to a reactive hydrazide form by reaction with nitrous acid [17]. The major problem with the celluloses, and any naturally occurring polysaccharides, is that they are susceptible to microbial attack and hence can only be used under rigorous sterile conditions. They are also not physically stable enough to stand up to the mechanical stresses imposed by many industrial processes [18].

Few other organic supports have found widespread industrial use, although they have been used in the research laboratory as support materials for a wide variety of enzymes (Table 4.1). Polystyrene supports do have some added advantage as they

Table 4.1 — Some examples of surfaces used for the covalent attachment of enzymes.

Support	Modification	Ref.
Poly-*p*-amino polystyrene	Diazotization	[18]
Maleic anhydride	Copolymerized with vinyl ether	[89]
Polyacrylamide	Aminoethyl and hydrazide derivatives	[90]
Methacrylamide	Allylglycidyl ether	[90]
Polyacrylamide	Diazotization	[15]
Nylon	*o*-alkylation	[91]
Nylon	*N*-alkylation	[92]

are hydrophobic in nature and can therefore be used where hydrophobicity is an advantage, but all these supports are uneconomical unless some means can be found to make them reusable.

Because of the problems of microbial growth on organic supports, and consequent loss in activity, collapse of the structure and product contamination, there has been an increasing interest in the use of inorganic support materials, in particular in ceramics and porous glass. All these supports are rigid but can usually be adapted to provide supports with good porosity and high mechanical strengths [14]. However, the major drawbacks of many of these inorganic materials are their cost and weight, which limits the size of columns which can be used. One of the most widely used materials is controlled-pore glass. These glasses provide a large surface area for a small weight and can easily be modified to provide different attachment bonds. The most commonly used method is to activate the glass beads with γ-aminopropyl triethoxysilane and to bond the enzymes covalently with reagents which bond to reactive amino groups [19].

A surface of increasing importance for the development of biosensors, the interface between electronics and biochemistry, is the carbon electrode to which enzymes, and occasionally cells, can be fixed to produce the intimate contact necessary between sensor and effector. Glucose oxidase has been immobilized to carbon by simple adsorption [20] and covalently by carbodimide linkages [21].

4.2.1.3 Immobilization to waste materials

The preparation of immobilized enzymes is expensive as the enzyme has to be isolated from the cell and purified and finally fixed to a surface or entrapped in a gel matrix which has finite cost. Indeed, in many cases the material has been modified in some way to make it a better immobilization material. With whole cells part of this cost can be saved by doing away with the need to purify enzymes, but the cost of the immobilization material is still present.

In order to make the use of immobilized biocatalysts cost-effective it is necessary to reduce the cost of immobilization. Consequently, there has been a shift towards using waste materials as surfaces for immobilization, which in theory can have a negligible or even a negative cost. Materials which have been examined include chitin (waste from shellfish and crab-meat industries), collagen (from bone) and whole-cell wastes like yeast from the brewing industry and fungal mycelia from the organic acid and antibiotic industries. After sterilization these latter materials can be thought of as inert wastes with good flocculating properties and many reactive functional groups which can be used directly, or modified by physical, chemical or biochemical treatments.

4.2.2 Immobilization by entrapment

4.2.2.1 Entrapment in polymeric gels

Gel entrapment of biocatalysts is used mostly with whole cells, as their size makes it relatively simple to prepare porous networks which combine the desirable properties of complete cell retention with high porosity for substrate and product diffusion. Different polymers which can be polymerized at low temperature, or without the application of denaturing conditions, have been widely used. The prepared particles can have a wide variety of shapes and must have sound chemical and mechanical properties such that they do not collapse under operating conditions.

Entrapment is usually carried out to give the maximum retention of the desired enzyme activity within the cell. It is not usually essential to ensure cell viability, as 'dead' cells retain enzyme activity. The cells only need to be viable if it is intended to recharge enzyme activity periodically by placing the cells in a growth medium. Indeed, it is not uncommon for the cells to be immobilized and then treated in some way to increase permeability of the cell membrane to substrate or product.

(a) Use of water-soluble gels which set on cooling

Polymers like agar and gelatin are soluble at high temperatures but set when allowed to cool to produce a porous network of cross-linked chains. Agar is probably the more widely used of the two as, unlike gelatin, it does not become liquid above 30°C [3]. However, cells have to be added to agar at around 45°C, which can be harmful to some thermolabile enzymes, but usually the short time the cells/enzymes are held at this temperature is not denaturing. Both gelatin and agar can act as growth substrates for bacteria and fungi. Therefore, operating conditions must be completely sterile to prevent the growth and establishment of contaminants and subsequent collapse of the gel, which leads to loss of enzyme activity. Agar also has desirable mechanical properties, being rigid and having high tensile strength; gelatin, on the other hand, is mechanically unstable and tends to compact under pressure, reducing flow rates of liquid streams.

(b) Use of ionotropic gels

These water-soluble gels set when subjected to a change in ionic conditions. The most commonly used are two polysaccharide gels derived from seaweed, k-carrageenan and alginate, which set in the presence of potassium ions, and calcium ions, respectively.

k-carrageenan is a heteropolysaccharide with β-D-galactose sulphate and 3,6-anhydro-α-D-galactose repeating units. It is soluble above 40°C and sets in the cold in the presence of monovalent cations, usually potassium. The gel can be used to produce blocks or beads with good mechanical properties. The gel agent is completely non-toxic, but fungi are known to grow on it and this can lead to collapse of the structure. Growth of cells in the matrix is possible but respiration of the cells can produce excess gas, which ruptures the matrix structure. Methods have been developed to improve the mechanical strength of the gel by mixing with hexamethylenediamine and glutaraldehyde as hardening agents, or with locust bean gum as a copolymerized gel matrix [22].

Alginic acid, first used in 1975 [23], is derived mostly from *Macrocystis pyrfera* and is composed of 1 : 4-linked anhydro-β-D-mannuronic acid residues. It is soluble in cold water and produces gels in the cold when dropped into calcium ions or other divalent cation solutions. The gels are rigid and very stable except in the presence of phosphate ions, unfortunately a common constituent of biological buffers and growth media. Phosphate ions chelate calcium ions from the gel, causing the collapse of the cross-linked chains and consequent release of enzymes and cells. Alginate is a very versatile matrix as its porosity can be varied by selecting different sources of gel and it can be moulded into a variety of shapes, although spherical beads are the commonest working form. More recently the substitution of other cations, particularly barium, for calcium has overcome some of the problems caused by phosphate chelation and has extended the range of functions for which alginate beads can be used. It is rare for enzymes to be immobilized in alginate, for industrial purposes at least, but for whole cells this is the gelling agent most widely used.

(c) Entrapment during polymerization

Together with alginate, polyacrylamide has been used in the bulk of gel immobilization experiments. Polyacrylamide is produced from a mixture of acrylamide monomer, the cross-linking agent *NN'*-methylene bisacrylamide plus the polymerization catalyst and inducer ammonium persulphate and *NNN'N*-tetramethylethylenediamine (TEMED) or riboflavin and ultraviolet light. The use of bisacrylamide as the cross-linker produces a relatively poorly cross-linked structure as it is not very soluble, so that for all intents and purposes polyacrylamide gel is considered as a microporous homogeneous structure which is easily accessible to high molecular weight substrates. This degree of porosity makes it an unsuitable matrix for the retention of enzyme activity and hence it is seldom used as a matrix for immobilizing enzymes. The polymer can be cast as slabs and mechanically cut into pieces or blended [15], or it can be dropped into a hydrophobic, water-immiscible solvent to produce beads. The most widely used non-toxic suspending liquid is dibutylphthalate, which produces particles up to 2 mm in diameter [24].

This polymer has an advantage over the polysaccharide-based polymeric materials described above in that it will not support the growth of micro-organisms, hence the structure is not liable to decay. It is also chemically inert and mechanically sound. However, in the monomeric form it is a potent neurotoxin and is also carcinogenic. Because of this problem it is highly unlikely that polyacrylamide gel immobilized enzymes or whole cells would be used to produce substances intended for human consumption, and, although it is widely used in the laboratory as a test system, it is not common in industry.

Collagen has also been used to produce membranous matrices, with the enzymes trapped between the membrane sheets. Collagen has numerous binding sites, mostly free amino groups available for covalent coupling and is very supple but mechanically strong [25]. The presence of binding sites allows covalent attachment within the matrix, thus preventing any enzyme leakage, which can be a problem with other more open pore structures like alginate.

(d) Use of photocross-linkable resin prepolymers

For the successful industrial development of immobilized microbial cell techniques, gel matrices that have a variety of physicochemical properties are required which can be adapted, depending on the nature of the reaction to be catalysed. It is very difficult to meet these requirements using natural polymers because it is not always possible to produce derivatives with altered chemical properties. Synthetic polymer gels may be prepared by simple procedures from some monomers or from prepolymer chains and the properties of these synthetic polymers can be altered by changing side chains and reactive groups.

Kumakura *et al.* [26,27] used a combination of hydrophilic and hydrophobic monomers derived from methacrylate and polymerized by γ irradiation at -78°C to immobilize cells and enzymes, but these very low temperatures are not ideal for producing preparations active and functional at room temperature. More success has been met using photocross-linkable resin prepolymers and urethane prepolymers. These materials are already polymerized when they come into contact with the cell or enzyme and are therefore unlikely to cause denaturation or kill the cell. Acrylamide monomers, on the other hand, are introduced in the monomeric form and are often taken up by the cells, thereby reducing viability. These prepolymers also form matrices under extremely mild conditions. The photocross-linkable resins polymerize in the presence of a photosensitizer (benzoin ethyl ether) and ultraviolet light for a few minutes [28] and the urethane prepolymers form a matrix when mixed with an aqueous solution of the cells or enzymes [29]. There is no change in pH, ionic strength or addition of toxic chemicals necessary. More importantly no heat is generated, unlike the case of acrylamide polymerization when localized temperatures can reach 60°C or more, causing denaturation.

Both types of prepolymer can be chemically altered in the absence of the biocatalyst to produce polymers capable of making different network sizes. The polyurethanes have a multitude of functional groups, particularly isocyanate groups, which can react with hydroxyl and amino groups of the catalysts to fix them in place and, in the presence of water, to cross-link with the release of carbon dioxide gas. The rate at which this gas is released from the solution as microbubbles is controlled to produce a variable pore size. The rate of release is dependent upon the temperature and pressure at which the reaction is carried out. The major drawback of the polyurethane system is the low cell loading that can be achieved compared to other systems. This means that more material is required for a reaction, but the versatility and stability of the matrix more than compensates for these shortcomings.

The photocross-linkable resins are derived from polyglycol oligomers reacted with hydroxyethylacrylate or methacrylate derivatives and isophorone diisocyanate, and the relative proportions of these prepolymers in the final matrix determines the hydrophobicity of the biocatalyst. A high proportion of the prepolymer synthesized from hydroxyethylacrylate, isophorone diisocyanate and poly(propylene glycol) produces a hydrophobic gel well suited to reactions involving steroids and other lipophilic reactions [30,31].

As with polyurethane prepolymers the cell loading is low but the ability to control network porosity by controlling the size of the polyethylene glycol precursor and the control over hydrophobicity more than compensates.

The use of prepolymers of this type is the method which in future years will become most widespread. Once problems of cell loading, viability and stability have been overcome this highly versatile system will be widely used, particularly in industrial applications.

4.2.2.2 Microencapsulation in a semipermeable membrane

Microencapsulated enzymes are formed by enclosing enzymes in semipermeable polymer membranes, or in fibres, which allow the diffusion of low molecular weight substrates and products but are impermeable to enzymes and cells.

There are two basic methods involved in the formation of microencapsulated biocatalysts. In the first a water-immiscible solvent containing a polymer (e.g. cellulose, nitrate, polyethylene, polyvinylacetate or polystyrene) is dispersed in an aqueous enzyme solution. The polymer separates out around the microdroplets containing the biocatalyst [32,33]. In the second method, an aqueous solution of the enzyme, or cells, and monomer is dispersed in a water-immiscible solvent and a hydrophobic monomer is added, resulting in a polymer being formed at the interface of the droplets. This method has been used with nylon and polyurethane [3].

The main advantage of this method is the large surface area available for contact between the biocatalyst and the substrate within a relatively small volume. Multi-step enzyme reactions are also possible as there is a very real chance of immobilizing all the necessary enzymes within the same droplet, whereas multi-step reactions are not possible using any other enzyme-immobilization process. The main disadvantage is that the molecular weight of the substrate has to be very low to allow diffusion across the membranous barrier and the capsules are very prone to enzyme leakage as they are relatively fragile.

This method may become more important in the future as a means of directing medically important drugs or enzymes to specific sites in the body using biologically compatible membranous preparations.

4.2.3 Carrier-free methods

This method is used to produce enzymes or whole cells in a particle form and which still possess enzyme activity. It makes use of the natural tendency of some strains of micro-organisms to flocculate during fermentation owing to changes in ionic strength or pH of a medium. Perhaps the most obvious use is with yeasts which flocculate during the brewing process and make clearing the beer easier, and many fungi which grow as hyphal masses, again making separation easier.

The major advantage of this process is that it is mild, thus there is no loss of activity, but the mechanical stability of the flocs is usually very poor, resulting in contamination due to shear forces. However, high activity within the flocs is of great use. This method is limited to those species which adhere to one another easily, such as yeasts, fungi and some bacterial species which can produce polysaccharide (e.g. *Zoogloea ramigera*), or which can be engineered to do so. However, it is usually easier to make the cells or enzymes floccular by using chemical bonding to a surface and to each other.

A second carrier-free method of immobilization is the cross-linking technique which is based on the formation of covalent bonds between enzyme molecules or cells by means of bifunctional or multifunctional reagents. This leads to the formation of a cross-linked biocatalyst which is insoluble in water but still retains the bulk of its enzyme activity.

Conditions for cross-linking have to be chosen to give the minimum of distortion of the enzyme structure and the minimum of stereo hinderance of the active site. Reagents with two identical functional groups have been most widely used to produce insoluble aggregates, with glutaraldehyde the most commonly used reagent [34]. The linkages formed are irreversible and tolerant to extremes of pH and temperature, but the retention of activity is very dependent upon concentration of both biocatalyst and reagent, and the pH, temperature and ionic conditions under which immobilization is conducted.

Immobilization by this method has met with limited application because of the large amounts of enzyme/cells required, the uncontrollable nature of the reaction which leads to inactivation, and the unsuitable mechanical properties of the floc-like preparations. However, these preparations can be further immobilized by any of the methods described above and it is one means of ensuring that more than one enzyme function is immobilized to a surface, although this method can lead to very low retention of enzyme activity.

4.3 ENZYME REACTORS

An enzyme reactor is described as the vessel in which a reaction, catalysed by free or immobilized enzymes or cells, takes place, together with all the devices necessary for sampling and control. Various types of reactor have been designed and used on a laboratory or industrial scale, some of which are described below.

4.3.1 Batch reactor

A batch reactor usually consists of a large vessel with a stirrer and sometimes with the addition of baffles to improve agitation. It is suitable for use with both soluble and immobilized enzymes. The principle of this type of reactor is that the enzyme reaction is allowed to go to completion, the vessel is then drained and the product separated from the enzyme. If an immobilized enzyme has been used in the reactor it is separated from the product by filtration or centrifugation and, unlike a soluble enzyme which is removed by heat treatment, can be reused in the following batch process.

4.3.2 Continuous-flow reactor

The principle of the continuous-flow reactor is that there is a continuous supply of substrate and removal of products, hence it can only be used with immobilized enzyme preparations. There are two basic types of reactor which vary on the degree of stirring: a continuous-flow stirred tank reactor is stirred whilst a plug-flow reactor is not.

4.3.2.1 Continuous-flow stirred tank reactor (CSTR)

The basic design of a CSTR consists of a large vessel with a stirrer, an inlet to supply substrate and an outlet for product removal. A characteristic feature is that the contents of the reactor are well mixed, and the output has a similar composition to the mixture in the reactor. The immobilized enzyme is retained in the vessel by filtration of the outlet materials, or by addition of a settling tank to recover enzyme removed with the outlet. Alternatively, the enzyme is immobilized on the paddles of the agitator or onto the magnetically active material used to stir the contents of the reactor.

4.3.2.2 Plug-flow reactor (PFR)

A plug-flow reactor consists of a column packed with the immobilized biocatalyst, and the substrate is passed into the column at one end and out at the other. Unlike the CSTR, the contents of the reactor are not uniform since there is no stirring. Several variations of this basic design have been developed with the immobilized enzyme packed in different ways, for example, in a packed-bed reactor the enzyme is packed into a tall column, whereas in flat-bed and filter-bed reactors the enzyme is packed into a short column in the form of a flat bed and filter bed, respectively. Alternatively, the enzyme can be retained in a hollow fibre placed in the reactor (hollow-fibre reactor) with the substrate passed around the fibre. Since the hollow fibre is impermeable to the enzyme, but permeable to the substrate, the substrate can come into contact with the enzyme and the product diffuses back out. This design can be modified so that the substrate passes through the hollow fibre and the immobilized enzyme is retained in the reactor.

An intermediate of the CSTR and PFR is the fluidized-bed reactor, in which the immobilized enzyme is loosely packed in the column and uplifted by the high flow rate of the substrate. This results in a slight mixing of the contents of the reactor.

4.3.3 Choice of reactor

When deciding on the most appropriate type of reactor to use with an immobilized enzyme several factors have to be considered. The first decision to be made is whether the process is to be operated batchwise or continuously. Usually a continuous method is preferred so that full advantage can be taken of the immobilized enzyme and its reusability. Although there is a greater capital investment with a continuous system, labour costs are reduced considerably.

Batch reactors are generally used with soluble inexpensive enzymes and have only limited use with immobilized enzymes. Reasons for this include loss of immobilized enzyme as a result of repeated recovery cycles and loss of enzyme activity through mechanical shearing. In addition, conditions in a batch reactor change continuously, thereby making control difficult. The type of reaction for which a batch reactor would be suitable is one requiring high oxygen transfer or the addition of acid or alkali for pH control.

In considering the two types of continuous reactors, the CSTR is less expensive and easier to construct than the PFR, and also has the advantage of ease of access, enabling it to be recharged by addition of fresh enzyme. Consequently, this type of reactor is suitable for use with an immobilized enzyme having a relatively short half-life. On the other hand, conditions in the CSTR (low catalyst concentration, low substrate input concentration and high product concentration) can lead to product inhibition. As a result, the reactor is not suitable where high conversion reactions are required. Furthermore, as with the batch reactor, there may be a loss of enzyme activity resulting from mechanical shearing. Despite the fact that conditions within the CSTR can be controlled, this type of reactor is difficult to automate.

Disadvantages of the plug-flow reactor include limited access, making it virtually impossible to recharge with fresh enzyme, and it is difficult to control conditions in the vessel, such as pH, if acid or alkali are liberated during the reaction. The PFR is also more prone to substrate inhibition than the CSTR because there is no mixing and consequently the substrate concentration varies with length from the inlet and outlet. This type of reactor is also prone to fouling by particulate material and self-compression, resulting in localized channelling, owing to the packed nature of the column. Substrates of high viscosity can create problems as the high substrate flow rate required can cause channelling. Despite this, the PFR has its advantages as higher substrate conversions can be achieved using less enzyme, hence it is kinetically more efficient than the CSTR. In addition, the reactor can be easily automated.

The fluidized-bed reactor has all the advantages of packed-bed reactor together with its own advantages. It operates with a high catalyst concentration, high flow rate and short residence time, problems of channelling are eliminated and it is suitable for viscous or insoluble substrates. However, it does require a large input of power. This type of reactor is suitable for highly exothermic reactions as heat transfer and removal from the column are more effective, but as yet it has only been used on a laboratory scale.

In conclusion, there are no hard and fast rules to apply when deciding the type of reactor to use for a particular process. The advantages and disadvantages of the various types of enzyme reactors must be considered in detail in order to develop an industrial process which produces high product yields at a rapid rate, in the smallest type of reactor and at a minimum cost.

4.4 CURRENT INDUSTRIAL APPLICATIONS OF IMMOBILIZED ENZYMES

Immobilized enzymes which are currently employed in industry include glucose isomerase, aminoacylase, lactase, penicillin G/V acylase and nitrilase. Details of each of these industrial processes together with the method of enzyme immobilization are given in Table 4.2. Only one enzyme, glucose isomerase, is used on a large scale, with an estimated usage of 1500–1750 tonnes/year (Table 4.3), the other enzymes being used in considerably smaller amounts [35].

Published data on specific immobilized enzyme processes are sparse. This is mainly because those companies producing a particular immobilized enzyme are also involved with the manufacture of its product and details of the process are regarded as confidential. The details given in this section are therefore based on the information available in the literature.

Although environmental uses of such enzymes are rare, conversion of waste materials into more useful end products is feasible with immobilized systems. The technology, for the moment, must be illustrated by describing non-environmental applications where substantial research and process developments have been completed.

4.4.1 Food industry

Several industrial plants using immobilized lactase are currently in operation to hydrolyse lactose in milk products to glucose and galactose. Considerable attention has been given to this enzyme for two main reasons. Firstly, whey, a by-product of cheese manufacturing which contains relatively high amounts of lactose, is disposed of in large quantities every year, giving rise to waste disposal problems and loss of valuable nutrients. Secondly, a significant proportion of the world population is intolerant to lactose and therefore unable to drink milk. This led to the development of industrial processes to hydrolyse lactose in both whey and milk products. The use of lactase has been studied by many researchers and is reviewed by Greenberg and Mahoney [40] and Moulin and Galzy [41]. In the initial stages of process development, the soluble lactase system which was used had several drawbacks. Firstly, since lactase is an expensive enzyme it was uneconomical to use in the soluble form and, secondly, the low operational temperatures required to reduce microbial contamination resulted in the need for high enzyme levels to minimize hydrolysis time [35].

The first process using immobilized lactase was introduced by Snam Progetti in

Table 4.2 — Industrial applications of immobilized enzymes.

Industry	Enzyme	Method of immobilization	Process	Ref.
Food	Glucose isomerase	DEAE – cellulose	Conversion of glucose to fructose	[36]
		Cell homogenates cross-linked		[37]
		with glutaraldehyde		[38]
	Aminoacylase	DEAE–Sephadex	Resolution of DL-amino acids to L-form	[39]
Dairy	Lactase	Cellulose acetate fibres	Hydrolysis of lactose to glucose and galactose	[42]
Pharmaceutical	Penicillin G/V acylases	BrCN-activated Sephadex	Production of 6-APA from pencillin G	[44]
		Cellulose triacetate fibres, polyacrylamide		[43]
Chemical	Nitrilase	Polyacrylamide	Production of acrylamide from acrylonitrile	[35]

Table 4.3 — Commercial processes using glucose isomerase.

Company	Immobilization method
Gist-Brocades, Netherlands	*Actinoplanes missouriensis* cells entrapped in gelatin and cross-linked with glutaraldehyde
Miles Labs Inc., USA	*Streptomyces* cells cross-linked with glutaraldehyde and granulated
Novo Industry, Denmark	*Bacillus coagulans* cells lysed, cross-linked with glutaraldehyde and granulated
UOP, USA	*Streptomyces olivochromogenes* purified and immobilized with polyethyleneimine and glutaraldehyde on ceramic carrier Al_2O_3

cooperation with the Dairy Plant of Milan, in 1975 [42], and a plant with a capacity of 10 000 l/day has been in operation since that time, hydrolysing lactose in milk. The process uses yeast lactase immobilized in cellulose acetate fibres in a packed-bed reactor which operates as a batch and recycles the milk for 21 hours at 7°C. To overcome bacterial contamination problems the system is flushed periodically with sterilizing agents.

A process hydrolysing lactose in whey was introduced by the Valio Finnish Coop Dairies Association in 1978 [35]. Today this system operates using *Aspergillus niger* lactase to treat 80 000 l/day of whey. Additional steps to the process have been developed and include ion-exchange to dimineralize the whey and a concentration step after hydrolysis.

Although processes hydrolysing lactose on an industrial scale have been in operation since the mid-1970s only a few small plants exist, and further development has been slow as a number of economic and practical constraints still need to be overcome [35]. In particular, enzyme stability needs to be improved and problems due to fouling of the support need to be overcome.

Other food-industry processes provide an insight into the process improvements which have been achieved in recent years.

4.4.1.1 Glucose isomerase

The largest application of immobilized enzymes is found in the sugar industry, where glucose isomerase is used to convert glucose into fructose. Corn starch, a cheap and readily available substrate, is first hydrolysed by α-amylase and glucoamylase to produce high-glucose syrups. Then, by conversion into fructose using glucose isomerase, the sweetness of the syrup is increased so that it is similar to the more expensive sucrose (Fig. 4.3).

Since there is no convenient chemical process available for the isomerization of glucose, an enzymatic process using glucose isomerase was developed with the production of a syrup consisting of 42 per cent fructose, 50 per cent glucose and 8 per cent sugars. Glucose isomerase is an intracellular enzyme produced by several organisms, including *Streptomyces, Corynebacterium, Curtobacterium, Bacillus stearothermophilus* and *Flavobacterium arborescens.*

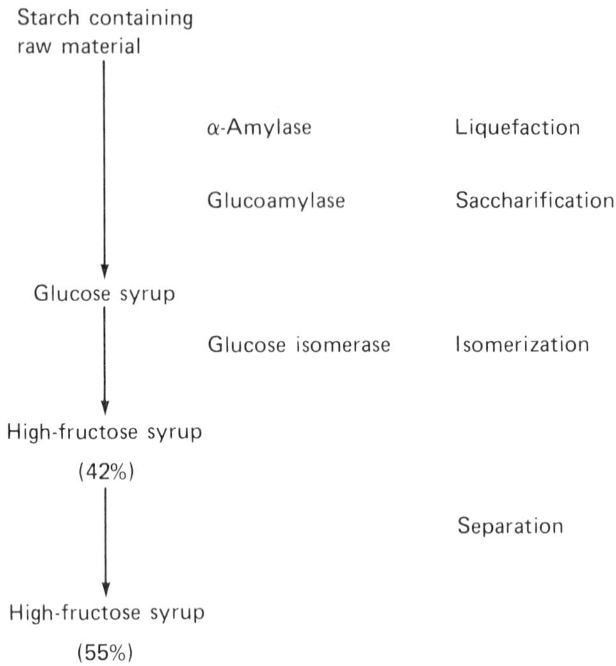

Fig. 4.3 — Production of fructose from starch.

The first immobilized enzyme system was introduced by Clinton Corn Products in 1969 [36] using glucose isomerase isolated from *Streptomyces* and adsorbed onto DEAE–cellulose. Unfortunately, this process had little success, mainly because it involved introducing sophisticated equipment into a well-esablished industry which used a soluble enzyme. However, with the continuing rise in price of raw sugar in the early 1970s the need for a reusable enzyme became obvious. Novo Industries introduced an immobilized enzyme process using cell homogenates of *Bacillus coagulans* cross-linked with glutaraldehyde [37,38] and, by the time the price of raw sugar fell in 1976, this new process had become well established. Initially, the process was operated as a batch system but since reaction conditions were not optimal, the long reaction time led to excessive colour and by-product formation. As a result, a packed-bed reactor was introduced, with optimal conditions and a shorter reaction time, producing purer products. Further developments then took place in 1978 with the production of a 55 per cent high-fructose syrup (HFS) resulting from improved ion-exchange techniques to separate fructose from glucose.

Several commercial processes have been developed using both cell-free and whole-cell preparations and these are listed in Table 4.2. The process developed by Novo Industries is now widely employed, with several plants operating in USA, Japan and Europe. Immobilized glucose isomerase is usually packed into a column reactor which is operated at about 60°C and pH 8 to produce syrups containing approximately 43 per cent (w/v) fructose. Enzyme preparations are generally stable for 2–4 months and it is estimated that 2–3 million tonnes of HFS are produced each year [36] and used mainly in the food and drinks industry.

4.4.1.2 Aminoacylase

Amino acids are used in the production of food supplements, medicines and cosmetic additives and are also the starting material for the synthesis of several other substances. They can be produced by fermentation or chemically. Several commercial processes have been developed using both cell-free and synthetic methods. Products of the latter tend to be optically inactive racemic mixtures of DL-amino acids which have to be resolved to the L form to be of much use (Fig. 4.4). Using

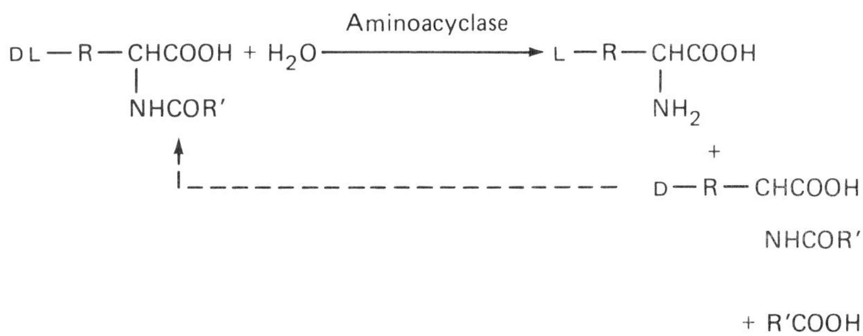

Fig. 4.4 — Optical resolution of DL-isomers.

aminoacylase, the DL-amino acid is hydrolysed to the L-amino acid and D-acylamino acid, which can be separated by their differences in solubility. The D form is then racemized to the DL form and used again.

Tanabe Seiyako Co. of Japan in 1969 developed a process using immobilized aminoacylase from *Aspergillus oryzae* for the industrial production of several amino acids [39]. This process was a success as it overcame the drawbacks of the soluble enzyme system, that is, the high costs for the separation of the enzyme and product. The method of immobilization used was that of DEAE–Sephadex and since this system could be regenerated by the addition of fresh enzyme, the enzyme having a half-life of 65 days at 50°C, this avoided having to discard the expensive support material. Other amino acids, including L-alanine, L-methionine, L-phenylalanine and L-valine, have been produced using this process.

4.4.2 Pharmaceutical developments

Examples drawn from the pharmaceutical industry illustrate how economics and the ability of immobilized enzyme methods to operate in continuous processes with very high reaction selectivity have stimulated major advancements in the technology. It is unlikely that profit margins in environmental treatment processes will ever be sufficient to support research and development on the scale seen in the pharmaceutical industry and so the latter will continue to be the source of technical innovations in this field. For this reason the processes for antibiotic conversions and manufacture of precursors of antibiotics are now described in some detail.

4.4.2.1 Production of antibiotics

(a) Semi-synthetic penicillins

Immobilized acylases have been successfully used for the conversion of 6-amino penicillanic acid (6-APA) to semi-synthetic penicillins. Abbott [45] reported on the synthesis of ampicillin from 6-APA and D-phenylglycine methyl ester using acylase from *Bacillus circulans* immobilized on DEAE–Sephadex (Fig. 4.6). Fibre-

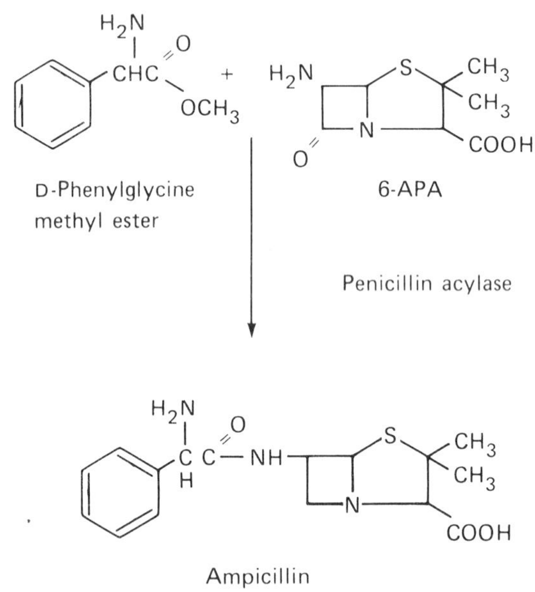

Fig. 4.5 — Production of ampicillin from D-phenylglycine methyl ester and 6-APA.

entrapped acylase (from *Escherichia coli*) has also been used to synthesize ampicillin and amoxycillin from 6-APA and esters of D-phenlglycine or *p*-hydroxyphenylglycine, respectively [46]. Owing to low yields and the availability of simple acylation procedures, these immobilized methods have not yet been developed on a commercial scale.

Two types of pencillins are produced by fermentation: penicillin G (phenyl acetyl-6-APA), and penicillin V (phenoxy acetyl-6-APA) both of which consist of a nucleus 6-APA and a side chain (Fig. 4.6). The antibiotic activity of the pencillin molecule is influenced by the side chain which, when removed and replaced with another, can alter the antibiotic spectrum and pharmokinetic properties. Removal of the side chain (deacylation) can be achieved by chemical and enzymatic procedures. With the increasing cost of chemical hydrolysis, enzymatic hydrolysis is becoming more economical to use, particularly with immobilized enzymes, as they can be reused and continuous bio-conversions can be carried out.

Several pharmaceutical companies, including Beecham, Bayer, Squibb and Astra, are currently operating immobilized enzyme processes for the production of 6-APA on an industrial scale [43]. It is estimated that about 60% of all APA

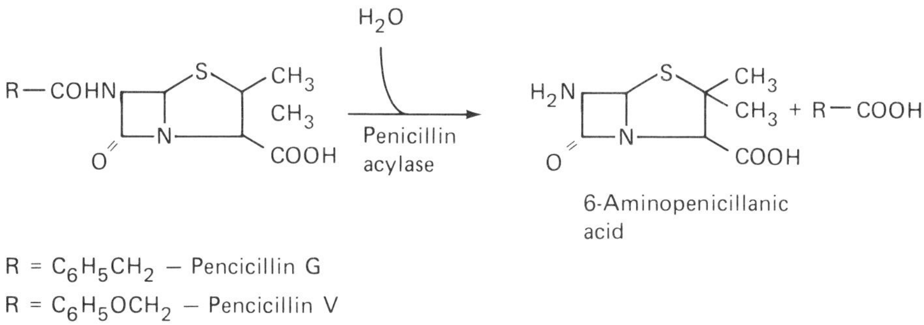

Fig. 4.6 — Formation of 6-APA by hydrolysis of penicillin.

produced today is made by the immobilized catalyst route and as an example of 6-APA production the process developed by Astra of Sweden has been described [44]. The hydrolysis of pencillin G to 6-APA is catalysed by penicillin acylase (from *E. coli*) immobilized on BrCN-activated Sephadex 200. When the immobilized enzyme process was first introduced by Astra it was operated as a batch system, hydrolysing 100 kg penicillin G at 35°C and pH 7.8. The immobilized enzyme could be used for up to 100 batches, provided that particular care was taken in the recovery and recharging of the enzyme to avoid loss of activity. To eliminate these problems, a recirculation process was introduced with added advantages of higher yields (90 per cent) and a purer product (98 per cent).

A major problem of 6-APA production is the formation of pencilloylated protein which, if not removed from the product, can cause serious allergenic reactions in man, such as anaphylactic shock. Astra found that there was no leakage of protein from the support and hence 6-APA was significantly less allergenic.

The wide range of techniques used to immobilize penicillin acylases have been reviewed by Vandamme [43] and include coupling to BrCN-activated polysaccharides (cellulose, Sepharose, Sephadex) and polyacrylamide supports, binding to resins with glutaraldehyde and entrapment in cellulose triacetate fibres.

(b) Cephalosporins

There are several reports on the use of immobilized enzymes to produce cephalosporins antibiotics. These antibiotics, which can either be synthesized from penicillins or made by direct fermentation, contain a 7-amino cephalosporonic acid nucleus (7-ACA) and a side chain (Fig. 4.7). Other antibiotics may be produced by removal of this side chain and addition of a required chain to yield antibiotics such as cephalothin (Fig. 4.8). Both deacylation and acylation can be accomplished using chemical or enzymatic procedures.

Cephalosporin can also be produced from penicillin by chemical expansion of the 5-membered thiazolidine ring of penicillin to the 6-membered dihydrothiazine ring of cephalosporins. The side chain can be removed either chemically or enzymatically to produce 7-aminodesacetoxycephalosporanic acid (7-ADCA), which can be acylated to produce semi-synthetic cephalosporins such as cephalexin.

Toyo Joco Co. Ltd have developed a process using acylase (from *Bacillus megaterium*) immobilized on celite to synthesize cephalothin from 7-ACA and 2-thiophenacetic acid, and cephacetile from 7-ACA and cyanoacetate [36]. Similar methods have also been used to produce cephalolysine and cephazoline. Snam

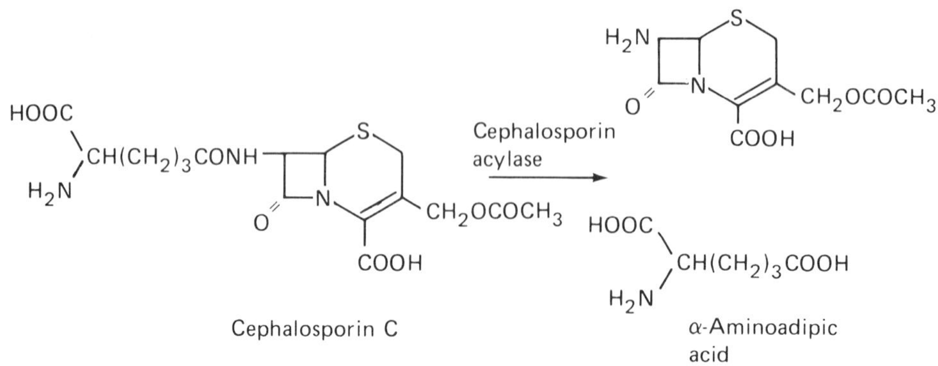

Fig. 4.7 — Hydrolysis of cephalosporin into 7-ACA.

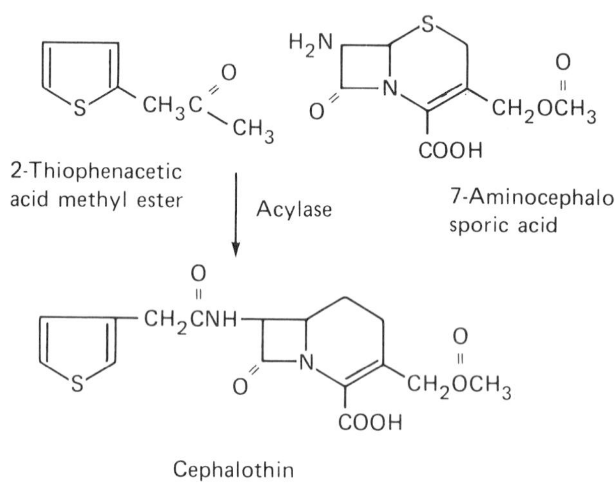

Fig. 4.8 — Formation of cephalosporin from 2-thiophenoacetic acid and 7-ACA.

Progetti used fibre-entrapped penicillin acylase for the synthesis of cephalexin from D-phenylglycine methyl ester and 7-ADCA.

The antibiotic activity of cephalosporin is not only dependent on the side chain but also on the substitution at the C_3 position and modification can be made at this position after deacylation. Ciba-Geigy Ltd have used acetylesterase from *Bacillus subtilis* immobilized on brick powder for the deacylation of cephalosporins [36].

It appears that immobilized enzymes for cephalosporin production should soon be developed on an industrial scale and might be able to compete with more conventional chemical procedures.

4.4.2.2 Enzymatic production of amino acids

Traditionally, amino acids are produced by microbial fermentation, but alternative methods of production have been investigated owing to problems associated with product purification and decontamination, together with the increasing use of amino acids as food additives.

Many systems have been developed for the production of L-lysine, two of which are described here. The first process involves a two-enzyme system consisting of L-α-amino-ε-caprolactam hydrolase (from *Cryptococcus laurentii*) and α-amino-ε-caprolactam racemase (from *Achromobacter cyclocraster*) immobilized on DEAE–Sephadex [2]. DL-α-Amino-ε-caprolactam, which is easily synthesized from cyclohexane, a by-product from nylon manufacturing, is hydrolysed by the first enzyme to produce L-lysine and D-α-amino-ε-caprolactam. The later product is then converted by the second by the second enzyme to the DL form. (Fig. 4.9).

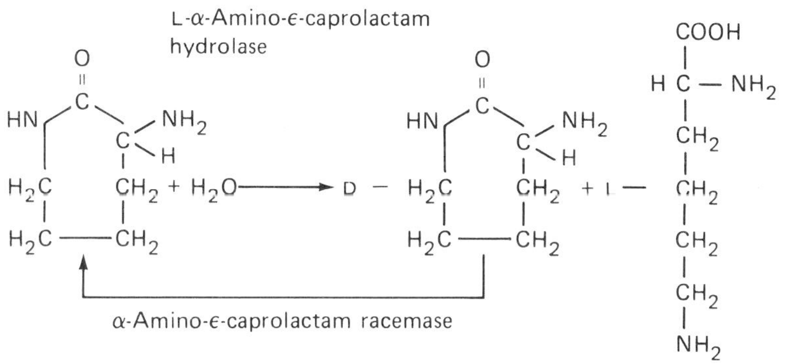

Fig. 4.9 — Production of L-lysine from DL-α-amino-ε-caprolactam.

A second process has been described which uses purified diaminopimelate decarboxylase (from *E. coli*) immobilized in polyacrylamide gel for the production of L-lysine acid from meso-2,6-diaminopimelic acid [36]. Attempts have also been made to produce L-lysine from threo-2,6-diaminopimelic acid, by first converting it to the meso form using diaminopinelate racemase. In these studies the two enzymes, diaminopimelate racemase and diaminopinelate decarboxylase, were immobilized separately and product yields were low. It was suggested that enzyme co-immobilization may result in increased yields.

L-Tryptophan has been produced from indole, pyruvate and ammonia using trytophanase from *E. coli*. This enzyme requires pyridoxal phosphate for activity and has been successfully immobilized onto Sepharose-bound pyridoxal phosphate [47]. High yields of tryptophan were obtained using a continuous-flow method or a repeated batch process and the immobilized enzymes showed increased stability compared with the soluble enzyme. It may be possible to use this immobilized enzyme preparation to catalyse long-term reactions.

It has also been reported that trytophan can be produced from indole and DL-serine using partially purified tryptophanase (from *E. coli*) immobilized in cellulose acetate fibres [49]. This process was found to be most successful when operated as a continuous rather than a batch system. The authors suggested that the process may compete with the traditional fermentation processes owing to the enzyme stability, reuse of D-serine after racemization and the easy isolation of the product.

Other amino acids produced by immobilized systems include aspartic acid, glutamic acid and alanine, but in these cases microbial cells were found to be more satisfactory for amino acid production than enzymes. Tanabe Seiyako Co. investigated the use of aspartase (from *E. coli*) immobilized in polyacrylamide gel for the production of aspartic acid. The partially purified aspartase preparations were heat-treated selectively to destroy the significant amounts of contaminating fumarase activity that catalysed unwanted side reactions. A solution of ammonium fumarate was passed over the immobilized aspartase and aspartic acid was produced. Since the immobilized enzyme was found to be unstable, this process was considered unsuitable for the production of aspartic acid on a large scale and a system using immobilized microbial cells was developed. Immobilization of the whole microbial cells resulted in more stable enzyme preparations, possibly because the binding of aspartase to membranes played an important role in the stability of this enzyme [50]. Tanabe Seiyako Co. has used a system employing immobilized *E. coli* cells for the production of L-aspartic acid on an industrial scale since 1973 [51].

4.5 POTENTIAL USES OF IMMOBILIZED ENZYMES IN INDUSTRY

A wide variety of soluble enzymes is currently used in industry and some of these, together with their applications, are listed in Table 4.4. The vast majority of enzymes is used in food processing, for example α-amylases used to hydrolyse starch in the baking, brewing and distilling industries, and glucose isomerase and glucoamylase employed for the production of glucose and fructose syrups in the sugar industry. Proteases, another group of important enzymes, are used in cheese manufacturing, dehazing of beer, tenderization of meat and as digestive aids.

Extensive research studies carried out over the past ten years have shown that many of these industrial processes are suitable for the application of immobilized enzymes (Table 4.5). The potential uses are well illustrated by the following two examples.

4.5.1 α-Amylase and glucoamylase

The two most widely used enzymes in industry, α-amylase and glucoamylase, hydrolyse starch to glucose (Fig. 4.3). Batch processes using soluble enzymes have produced very large amounts of glucose for many years. A significant amount of research has been carried out on the immobilization of these enzymes in order to benefit from the advantages of a continuous process. In addition, since several industrial plants using immobilized glucose isomerase are currently in operation, it would be ideal to immobilize α-amylase and glucoamylase in order to make high-fructose syrup production a continuous process. So far, progress has been relatively unsuccessful, mainly because the soluble enzyme is inexpensive and therefore, the immobilized enzyme process must provide distinct advantages if it is to compete with the soluble enzyme process.

α-Amylase from *Bacillus subtilis* has been immobilized on BrCN-activated carboxymethyl cellulose and used to hydrolyse wheat starch in a stirred tank reactor [52]. The initial activity of the immobilized enzyme was found to be lower than that of

Table 4.4 — Some enzymes used in industry

Enzyme	Use
Aminoacylase	Resolution of racemic amino acid mixtures
Amylase	Degradation of starch; brewing, baking, textile industry
Aspartase	Production of aspartic acid
Aspartate decarboxylase	Production of alanine
Catalase	Sterilization of dairy products
Cellulase	Fruit and vegetable processing
Dextranase	Hydrolysis of polysaccharides, sugar industry
Galactosidase	Hydrolysis of oligosaccharides; sugar refining
Glucanase	Polysaccharide hydrolysis; brewing industry
Glucoamylase	Glucose production from starch; used in brewing, baking, textile industry
Glucose isomerase	Isomerization of glucose to fructose
Glucose oxidase	Antioxidant
Invertase	Production of invert sugar; confectionary, brewing industry
Lipase	Leather and wool processing, waste treatment
Pectinase	Pectin degradation in fruit and vegetable processing
Pencillinase	Removal of antibiotics from milk
Proteases	Food processing, detergents, leather industry
Rennin	Coagulation of milk in cheese manufacturing
Ribonucleases	Formation of nucleotides for flavour enhancement
Tannase	Drinks industry
Trytophanase	Production of tryptophan
Xylanase	Processing of cereals

the soluble enzyme, but owing to increased thermal stability the productivity of the immobilized enzyme was greater. Immobilization of the enzyme also resulted in increased glucose and maltose production, possibly due to diffusion limitation with larger substrate molecules. Small substrate molecules were probably able to diffuse more easily into the polymer, where they were completely hydrolysed.

Glucoamylase is an extracellular enzyme produced by fungi such as *Aspergillus* and *Rhizopus* species. Using the soluble enzyme, glucose at a concentration of 95–96 per cent is obtained but the process has the disadvantage in that the residence time is long and hence large tanks are required. Attempts have been made to improve the economics of the process by using immobilized glucoamylase and smaller tanks. This proved to be unsatisfactory since the highest concentration of glucose which can be obtained is 94 per cent which is significantly less than that produced by the soluble enzyme.

Other reports of glucoamylase, immobilized on supports such as porous glass [53] and macroreticular polystyrene [54], have shown several advantages in that the reaction time can be drastically shortened from 75 h using the soluble enzyme to 1 h

Table 4.5 — Potential uses of immobilized enzymes.

Industry	Enzyme	Method of immobilization	Process	Ref.
Sugar	Invertase	Cellulose triacetate fibres	Conversion of sucrose to glucose and fructose	[93]
	Glucose oxidase and catalase	Copolymer of phenylene diamine and glutaraldehyde	Production of gluconic acid from glucose	[94]
	α-Amylase and glucoamylase	BrCN-activated carboxymethyl cellulose	Production of glucose from starch	[52]
		Porous glass		[19]
Dairy	Rennet, proteases	Porous glass	Coagulation of milk for cheese making	[95]
	Catalase	Collagen membrane	Sterilization of dairy products	[96]
	Trypsin	Porous glass	Prevention of oxidized flavour in milk	[97]
	Sulphydryl oxidase	Porous glass	Prevention of sulphydryl groups in UHT milk to elimate cooked flavour	[98]
Drinks	Papain, proteases	Papain–collagen membranes	Chill-proofing beer, wines and fruit juices	[99]
Production of nucelotides	Phosphate diesterase and AMP deaminase	Porous ceramic	Production of nucleotides to increase flavour enhancement of monosodium glutamate	[100]
Pharmaceutical	Amino acid oxidase and catalase	Alkylamine glass	Production of α-keto acids from their corresponding amino acid	[101]
	Glutamate dehydrogenase and transaminase	*N*-hydroxysuccinimide derivative of silica beads	Synthesis of radioactive compounds, e.g. [^{13}N]alanine	[102]
Production of amino acids	L-α-Amino-ε-capro-ε-lactam and α-amino-ε-caprolactam racemase	DEAE–Sephadex	Synthesis of L-lysine	[36]
	Tryptophanase	Sepharose-bound pyridoxal phosphate	Synthesis of L-tryptophan	[47]
	B-Tyrosinase	BrCN-activated Sepharose	Synthesis of L-tyrosine	[47]

using the immobilized enzyme. As a result, there are likely to be fewer side reactions, so purification of the final product would be easier and less expensive.

Lee *et al.* [55] developed a pilot plant using glucoamylase bound to glutaraldehyde-treated alkylamine silica beads packed in a column. On the basis of the results obtained, a reactor suitable for use on an industrial scale was proposed. It was suggested that seven columns would be necessary to keep production at a constant rate and the process would have to operate at a low temperature to compete with the soluble enzyme. Processes operating at temperatures below 55–60°C are not acceptable because of the risk of microbial contamination. It therefore seems likely that a process using a heat-stable glucoamylase will prove to be more successful.

In conclusion, the immobilized enzymes described above have all been shown to have a potential application in industry, but further development and improvement of enzymes extraction and purification, and of immobilization techniques and reactor designs, are still needed before these enzymes will be used on an industrial scale. Once introduced, the 'new' immobilized enzyme process has to show distinct advantages over the well-established systems if it is to be successful. Generally, there is a greater chance of survival if the product and immobilized enzyme system are developed and introduced simultaneously.

4.6 IMMOBILIZED ENZYMES IN WASTE TREATMENT

A more recent development in the field of immobilized enzymes is their use in waste treatment. This aspect is of considerable interest owing to the low cost of the substrate, the production of reusable material, and the elimination of waste-disposal problems.

One of the most important developments appears to be the use of immobilized lactase for the hydrolysis of whey, waste material from cheese manufacturing.

The conversion of waste cellulose into glucose is another exciting area which has attracted the attention of many researchers. Cellulose is a major constituent of domestic and commercial waste and is hydrolysed by a complex of enzymes known as cellulases. The end product, glucose, can be used for single-cell protein production, conversion to fuels, as a sweetener and as the starting material for other industries. Owing to the high cost of cellulase production there have been several attempts to immobilize cellulases [56,57] but owing to the insoluble nature of cellulose only a limited number of immobilization methods can be used. Rao and Misthra [56] immobilized cellulase from *Penicillium funiculosum* on a soluble polymer (polyvinyl alcohol) and found that this preparation was as active as the soluble enzyme. Cellulose hydrolysis is complicated by the fact that cellulose is often found in a very crystalline form which limits enzyme access and is found in close association with recalcitrant material such as lignin. It therefore becomes necessary to pretreat the cellulose to make it more susceptible to attack by the immobilized enzyme preparation.

Industrial effluents containing heavy loads of pollutants (Table 4.6) can have adverse effects on biological treatment processes, thereby creating a disposal problem. One solution to this problem might be to treat such effluents with immobilized enzymes which are capable of degrading the polluting material. With

Table 4.6 — Sources of major pollutants in water (adapted from Forster *et al.* 1977 [103]).

	Source					
Pollutant	Agriculture	Chemical	Domestic	Food	Iron and steel	Metal finishing
Solids	+		+	+		
BOD	+	+	+	+		
Ammonia	+	+	+			
Cyanide					+	+
Copper						+
Cadmium					+	+
Chromium						+
Detergents			+			
Nickel			+			
Nitrate	+	+	+			
Acidity/alkalinity		+			+	+
Phenols		+			+	
Phosphates	+		+			
Pesticides	+	+				
Sulphates		+				

+ indicates the presence of an established pollutant in a typical effluent from the type of process indicated.

the pollutant as a substrate, the wastewater would be brought in contact with the enzyme for a time sufficient for the pollutant to be converted to a less toxic form. A considerable amount of research has been carried out into the enzymatic degradation of pollutants such as pesticides, detergents and oils, thus allowing the appropriate enzyme to be selected for immobilization.

Methods which are currently used in the disposal of pesticides include incineration, land-fill burial, solvent extraction or distillation of pesticide-manufacturing waste streams, chemical detoxification processes (e.g. oxidation), microbial degradation in activated treatment systems and degradation by micro-flora and macro-fauna [58]. Usually it is necessary to use more than one of these methods to ensure that the pesticide is converted to a non-toxic form. As a result of the rapid increase in pesticide use over the past decade, laws governing pesticide disposal and discharge have become more demanding and the need to improve pesticide detoxification methods has arisen. There is now growing interest in the use of immobilized enzymes for pesticide disposal [58,59]. The vast majority of pesticides on the market today can be degraded by micro-organisms to produce less toxic metabolites, and enzymes capable of detoxifying phenylurea, phenylcarbamate, acid anilide, phenoxyacetate and organophosphate pesticides have been obtained. Munnecke [58] has shown that parathion hydrolase, covalently immobilized on glass, can be used to detoxify organophosphate pesticides in industrial wastewater conditions. Talbot *et al.* [59]

described the use of immobilized parathion hydrolase to degrade parathion to *p*-nitrophenol and diethyl thiophosphoric acid.

Another enzyme which has a potential use in wastewater treatment is α-amylase. The soluble form of this enzyme has been used to clarify the starch–clay suspensions produced in large volumes by the paper industry [60]. Starch present in the water is partially hydrolysed to produce solids which easily flocculate with the addition of alum. The advantages of using immobilized α-amylase include elimination of the enzyme-denaturing step which is required with soluble α-amylase and it would enable large volumes of water to be treated continuously.

Other potential uses of immobilized enzymes in wastewater treatment include the removal of carcinogenic aromatic amines such as benzidine, napthylamine and aminophenyl found in wastewaters from the coal, resin, plastic and textile industries using immobilized peroxidase [61].

4.7 ENVIRONMENTAL APPLICATIONS OF IMMOBILIZED ENZYMES

4.7.1 Biosensors

Immobilized enzymes which are used for analytical purposes are referred to as biosensors and in such cases the enzyme is usually immobilized in conjunction with a physicochemical sensing device like an ion-specific electrode. The great advantage of biosensors over chemical instrumentation is that they are very specific, as the enzymes used are themselves very specific. Enzyme reactions can be monitored with ease using colorimetric, spectrophotometric or amperometric methods which allow the development of other devices such as enzymes immobilized in auto-analyses for the determination of the concentration of specific substances in environmental samples [62]. Using immobilized enzymes can reduce costs, particularly in the clinical and environmental areas where assays are carried out for the routine evaluation of a great many samples.

In most of the cases reported in the literature, immobilized enzymes have been used preferentially because unwanted side reactions, present in whole cells for example, can be eliminated. However, the use of enzymes in this way requires their purification and this can add to the cost of the assays. The use of whole cells or organelles reduces this cost but there is some loss of sensitivity owing to the extra diffusion barrier imposed and owing to side reactions. However, it is now possible to remove or greatly reduce unwanted reactions via genetic manipulations designed to increase production of the enzyme of interest or to reduce the synthesis of unwanted enzymes.

To date biosensors have been developed primarily for clinical use, with industrial applications following closely, particularly in the control of fermentation processes. However, few reports mention the potential of these instruments in environmental monitoring of trace amounts of substrates or pollutants. Sternberg *et al.* [63] discussed the use of a trace glucose detector for environmental analyses and Neujahr [64] has reviewed some possible applications of biosensors, including their use in environmental areas. Most of the biosensors so far designed and described are for the detection of specific substances which are almost invariably the substrate for the immobilized enzymes. If biosensors are to be used for the detection of pollutants they have to be designed so that it is the inhibition of enzyme reaction which is being monitored. This change in emphasis will require some rethinking of basic enzyme electrode/biosensor design and construction, as well as changes in their mode of operation.

There are two types of immobilized enzyme systems which could be used for the detection of environmental pollutants. In the first type — a bioprobe — the enzyme is immobilized in close contact with the sensor, usually fixed covalently onto a membrane, entrapped between membranes or between the membrane and the electrode surface. Guilbault [15] has described a typical enzyme electrode which could be used for the detection of glucose. This incorporated a platinum disk embedded in the end of a glass cylindrical insulated support with a platinum wire connecting the disk with the detection instrument. The enzyme, in this case glucose oxidase, was covalently fixed to a collagen membrane, or to the surface of preformed polyacrylamide beads which were then held by a cellophane membrane in contract with the electrode.

An alternative system is the bioreactor based on the autoanalyser. Here, the enzyme is attached by covalent bonding to the inside of a nylon tube or entrapped in a polymeric matrix which is then inserted in the autoanalyser. This type of instrument has been used to determine the concentration of glucose, urea, creatinine, glycerol, pyruvate and citrulline in clinical specimens [62,15] and would probably be of more importance than the bioprobe in the area of monitoring for trace environmental pollutants. The mode of operation would be to pass the polluted water through the enzyme for some fixed period of time and then to assay for residual enzyme activity by replacing the water stream with substrate plus buffer. The pollutants/inhibitors should react with the enzyme causing inhibition and, knowing the time for which the water stream was passed and the volume passed, an average pollution load could be calculated.

Many substrates can now be quantitatively determined by sensors using enzymes as biological catalysts; some of these listed in Table 4.7. Over 50 substrate electodes have been described. Many of them are totally specific and unaffected by the other constituents of the medium or clinical specimen being examined. In some cases, notably glucose and urea, a number of different sensors have been used, showing the versatility of these biosensors. Most sensors give a full response in less than one minute and can be calibrated to give a direct quantitative estimate of substrate concentration. Response time is dependent upon the concentration of both substrate and enzyme, with optimum operation conditions requiring a highly active preparation, usually with greater than 10 international units of activity immobilized on each sensor. Most electrodes give a linear response to substrate concentrations between 10^{-2} and 10^{-4} M, although some will give estimates of concentrations below 10^{-4} M. However, these concentrations are far above those found in nature, illustrating their lack of usefulness in environmental situations. The stability of the electrode is dependent upon the stability of the enzyme, which in turn is dependent upon the method of immobilization, as most activity is lost in the initial stages of operation through leaching of loosely or inadequately bound enzyme. Chemically bonded enzyme electrodes can usually be used for many thousands of assays, usually until the enzyme becomes irreversibly denatured through physicochemical conditions or by inhibition. Longer lifetimes are possible in the laboratory because

Table 4.7 — A range of substrates which can be quantitatively measured using an enzyme-based biosensor.

Substrate	Enzyme
Acetic acid	Alcohol oxidase
Acetylcholine	Acetylcholinesterase
AMP	5-Adenylate deaminase
ATP	Glucose oxidase/hexokinase
Alcohol	Alcohol dehydrogenase
D-Amino acids	D-Amino acid oxidase
L-Amino acids	L-Amino acid oxidase
L-Arginine	Arginase
L-Asparagine	Asparaginase
Amylogladin	β-Glucosidase
Butyrylthiocholine	Cholinesterase
Cathechol	Catechol-1,2-oxygenase
Cholesterol	Cholesterol oxidase/cholesterol esterase
Creatinine	Creatininase
Glucose	Glucose oxidase
Glucose-6-phosphate	Glucose-6-phosphate dehydrogenase
L-Glutamine	Glutaminase
L-Glutamic acid	Glutamate dehydrogenase/glucose oxidase
L-Histidine	Histidinase
Hypoxanthine	Xanthine oxidase
Inosine	Nucleotide phosphorylase
Lactic acid	Lactate dehydrogenase
Lactose	β-Galactosidase/glucose oxidase
Lectin	Glucose oxidase
L-Lysine	Lysine decarboxylase
Maltose	Maltase/glucose oxidase
L-Methionine	Methionine ammonia lyase
NADH	Alcohol dehydrogenase
Nitrate	Nitrate reductase/nitrite reductase
Nitrite	Nitrite reductase
Oxalic acid	Oxalate decarboxylase
Penicillin	Penicillinase
Peroxide	Peroxidase
L-Phenylalanine	Phenylalanine ammonia lyase
Phosphate	Phosphatase/glucose oxidase
Pyruvate	Lactate dehydrogenase
Saccharose	Invertase/mutarotase/glucose oxidase
Succinic acid	Succinate dehydrogenase
Sucrose	Sucrase/glucose oxidase
Sulphate	Amyl sulphatase
Thiosulphate	Rhodanase
L-Tyrosine	Tyrosine decarboxylase
Urea	Urease
Uric acid	Uriase

conditions under which the electrodes operate can be more rigorously controlled than in industrial or clinical situations.

One of the drawbacks of many enzyme electrodes is the need to supply expensive cofactors, which are often not recoverable, although the co-immobilization of enzyme and cofactors has now been achieved [65]. A number of sensors using whole microbial cells have been developed and here the need to supply cofactors is eliminated as they are already present within the cell and are easily recycled through the cell's own metabolic systems.

4.7.2 Detection of environmental pollutants using biosensors

In comparison with those of clinical or industrial use, relatively few biosensors detecting environmental pollutants have been reported. The types of pollutants which can be detected can be divided into three groups.

(a) Pesticides

Perhaps the most studied biosensor for environmental control is that of acetyl cholinesterase, which is inhibited by organophosphorus insecticides and carbamate pesticides [66–68]. both groups used a non-specific enzyme and, after exposure to inhibitors in air and water, measured residual activity by a spectrophotometric method [68], or by a platinum electrode potentiometric method [67]. This enzyme is a very useful tool for the study of inhibition as it has an extremely high turnover number ($>$80 000/min). This means that the inhibition of a single active site leads to the loss of formation of 80 000 molecules of product per minute and this makes the test extremely sensitive. Goodson and Jacobs [67] reported the detection limit to be 0.1 mg/l for paraoxon, 5 mg/l for parathion, 1 mg/l for DDUP and 1.2 mg/l for diazinon. Bhattacharya *et al.* [68] were able to detect 0.022 mg/l paraoxon using a continuous-flow system where the enzyme was continuously exposed to this concentration of inhibitor. They also claimed to have detected unspecified organophosphorus inhibitors in German drinking water at a concentration equivalent to 0.002 mg/l paraoxon. The inhibition caused by organophosphorus compounds and by carbamates can easily be differentiated by exposing the inhibited enzyme to obidoxime. This causes reversion of inhibition caused by organophosphorus compounds but not carbamates.

(b) Phenolic compounds

Two enzymes (phenol oxidase from fungi and phenol monoxygenase from *Trichosporon cutaneum*) have been used to construct electrodes to detect phenols and related compounds like catechol. A non-specific polyphenol oxidase covalently bonded by glutaraldehyde to a polyacrylamide membrane in a Clark oxygen electrode could detect 0.62 mg/l phenol [69]. An electrode based on polyacrylamide-entrapped tyrosinase was able to detect 0.036 mg/l phenol [70]. The authors reported that this system could be developed into a field monitor for phenols as it was unaffected by the majority of inorganic and organic chemicals likely to be encountered in wastewater streams from chemical plants, with the exception of benzoic acid and aniline.

Using phenol *o*-hydroxylase, covalently linked via a carboxyl group by CNBr or membranes, and an oxygen electrode, Kjellen and Neujahr [71] reported a detection limit of 0.047 mg/l for phenol and suggested that the detectors could be used, again near chemical plants or at sewage works, but they believed that their system was not sensitive enough for use in water-abstraction protection. Immobilization of the enzyme in polyacrylamide made the response slower but did not affect the detection limit. The major problem with this method is that it requires NADPH as a cofactor, which amounts to 80 per cent of the assay cost. Co-immobilization with the enzyme is possible but diffusion problems in polyacrylamide and instability on the surface limit its effectiveness [72].

(c) Heavy metals and anions
Using the concept of enzyme activation or inhibition, biosensors have also been developed to detect heavy metals and anions. Mattiasson *et al.* [73] described an enzyme electrode which could detect the presence of Cu^{2+}. Tyrosinase, an apoenzyme requiring Cu^{2+} as a cofactor, was immobilized on nylon netting, stripped of Cu^{2+} and mounted in an oxygen electrode. Incubation with a sample containing Cu^{2+} reactivated the enzyme and the activity measured was proportional to the amount of Cu^{2+} present. Polyphenol oxidase, another apoenzyme requiring Cu^{2+}, immobilized in polyacrylamide gel can also detect Cu^{2+} [74]. In principle it should be possible to develop biosensors to detect other metal ions, once the appropriate enzyme is found.

Chemicals such as nitrate, nitrite, phosphate and sulphate, although naturally occurring, are potentially hazardous when they accumulate and their presence may be determined using enzymes which use the particular anion as a substrate. Using nitrate reductase immobilized on glass beads by the diazonium salt procedure, nitrate ions can be detected at the p.p.b. level [75]. Nitrates can be detected using immobilized nitrite reductase [76], sulphates using aryl sulphatase [77] and phosphate with phosphatase/glucose oxidase [78].

The types of biosensors which are described above offer a potential application in the detection of pollutants in river water and water used for drinking purposes. At the present time, the presence of pollutants in drinking-water supplies is determined using a range of bioassays. These tests range from the use of mammalian subcellular components through to whole cells and micro-organisms. However, all of these tests, with the exception of the fish cough monitor [79], are long-term tests and therefore unsuitable for the protection of drinking-water supplies from pollution caused by accidental spillage. Biosensors offer several advantages over these traditional assays as a specific or broad range of inhibitors can be identified, depending on the need and the enzyme selected. Reproducible results are obtained, provided that a standard or purified enzyme preparation is used. Biosensors are also versatile owing to the wide range of immobilization techniques available and maintenance costs are reduced as biosensors, unlike fish which need feeding and handling, can be left in an unattended module.

4.7.3 The use of immobilized phosphatase to detect river pollutants
As an example of one of the ways in which immobilized enzymes can be used in environmental studies, neutral phosphatase has been used as a model enzyme for the detection of oxyanions, particularly vanadate, in river water [80]. Neutral phosphatase was selected as it is a stable enzyme which can easily be assayed colorimetrically using *p*-nitrophenyl phosphate (*p*NPP) and immobilized in gels or on surfaces.

Vanadium occurs as a vanadate in waters, although the oxidation state is dependent upon ionic concentration and on pH [81]. It is acutely toxic to fish [82], lichens [83] and plants [84]. The mechanism of this toxicity is believed to be via inhibition of phosphatase or ATPase function [85,86]. Vanadate is a common constituent of many crude oils and it is possible that vanadate could be used as an indicator or a tracer of oil pollution in marine or fresh waters.

A crude extract of neutral phosphatase (from *Pseudomonas fluorescens*) was immobilized in polyacrylamide gel and its potential for use as a monitor was studied. Virtually all enzyme activity was retained after immobilization in the gel, and the immobilized enzyme preparation remained stable over a considerable time period. In addition, the polyacrylamide gel retained its physical and mechanical stability and was not susceptible to microbial attack.

Studies of inhibition of enzyme activity indicated that vanadate and tungstate at 0.51 mg/l and 0.92 mg/l, respectively, caused 50 per cent inhibition of phosphatase activity. The two types of inhibition could be differentiated as vanadate inhibition was reversible whereas that caused by tungstate was not. Although this system has only been used as a batch process it may be possible to detect lower concentrations of vanadate and tungstate using a flow system in which the polluted water is passed over the enzyme for a fixed period of time and then assayed for residual activity. The use of immobilized phosphatase is by far the most rapid and simple method for the detection of vanadium as an oxyanion, but unfortunately it is not specific as neutral phosphatase enzymes are also inhibited by other oxyanions and some metals, although most of these are at much higher concentrations.

4.8 CONCLUSION

With only two immobilized enzyme systems currently operating on a large scale (glucose isomerase and pencillin G and V acylases), it appears that the commercial application of immobilized enzymes is still at an early stage of development. Many major problems have yet to be overcome before the full potential of immobilized enzymes is realized. Some of these problems will be considered here.

(a) Cofactor regeneration

Further research and development is needed in the area of cofactor regeneration *in situ* so that oxidation/reduction reactions can be performed. This is important because at least one-third of the 2000 enzymes that have been listed require cofactors and because immobilized enzymes catalysing synthetic reactions require the continuous addition of these expensive cofactors.

(b) Co-immobilization of enzymes

Usually single enzymes are immobilized but the co-immobilization of two or more enzymes would enable multi-step reactions to be carried out. The complete enzymatic synthesis of the antibiotic gramicidin S, a growth factor used in animal feed, has been demonstrated [87]. Several enzymes are required for the synthesis of this antibiotic from its constituent amino acids, together with the enzymes adenylate kinase and acetate kinase, which are required to regenerate ATP. It is hoped that by applying co-immobilized enzymes to systems of this type, many more multi-step enzyme reactions will be made possible.

(c) Use of water-insoluble and water-immiscible substrates
Substrates of this nature are required, for example, in the synthesis of steroids such as hydrocortisone and prednisolone from Reichstein's compound S, and also in steroid transformation. In order that steroid conversions can be carried out, procedures for handling water-insoluble substrates in a reactor must be developed.

Thc usc of immobilizcd cclls in industry has bccn of incrcasing importance as they overcome many of the problems associated with immobilized enzymes. For example, there is no need to supply cofactors as they are already present in the cell and recycled through the cell's own metabolic system. Moreover, cells can carry out multi-step reactions as the enzymes required are contained within the cell, and hence such cells eliminate the need to purify and co-immobilize a variety of enzymes. Another factor favouring the use of immobilized cells is that the industrial use of enzymes is confined by the limited number available in commercial quantities.

Microbial cells do, however, have their disadvantages, as side reactions need to be suppressed and specific activity is low in comparison with enzymes. In addition, cell multiplication needs to be controlled and there are also problems associated with the leaching of cells and cell contents. Nevertheless, a great deal of research is being carried out on immobilized microbial cells and their potential uses and it may be possible that they will find a greater application than enzymes. Perhaps the future of immobilized enzymes will lie in the area of relatively small specialized processes [18] with the production of high-value, low-bulk substances such as antibiotics.

REFERENCES

[1] Andresen, O. and Poulsen, P. B. (1982). Application for enzymes to organic synthesis. In: Lafferty, R. M. (ed.) *Enzyme Technology,* Rotenburg Ferment Symp. 3rd, Springer, Berlin.
[2] Trevan, M. D. (1980). *Immobilized Enzymes: An Introduction and Applications in Biotechnology* Wiley, Chichester.
[3] Chibata, I. (1978). Immobilized Enzymes. Wiley, New York.
[4] Kolot, F. B. (1981). Microbial carriers—strategy for selection. *Process Biochemistry,* **16**, 2–9.
[5] Kolot, F. B. (1981). Microbial carriers—strategy for selection, part 2. *Process Biochemistry,* **16**, 30–33.
[6] Fukui, S., Ikeda, S., Fujimura, M., Yamada, H. and Kumagi, H. (1975). Comparative studies on the properties of tryptophanase and tryosine phenollyase immobilised directly on Sepharose or by use of Sepharose-bound pyridoxal 5′ phosphate. *European Journal of Biochemistry,* **51,** 155–164.

[7] Tramper, J., Angelino, S. A. G. F., Muller, F. and Van der Plas, H. C. (1979). Kinetics and stability of immobilised chicken liver xanthine dehydrogenase. *Biotechnology and Bioengineering,* **21**, 1767–1786.

[8] Cashion, P., Lentini, V., Harrison, D. and Javed, A. (1982). Enzyme immobilisation on tritylagarose: reusability of both matrix and enzyme. *Biotechnology & Bioengineering,* **24,** 1221–1224.

[9] Navaroo, J. M. and Durrand, G. (1977). Modification of yeast metabolism by immobilization onto porous glass. *European Journal of Applied Microbiology,* **4,** 243–254.

[10] Vijayalakshmi, M., Marcipar, A., Segard, E. and Broun, G. B. (1979). Matrix-bound transition metal for continuous fermentation tower packing. *Ann. NY Acad. Sci.,* **326,** 249–254.

[11] Maccipar, A., Cochet, N., Brackenridge, L. and Lebeault, J. M. (1979). Immobilization of yeasts on ceramic supports. *Biotechnology Letters,* **1,** 65–70.

[12] Tosa, T., Mori, T., Fuse, N. and Chibata, I. (1969). Studies on continuous enzyme reactions. Part V. Kinetics and industrial applications of amino-acylase column for continuous optical resolution of acyl, D, L-amino acids. *Agricultural and Biological Chemistry,* **33,** 1047–1052.

[13] Mosbach, K. (1976). Immobilized enzymes. In: *Methods in Enzymology,* Vol. 44, Academic Press, New York.

[14] Kent, C., Rozevear, A. and Thomson, A. R. (1978). Enzymes immobilised on inorganic supports. In: Wiseman, A. (ed.) *Topics in Enzyme and Fermentation Biotechnology,* Vol. 2, Ellis Horwood, Chichester, pp. 13–119.

[15] Guilbault, G. G. (1983). Immobilised enzyme electrode probes. In: Scouten, W. H. (ed.) *Solid Phase Biochemistry, Analytical and Synthetic Aspects,* Wiley, New York, pp. 479–505.

[16] Axen, R., Porath, J. and Ernback, S. (1967). Chemical coupling of peptides and proteins to polysaccharides by means of cyanogen halides. *Nature,* **214,** 1302–1304.

[17] Mitz, M. A. and Summaria, L. J. (1961). Synthesis of biologically active cellulose derivatives of enzymes. *Nature,* **189,** 576–577.

[18] Powell, L. W. (1984). Developments in immobilised enzyme technology. *Biotechnology and Genetic Engineering Reviews,* **2,** 409–438.

[19] Weetall, H. H. and Filbert, A. Y. (1974). Porous glass for affinity chromatography applications. In: Jakobj, W. B. and Wilchek, M. (eds) *Methods in Enzymology,* Vol. 34, Academic Press, New York, pp. 59–72.

[20] Cho, Y. K. and Bailey, J. E. (1979). Immobilisation of enzymes on activated carbon: selection and preparation of carbon supports. *Biotechnology and Bioengineering,* **21,** 461–476.

[21] Bourdillon, C., Bourgeois, P. and Thomas, D. (1980). Covalent linkage of glucose oxidase on modified glassy carbon electrodes. Kinetic phenomena. *Journal of the American Chemical Society,* **102,** 4231–4235.

[22] Nishida, Y., Sato, T., Tosa, T. and Chibata, I. (1979). Immobilization of *Escherichia coli* cells having aspartase activity with carrageenan and locust bean gum. *Enzyme and Microbial Technology,* **1,** 95–99.

[23] Hackel, U., Klein, J., Megnet, R. and Wagner, F. (1975). Immobilization of

microbial cells in polymeric matrices. *European Journal of Applied Microbiology,* **1,** 291–293.
[24] Klein, J., Washausen, P., Kluge, M. and Eng, H. (1980). Physical characterization of biocatalyst particles obtained from polymer entrapment of whole cells. In: Weetall, H. H. and Royer, G. P. (eds) *Enzyme Engineering,* **5**, 359–362.
[25] Coulet, P. R., Julliard, J. H. and Gautheron, D. C. (1974). A mild method of general use for covalent coupling of enzymes to chemically activated collagen films. *Biotechnology and Bioengineering,* **16,** 1055–1068.
[26] Kumakura, M., Yoshida, M. and Kaetsu, I. (1978). Immobilization of *Streptomyces phaeochromogenes* cells at a high concentration by radiation-induced polymerization of glass-forming monomers. *European Journal of Applied Microbiology and Biotechnology,* **6,** 13–22.
[27] Kumakura, M., Yoshida, M. and Kaetsu, I. (1979). Immobilization of glucose isomerase containing *Streptomyces phaeochromogenes* cells in fine particle form. *Applied Environmental Microbiology,* **37,** 310–315.
[28] Fukui, S., Sonomoto, K., Itoh, N. and Tanaka, A. (1980). Several novel methods for immobilisation of enzymes, microbial cells and organelles. *Biochimie,* **62,** 381–386.
[29] Fukushima, S., Nagai, T., Fujita, K., Tanaka, A. and Fukui, S. (1978). Hydrophilic urethane prepolymers: convenient materials for enzyme entrapment. *Biotechnology and Bioengineering,* **20,** 1465–1469.
[30] Omata, T., Iida, T., Tanaka, A. and Fukui, S. (1979). Transformation of steroids by gel entrapped *Nocardia rhodocrous* cells in organic solvent. *European Journal of Applied Microbiology and Biotechnology,* **8,** 143–155.
[31] Omata, T., Iwamoto, N., Kimura, T., Tanaka, A. and Fukui, S. (1981). Stereoselective hydrolysis of di-methyl succinate by gel-entrapped *Rhodotorula minuta* var. Texensis. Cells in organic solvent. *European Journal of Applied Microbiology and Biotechnology,* **11,** 199–204.
[32] Chang, T. M. S. (1976). Microencapsulation of enzymes and biologicals. In: Mosbach, K. (ed.) *Methods in Enzymology,* Vol. 44, Academic Press, New York, pp. 201–218.
[33] Chang, T. M. S. (1976). Methods for the therapeutic application of immobilised enzymes. In: Mosbach, K. (ed.) *Methods in Enzymology,* Vol. 44, Academic Press, New York, pp. 676–697.
[34] Quiocho, F. A. and Richards, F. M. (1964). Intermolecular cross linking of a protein in the crystalline state: carboxypeptide-A. *Proceedings of the National Academy of Sciences, New York,* **52,** 833–839.
[35] Poulsen, P. B. (1984). Current applications of immobilized enzymes for manufacturing purposes. *Biotechnology and Genetic Engineering Reviews,* **1,** 121–140.
[36] Brodelius, P. (1978). Industrial application of immobilised biocatalysts. In: Ghose, T. K., Fiechter, A. and Blakebrough, N. (eds) *Immobilised Enzymes 1, Advances in Biochemical Engineering 10,* Springer-Verlag, Berlin, pp. 75–129.
[37] Hemmingsen, S. H. (1979). Development of an immobilised glucose isomerase for industrial application. *Applied Biochemistry and Bioengineering,* **2,** 157–183.

[38] Poulsen, P. B. and Zittan, L. (1976). Continuous production of high fructose syrup by cross-linked cell homogenates containing glucose isomerase. In: Mosbach, K. (ed.) *Methods in Enzymology,* Vol. 44, Academic Press, New York, p. 809–821.

[39] Chibata, I., Tsao, T., Sato, T. and Mori, T. (1976). Production of L-amino acids by aminoacylase adsorbed on DEAE–Sephadex. In: Mosbach, K. (ed.) *Methods in Enzymology 44,* Academic Press, New York, pp. 746–759.

[40] Greenberg, N. A. and Mahoney, R. R. (1981). Immobilisation of lactase (β-galactosidase) for use in dairy processing: a review. *Process Biochemistry,* **16,** 2–8.

[41] Moulin, G. and Galzy, P. (1984). Whey, a potential substrate for biotechnology. *Biotechnology and Genetic Engineering Reviews,* **1,** pp. 347–374.

[42] Marconi, W. and Morisi, F. (1979). Industrial applications of fiber entrapped enzymes. *Applied Biochemistry and Bioengineering,* **2,** 219–258.

[43] Vandamme, E. J. (1982). Immobilised enzyme and cell technology to produce peptide antibiotics. In: Lafferty, R. M. (ed.) *Enzyme Technology. Rotenburg. Fermentation Symposium (3rd),* Springer, Berlin, pp. 237–270.

[44] Lagerlof, E., Nathorst-Westfelt, L., Ekstrom, B. and Sjoberg, B. (1976). Production of 6-aminopenicillanic acid with immobilised *Escherichia coli* acylase. In: Mosbach, K. (ed.) *Methods in Enzymology 44,* Academic Press, New York, pp. 759–768.

[45] Abbott, B. J. (1977). Immobilized cells. *Annual Report on Fermentation Processes,* **1,** 205–233.

[46] Marconi, W., Bartoli, F., Cecere, F., Galli, G. and Morisi, F. (1975). Synthesis of penicillins and cephalosporins by penicillin acylase entrapped in fibers. *Agricultural and Biological Chemistry,* **39,** 277–279.

[47] Fukui, S., Ikeda, S., Fujimura, M., Yamanda, H. and Kumagai, H. (1975). Production of L-tryptophan, L-tyrosine and their analogues by use of immobilised L-tryptophanase and immobilised β-tyrosinase. *European Journal of Applied Microbiology,* **1,** 25–39.

[49] Zaffaroni, P., Vitobello, V., Cecere, F., Giacomozzi, E. and Morisi, F. (1974). Synthesis of L-tryptophan from indole and DL-serine by tryptophan synthetase in fibers. I. Preparation and properties of free and entrapped enzyme. *Agricultural and Biological Chemistry,* **38,** 1335–1342.

[50] Tosa, T., Sato, T., Nishida, Y. and Chibata, I. (1977). Reason for higher stability of aspartase activity of immobilized *Escherichia coli* cells. *Biochimica et Biophysica Acta,* **483,** 193–202.

[51] Cheetham, P. S. J. (1985). Principles of industrial enzymology: basic utilization of soluble and immobilised enzymes in industrial processes. In: Wiseman, A. (ed.) *Handbook of Enzyme Biotechnology,* Ellis Horwood, Chichester, pp. 54–146.

[52] Linko, Y., Saarinen, P. and Linko, M. (1975). Starch conversion by soluble and immobilized α-amylase. *Biotechnology and Bioengineering,* **17,** 153–165.

[53] Weetall, H. H., Havewala, N. B., Garfinkel, H. M., Buehl, W. M. and Baum, G. (1974). Covalent bond between the enzyme amyloglucosidase and a porous

glass carrier: the effect of shearing. *Biotechnology and Bioengineering,* **16,** 169–179.
[54] Baum, G. (1975). Enzyme immobilisation on macroeticular polystyrene. *Biotechnology and Bioengineering,* **17,** 253–270.
[55] Lee, D. D., Lee, Y. Y., Reilly, P. J., Collins, E. V., Jr. and Tsao, G. T. (1976). Pilot plant production of glucose with glucoamylase immobilized to porous silica. *Biotechnology and Bioengineering,* **18,** 253–267.
[56] Rao, M. and Mishra, C. (1984). Properties and applications of *Penicillium funiculosum* cellulase immobilised on a soluble polymer. *Biotechnology Letters,* **6,** 319–322.
[57] Dessi, M. R., Mauria, R., Rinaldi, A. and Satta, G. (1984). Highly efficient solubilisation of natural cellulosic materials by a commercial cellulase immobilised on various solid supports. *Applied Microbiology and Biotechnology,* **19,** 306–311.
[58] Munnecke, D. M. (1978). Detoxification of pesticides using soluble or immobilised enzymes. *Process Biochem.,* **13**(2), 14–16, 31.
[59] Talbot, H. W., Johnson, L., Barik, S. and Williams, D. (1982). Properties of a *Pseudomonas* sp-derived parathion hydrolase immobilized to porous glass and activated alumina. *Biotechnology Letters,* **4,** 209–214.
[60] Smiley, K. L., Boundy, J. A., Hofreiter, B. T. and Rogovin, S. P. (1974). Immobilised α-amylase for clarification of colloidal starch–clay suspensions. In: Olson, A. C. and Cooney, C. L. (eds) *Immobilised Enzymes in Food and Microbial Processes,* Plenum Press, New York, pp. 133–147.
[61] Klibanov, A. M. and Morris, E. D. (1981). Horseradish peroxidase for the removal of carcinogenic aromatic amines from water. *Enzyme and Microbial Technology,* **3,** 119–122.
[62] Sundaram, P. V., Blumenberg, B. and Hinsch, W. (1979). Routine glucose determination in serum by use of an immobilised glucose dehydrogenase nylon-tube reactor. *Clinical Chemistry,* **25,** 1436–1439.
[63] Sternberg, R., Apoteker, A. and Thevanot, C. D. R. (1980). Trace glucose electrode for clinical, food and environmental determinations. *Analytical Chemistry Symposia Series 2,* 461–473.
[64] Neujahr, H. Y. (1984). Biosensors for environmental control. *Biotechnology and Genetic Engineering Reviews,* **1,** 167–186.
[65] Keyes, M. H., Semersky, F. E. and Gray, D. N. (1979). Glucose analysis utilising immobilised enzymes. *Enzyme and Microbial Technology,* **1,** 91–94.
[66] Goodson, L. H. and Jacobs, W. B. (1974). Application of immobilised enzymes to detection and monitoring. In: Pye, E. K., Wingard, L. B. and Lemuel, B., Jr (eds) *Enzyme Engineering 2,* Plenum Press, New York, pp. 393–400.
[67] Goodson, L. H. and Jacobs, W. B. (1976). Monitoring of air and water for enzyme inhibitors. In: Mosbach, K. (ed.) *Methods in Enzymology 44,* Academic Press, New York, pp. 647–658.
[68] Bhattacharya, S., Alsen, C., Kruse, H. and Valentin, P. (1981). Direction of organophosphate insecticide by an immobilised enzyme system. *Environmental Science and Technology,* **15,** 1352–1355.
[69] Macholan, L. and Schanel, L. (1977). Enzyme electrode with immobilised

polyphenol oxidase for determination of phenolic substrates. *Collection of Czechoslovak Chemical Communications,* **42,** 3667–3675.
[70] Schiller, J. G., Chen, A. K. and Liu, C. C. (1978). Determination of phenol concentrations by an electrochemical system with immobilised tyrosinase. *Analytical Biochemistry,* **85,** 25–33.
[71] Kjellen, K. G. and Neujahr, H. Y. (1979). Immobilisation of phenol hydroxylase. *Biotechnology and Bioengineering,* **21,** 715–719.
[72] Kjellen, K. G. and Neujahr, H. Y. (1980). Enzyme electrode for phenol. *Biotechnology and Bioengineering,* **22,** 299–310.
[73] Mattiasson, B., Nilsson, H. and Olsson, B. (1979). An apoenzyme electrode. *Journal of Applied Biochemistry,* **1,** 377–384.
[74] Stone, J. V. and Townsend, A. (1973). Determination of traces of copper by activation of water-insoluble apopolyphenol oxidase. *Journal of the Chemistry Society, Dalton Transactions,* **5,** 495–501.
[75] Senn, D. R., Carr, P. W. and Klatt, L. N. (1976). Determination of nitrate ion at the part per billion level in environmental samples with a continuous flow immobilised enzyme. *Analytical Chemistry,* **48,** 954–958.
[76] Kiang, C. H., Kuan, S. S. and Guilbault, G. G. (1975). A novel enzyme electrode method for the determination of nitrate based on nitrite reductase. *Analytica Chimica Acta,* **80,** 209–214.
[77] Cserfalvi, T. and Guilbault, G. G. (1976). An enzyme electrode based on immobilised arylsulphatase for the selective assay of sulphate ions. *Analytica Chimica Acta,* **84,** 259–270.
[78] Guilbault, G. G. and Nanjo, M. (1975). A phosphate-selective electrode based on immobilised alkaline phosphatase and glucose oxidase. *Analytica Chimica Acta,* **78,** 69–80.
[79] Cairns, J. J., Thompson, K. W., Landers, J. D., McKee, M. J. and Hendricks, A. C. (1980). Suitability of some fresh water and marine fishes for use with a mini-computer interfaced biological monitoring system. *Water Resources Bulletin,* **16,** 421–427.
[80] Harrison, L. A. and Flint, K. P. (1986). The use of imobilised enzymes to detect river pollutants. In: Hopton, J. W. and Hill, E. C. (eds) *Industrial Microbiology Testing,* in press.
[81] Pope, M. T. and Dale, B. W. (1968). Isopoly-vanadates, -niobates and -tantalates. *Quarterly Review of the Chemical Society,* **22,** 527–548.
[82] Stendahl, D. H. and Sprague, J. B. (1982). Effects of water hardness and pH on vanadium lethality to rainbow trout. *Water Research,* **16,** 1479–1488.
[83] Le Seur, P. and Puckett, K. J. (1980). Effect of vanadium on the phosphatase activity of lichens. *Canadian Journal of Botany,* **58,** 502–504.
[84] Saxe, H. and Rajagopal, R. (1981). Effect of vanadate on bean leaf movement, stomatal conductance, barley leaf unrolling, respiration and phosphatase activity. *Plant Physiology,* **68,** 880–884.
[85] Bowman, B. J. and Slayman, C. W. (1979). The effects of vanadate on the plasma membrane ATPase of *Neurospora crassa. Journal of Biological Chemistry,* **254,** 2928–2934.
[86] Wu, P. H. and Phillis, J. W. (1979). Effects of vanadate on brain (Na^+-K^+) dependent ATPase and *p*-nitrophenyl-phosphatose interaction with mono- and

divalent ions and with noradrenaline. *International Journal of Biochemistry,* **10,** 629–635.

[87] Demain, A. L., Piret, J. M., Friebel, T. O. E., Vandamme, E. J. and Matteo, C. C. (1976). Studies on *Bacillus brevis* directed towards cell free synthesis of gramicidin S. In: Schlessinger, D. (ed.) *Microbiology,* American Society for Microbiology, Washington, DC, pp. 437–443.

[88] Chibata, I., Tosa, T., Sato, T., Mori, T. and Matsuo, Y. (1972). Preparation and industrial application of immobilised aminoacylases. *Proc. Int. Fermentation Symp. 4th Fermentation Technology Today,* pp. 383–389.

[89] Smith, R. A. G. (1981). Enzyme preparation having affinity for water-immiscible liquids. US Patent Number 4,267,273.

[90] Hannibal-Friedrich, O., Chun, M. and Sernetz, M. (1980). Immobilization of β-galactosidase, albumin and α-globulin on epoxy-activated acrylic beads. *Biotechnology and Bioengineering,* **22,** 157–175.

[91] Campbell, J., Hornby, W. E. and Morris, D. L. (1975). The preparation of several new nylon tube glucose oxidase derivatives and their incorporation into the reagentless automated analysis of glucose. *Biochimica et Biophysica Acta,* **384,** 307–316.

[92] Goldstein, L. and Mannecke, G. (1976). The chemistry of enzyme immobilisation. In: Wingard, L., Katchalski, Katzir, E. and Goldstein, L. (eds) *Applied Biochemistry and Bioengineering,* Vol. 1, Academic Press, New York, pp. 23–216.

[93] Marconi, W., Gulinelli, S. and Morisi, F. (1974). Properties and use of invertase entrapped in fibers. *Biotechnology and Bioengineering,* **16,** 501–511.

[94] Krasnobajew, B. and Boniger, R. (1975). Application possibilities of PAG (phenylenediamine-glutaraldehyde copolymer). *Chimia,* **29,** 123–131.

[95] Cheryan, M., van Wyk, P. J., Olson, N. F. and Richardson, T. (1975). Continuous coagulation of milk using immobilised enzymes in a fluidized-bed reactor. *Biotechnology and Bioengineering,* **17,** 585–598.

[96] Wang, S. S., Gallili, G. E., Gilbert, S. G. and Leeder, J. G. (1974). Inactivation and regeneration of immobilised catalase. *Journal of Food Science,* **39,** 338–341.

[97] Lee, E. C., Senyk, G. F. and Shipe, W. F. (1974). Preparation and stability of trypsin immobilised on porous glass. *Journal of Food Science,* **39,** 927–929.

[98] Swaisgood, H. E. (1980). Sulfhydryl oxidase: properties and applications. *Enzyme and Microbial Technology,* **2,** 265–272.

[99] Venkatasubramanian, K., Saini, R. and Vieth, W. R. (1975). Immobilisation of papain on collagen and the use of collagen–papain membranes in beer chill-proofing. *Journal of Food Science,* **40,** 109–113.

[100] Noguchi, S., Shimura, G., Kimura, K. and Samejima, H. (1976). Production of 5′ mononucleotides using immobilized 5′-phosphodiesterase and 5′ AMP deaminase. *Journal of Solid Phase Biochemistry,* **1,** 105–118.

[101] Fink, D. J., Falb, R. D. and Bean, M. K. (1976). Cited by Brodelius, P. (1978). Industrial applications of immobilized biocatalysts. In: Ghose, T. K., Fiechter, A. and Blakebrough, N. (eds) *Immobilized Enzymes 1. Advances in Biochemical Engineering 10,* Springer-Verlag, Berlin, pp. 75–129.

[102] Cohen, M. B., Spolter, L., Chang, C. C., MacDonald, N. S., Takahashi, J.

and Bobinet, D. D. (1974). Immobilised enzymes in the production of radiopharmaceutically pure amino acids labelled with nitrogen-13. *Journal of Nuclear Medicine,* **15,** 1192–1195.

[103] Forster, C. R., Stafford, D. A. and Templeton, W. E. (1977). Waste water treatment—problems of control and management. In: Callely, A. G., Forster, C. F. and Stafford, D. A. (eds) *Treatment of Industrial Effluents,* Hodder & Stoughton, London, pp. 7–17.

5

Process engineering: macro-kinetic aspects of aerobic wastewater-treatment processes

S. P. P. Ottengraf
Technisch Hogeschool Eindhoven, The Netherlands

5.1 GENERAL DESCRIPTION OF AEROBIC WASTEWATER-TREATMENT PROCESSES

5.1.1 Introduction

The purpose of this chapter is to describe some current process-engineering knowledge, hopefully to demonstrate that the process engineer has a role to play today if wastewater-treatment plants are to operate efficiently.

Until, perhaps, 25 years ago wastewater treatment was more of an art than a science. Treatment plants were designed by civil engineers who followed rule-of-thumb practices based on empirical experience. Other disciplines were associated with wastewater treatment, but almost always at the operational level: it was very unusual for chemists, biologists or chemical engineers even to be consulted at the design stage. After all, all the engineer needed to know was the retention time or the biological-filter BOD loading that were used by everyone by rote! And he was right because, at that time, little was understood of the mechanisms involved in wastewater treatment: certain things happened under certain conditions — somehow! But the situation is very different now. Over the past quarter of a century a huge fund of knowledge has developed and process engineering is now a science that is left to the unskilled only at great risk. It is hoped that this chapter will demonstrate that this is so.

Aerobic treatment processes are frequently used in the biological treatment of domestic and industrial wastewaters. The foundations of these processes were laid by Clark in Boston and Fowler in Manchester in 1910, who cultivated certain strains of micro-organisms to eliminate dissolved pollutants from wastewaters. However, the technical application of monocultures has been employed only sporadically, e.g. in the treatment of industrial wastewaters containing single carbon sources. Ardern and Lockett [1] at Manchester in 1914 cultivated a mixed culture of micro-organisms:

activated sludge. Since then this process has been widely known as the activated-sludge process.

In current biological wastewater treatment processes two stages can be generally distinguished (Fig. 5.1): a mechanical stage for the separation of settled, floating or suspended materials and a biological stage for the elimination of mainly colloidal and dissolved compounds.

The raw wastewater is generally pretreated mechanically in order to separate large particles and inorganic solids (e.g. sand) by means of screens, sieves, grid separator, etc. Settled organic solid particles are then separated by gravity settling in the primary settling basin. The settled primary sludge, having a dry matter content of about 5 per cent w/w, usually needs to be treated in order to reduce its volume and to increase its biological stability (e.g. by anaerobic digestion). The mechanically pretreated water still contains colloidal and dissolved components, which need biological treatment in, for example, an activated-sludge plant, trickling filter or oxidation pond. Since these microbial (oxidation) processes are under aerobic conditions, air (oxygen) has to be continuously supplied to the system.

As the activated-sludge organisms tend to agglomerate into small porous flocs, separation from the treated liquid can easily occur by gravity in a final settling basin. The supernatant in this separation stage is the clarified effluent.

Part of the thickened activated sludge is recirculated to the aeration basin in order to keep the concentration of active micro-organisms therein as high as possible.

After this some effluents still need further treatment in a third stage: for example, for the elimination of nitrate (NO_3^-) and/or phosphate (PO_4^-). However, these additional treatment processes have not yet been applied on a wide scale.

5.1.2 Biological oxidation and aeration

Although the composition, concentration and condition of wastewaters may differ widely, dependent on the sources of origin, biological treatment processes have one primary aim in common: the reduction of the oxygen demand of the wastewater. Total oxygen demand is usually expressed as BOD_5 (biochemical oxygen demand) or COD (chemical oxygen demand). The BOD_5 is defined as the amount of oxygen required for the stabilization of the microbiologically oxidizable organic matter during 5 days' incubation at 20°C. The total organic matter content of a wastewater which is oxidizable by dichromate in an acid solution is measured in a COD test. The elimination of biodegradable compounds (the substrate) by micro-organisms is due to two different types of overall reactions (Fig. 5.2):

- cell synthesis, or anabolism, and
- energy production, or catabolism.

It may be concluded from Fig. 5.2 that microbial oxygen consumption is due to the substrate oxidation reactions and, to a smaller extent, to the endogenous respiration of the cells, due to the oxidation of intracellularly stored constituents.

Aeration processes are primarily used for transferring oxygen to the microbial population and hence to provide for the total oxygen demand of the wastewater. Aeration equipment commonly applied in wastewater treatment plants may be differentiated as:

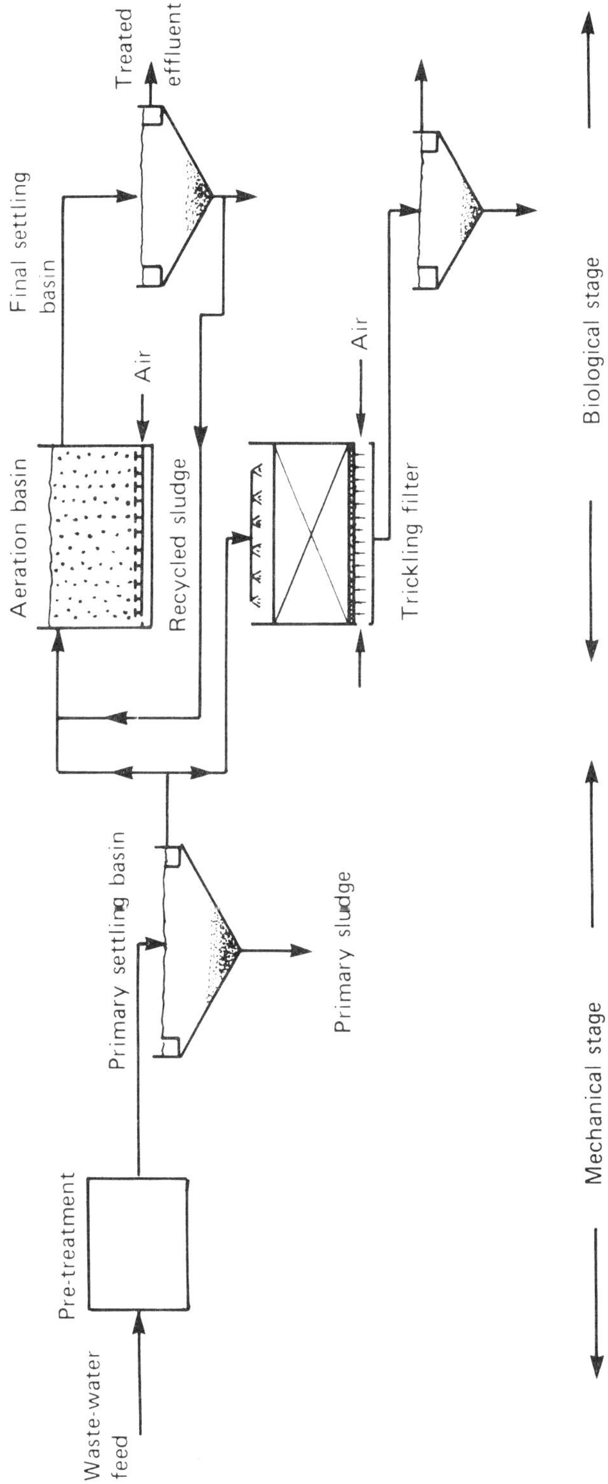

Fig. 5.1 — Flow sheet of a conventional waste-water-treatment plant.

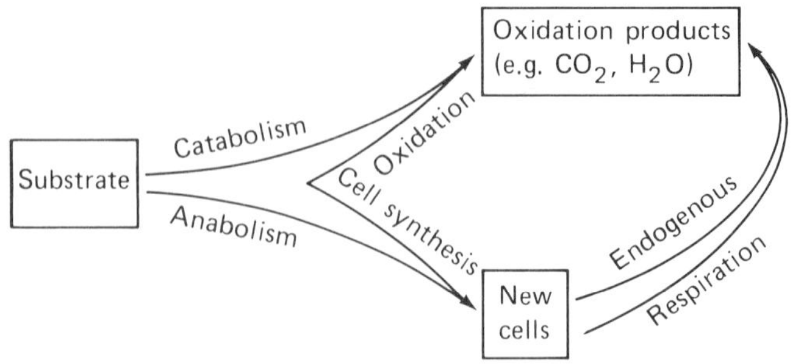

Fig. 5.2 — Substrate elimination due to microbial oxidation.

- diffused air systems: units producing bubbles from submerged porous media such as tubes, plates or grids;
- mechanical aeration equipment such as rotating brushes and surface impellers.

Different types of aeration systems are shown in Fig. 5.3.

As a result of the aeration process, circulating flows, turbulence and mixing are introduced in the aeration basin [2,3]. These mixing phenomena are necessary in order to keep the activated sludge in suspension, to distribute it throughout the reactor volume and for the promotion of the physical mass-transfer processes.

Besides transverse mixing, longitudinal mixing is also induced in the system. A strong longitudinal mixing in a continuously operating aeration basin may be advantageous in cases of fluctutating hydraulic loadings to the basin, or wide variations in the concentration of organics, temperature or pH of the influent stream. In the treatment of certain industrial wastewaters, which may contain substances with toxic or inhibitory effects on the activated sludge, the buffering capacity of a well-mixed system may be preferable. Moreover, uniform conditions are created with respect to the oxgen requirement, which generally favour the oxygen transfer processes. Also, a more uniform physical environment for the biological system is provided, which generally promotes its activity. On the other hand, longitudinal mixing is generally detrimental to the degree of conversion within the process. This will be illustrated in more detail in Section 5.4. Also there are indications that the settling properties of the activated sludge deteriorate with increasing longitudinal mixing [4].

5.2 KINETICS OF ORGANISM GROWTH AND SUBSTRATE ELIMINATION

Several models have been offered to explain the mechanism of substrate removal by the biological oxidation process. These models are partly based on theoretical considerations concerning microbial growth kinetics, and partly on empirical relationships. In modelling, wastewater-treatment processes simplifying assumptions are necessary owing to the generally very complex and different nature of the constituent nutrients and the heterogeneous composition of the activated-sludge

(b)

(a)

Fig. 5.3 — (a) Aeration by dispersing air bubbles through perforated grids (Inka aerator). (b) Aeration by rotating brushes (Kessener system). (c) Turbine aeration system with draught tube (Simplex cone aerator).

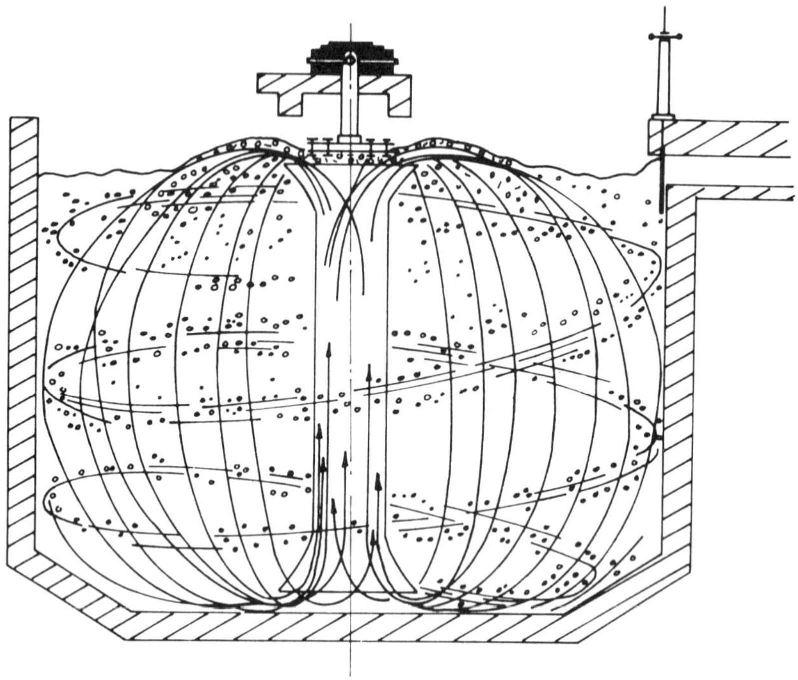

Fig. 5.3 — (c) Turbine aeration system with draught tube (Simplex cone aerator).

micro-organisms. Only for so-called monocultures, consisting of one species of organism, have growth kinetics been thoroughly investigated and modelled. For heterogeneous cultures like activated sludge, there is a lack in this field. For such cultures growth-kinetic phenomena are much more complex.

The growth of a monoculture can be visualized by means of the growth curve giving the path of the cell count as a function of time in a nutrient solution. In a typical growth curve (Fig. 5.4) several growth phases can be distinguished:

PHASE I: The lag phase

In this phase the number of cells remains nearly constant. During this phase the micro-organisms generally adapt themselves to the new environment by enzyme synthesis. The duration of the lag time is, *inter alia*, dependent on the age of the inoculum and its degree of adaptation to the nutrient solution.

PHASE II: The logarithmic or exponential growth phase

This phase is characterized by a constant and maximal division rate not limited by the supply of nutrients in the growth environment. During the exponential growth phase this rate may be very different for the various species of organisms. Fast-growing bacteria duplicate every 15–30 min, slow growing bacteria need hours or even days.

PHASE III: The linear or retardation phase

This transition state is generally caused by the fall in concentration of a key substrate to a level limiting the rate of division. For this special case the path of the substrate concentration is also shown Fig. 5.4.

PHASE IV: The stationary phase

During this phase the number of living cells generally remains nearly constant.

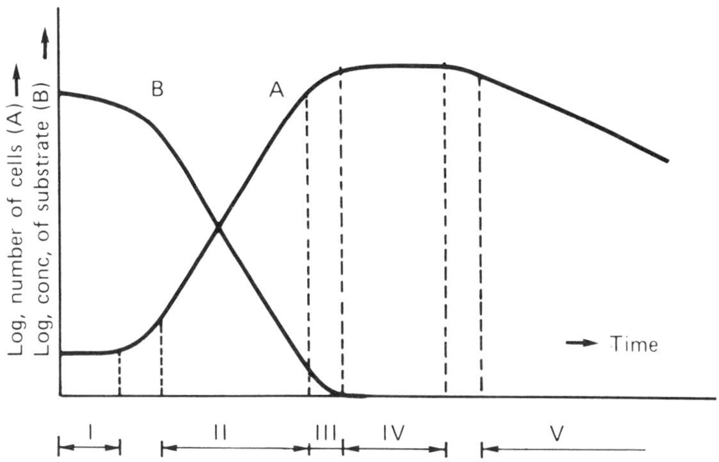

Fig. 5.4 — Diagrammatic growth curve.

Besides a lack of substrate the accumulation of a toxic metabolic product may initiate this phase. During it stored nutrients are consumed and essential cell substances are eventually respired. This process is often described as auto-oxidation.

PHASE V: The cell decay phase

This phase generally shows the behaviour of a first-order reaction, that is to say the rate of cell decay is proportional to the concentration of residual viable cells.

The degradation of substrate by microbial oxidation reactions takes place in a complicated chain of enzyme-catalysed reactions. The reaction rate generally shows a dependency on the substrate concentration. The experimentally determined path at constant enzyme concentration is shown in Fig. 5.5.

At low values of substrate concentration the reaction rate is proportional to this concentration, but at higher concentrations the reaction rate increases to a smaller extent and reaches a constant value at very high concentration levels. Moreover, the reaction rate depends linearly on the enzyme concentration.

This behaviour was first explained by Michaelis and Menten [5] in 1913. A modification of their theory was given by Briggs and Haldane [6] in 1925. The Michaelis–Menten relationship was derived for systems with a constant enzyme concentration. In growing cultures this condition is not satisfied and so the Michaelis–Menten theory may not be applied to such systems without modification.

However, Monod [7,8] showed experimentally that for growing cultures, the substrate elimination rate, as well as the growth rate of the micro-organisms, can very well be described by the Michaelis–Menten relationship. According to this model the microbial growth rate is given by:

$$\left(\frac{\mathrm{d}x}{\mathrm{d}t}\right)_{\text{growth}} = \mu_m \frac{L}{L + K_s} X \qquad (1)$$

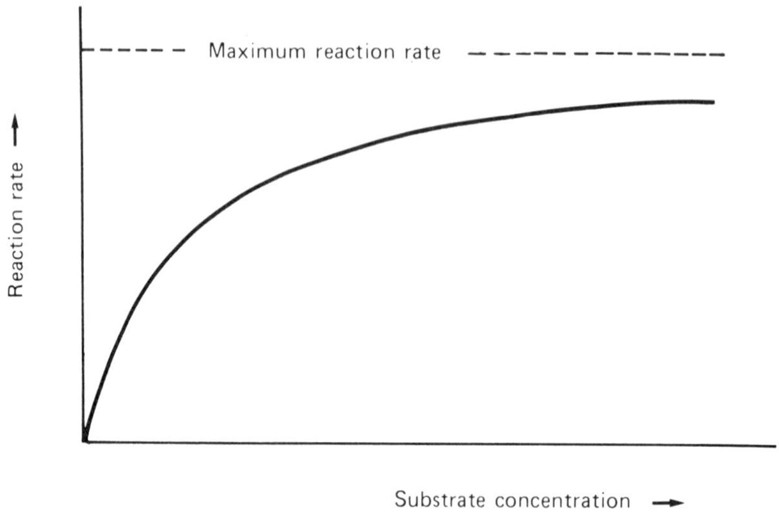

Fig. 5.5 — Reaction rate as a function of substrate concentration at constant enzyme concentration.

where X is the organism concentration, t is time, μ_m is the maximum growth rate, L is the substrate concentration and K_s is a saturation constant, which is often denoted as the Michaelis–Menten constant.

With respect to the biological oxidation of wastewater components the total substrate concentration L is in most cases expressed in terms of the equivalent oxygen demand (BOD_5 or COD), and the microbial concentration in terms of sludge solids content (VSS = volatile suspended solids).

In developing an expression for the rate of substrate removal one generally starts from the concept that part of the eliminated substrate is converted to new cell mass. Several investigators have shown that a constant mass of biological cells is synthesized from a given mass of organic matter.

The cell-yield coefficient (Y) is an important parameter. It is defined as g VSS/g COD or BOD removed. Data [9] for a large variety of substrates give an average value of the cell-yield coefficient as 0.39 g VSS/g COD removed and 0.57 g VSS/g BOD removed. This relationship may be expressed as:

$$\left(\frac{dX}{dt}\right)_{growth} = -Y\left(\frac{dL}{dt}\right) \tag{2}$$

From Eqns. (1) and (2) it follows that:

$$-\frac{dL}{dt} = \frac{\mu_m}{Y}\frac{L}{L+K_s}X \tag{3}$$

The effects of microbial cell decay have not been taken into account so far. Since most wastewater-treatment systems operate with the sludge in the declining, stationary or endogeneous growth phase, microbial cell decay is likely to have a significant effect on the performance of the process [10].

Microbial cell decay is usually assumed to follow first-order kinetics, so that the rate of cell decay is proportional to the concentration of residual viable cells:

$$\left(\frac{\mathrm{d}X}{\mathrm{d}t}\right)_{\text{dec.}} = -K_2 X \tag{4}$$

where K_2 is the specific decay rate constant. From Eqns. (1) and (4) it follows for the net growth rate of the organisms:

$$\frac{\mathrm{d}X}{\mathrm{d}t} = \left(\frac{\mathrm{d}X}{\mathrm{d}t}\right)_{\text{growth}} + \left(\frac{\mathrm{d}X}{\mathrm{d}t}\right)_{\text{dec.}} = \mu_m \frac{L}{L+K_s} X - K_2 X \tag{5}$$

It should be borne in mind that the given relationships hold only for monocultures and individual substrates: these conditions are hardly ever encountered in the field of wastewater treatment. Although more advanced and inherently more complex models have been proposed (e.g. by Wuhrmann [11]), the use of the rate expressions above, or their modifications, is very common in modelling the kinetic aspects of wastewater-treatment processes. These models have proved valuable not only in the prediction of plant performances, but also in identifying key process parameters and indicating which aspects of the process would profit most from further investigation [10].

5.3 RESIDENCE TIME DISTRIBUTION AND MIXING PHENOMENA IN AERATED SYSTEMS

In recent years the clear trend is for process engineering to be more and more applied to wastewater treatment. Increasingly, studies have been made of the kinetic behaviour of homogeneous and heterogeneous microbial populations in the biological treatment of wastewater. From the viewpoint of process engineering, mixing phenomena and residence-time distribution in aerated systems are amongst the important factors in determining the rate of conversion in a continuously operating reaction system.

The conversion achieved by a homogeneous reaction in a continuous-flow system is generally determined by the reaction rate (this is micro-kinetics), the residence-time distribution and the nature of the mixing. The interaction of factors affecting the overall behaviour of a continuous reaction system is often denoted as the macro-kinetics of the process. It can be shown that the effect of the mixing is satisfactorily described by the residence-time distribution only for first-order reactions. Hence, for most other types of reaction, information about the mixing and the mixing mechanism is necessary.

Mixing phenomena in aerated systems are mainly determined by the shape of the aeration basin and the method and intensity of the aeration.

With respect to the shape of the basin one can distinguish between types having a large length : depth : width ratio, and those having a value of the order 1 (Fig. 5.3). With respect to the method of aeration, which is often dependent on the shape of the basin, point aeration systems (e.g. turbine aerators) and diffused air systems generally result in different mixing phenomena.

Point aerators are usually placed in the centre of the aeration basin, in contrast to diffused air systems which are generally located along one side of the basin.

Basins with a length : depth : width ratio of the order of 1 are generally aerated by turbine aerators. Owing to the induced turbulent circulating flows these systems are generally very well mixed, i.e. the circulation time is considerably smaller than the average residence time in the basin. The residence-time distribution approximates that of an ideally mixed system (see Ch. 2).

Aeration of oblong basins by a series of turbine aerators generally results in a number of perfectly mixed stages. However, in such systems backmixing phenomena are generally introduced owing to a considerable exchange between the successive mixing stages. Residence-time distribution of such systems is described by the so-called stagewise backflow model. In order to suppress the longitudinal mixing phenomena, partitions are occasionally located between the different mixing stages. Owing to the continuous nature of the aeration process caused by diffused air systems in oblong aeration basins the longitudinal mixing phenomena in such systems are also more or less continuous. Hence the residence-time distribution may be expected to approach the behaviour of the continuous backflow model. This will be pointed out in more detail in the next section.

5.3.1 Residence-time distribution in oblong aeration basins

If a high concentration of a tracer is injected into the inlet stream of a continuous process during a very short period and the outlet concentration of the tracer is then measured, a method, in principle, has been identified to measure the residence-time distribution (RTD). Such a tracer has to satisfy several conditions:

- it must have a negligible volume to avoid changes in the process flow at the moment of injection;
- it must be detectable in low concentrations;
- it must not influence the physical properties of the fluid; and
- it must not be adsorbed or undergo a chemical reaction

Highly concentrated aqueous solutions of electrolytes (e.g. salts such as Li_2SO_4, Na_2SO_4, NaCl) or dyestuffs, have experimentally proved to be suitable tracers for measuring RTDs in wastewater-treatment plants. Also radioactive tracers have proved their usefulness in this respect; however, their application obviously requires caution.

In oblong aerated systems, which are typically 6–10 m wide, 30–100 m long and 4–5 m deep, plug-flow conditions are usually assumed. However, experimental investigations carried out in several types of such systems [3,12] have shown considerable longitudinal mixing. Experiments were carried out in two different types of aeration basins: the Inka aeration basin and the Brandol system, representing diffused air systems; and a system which was mechanically aerated by rotating brushes located along the long side of the basin.

As an example a flow sheet of the experimental set-up for the RTD measurements in the Inka aeration system is shown in Fig. 5.6. The system consisted of two

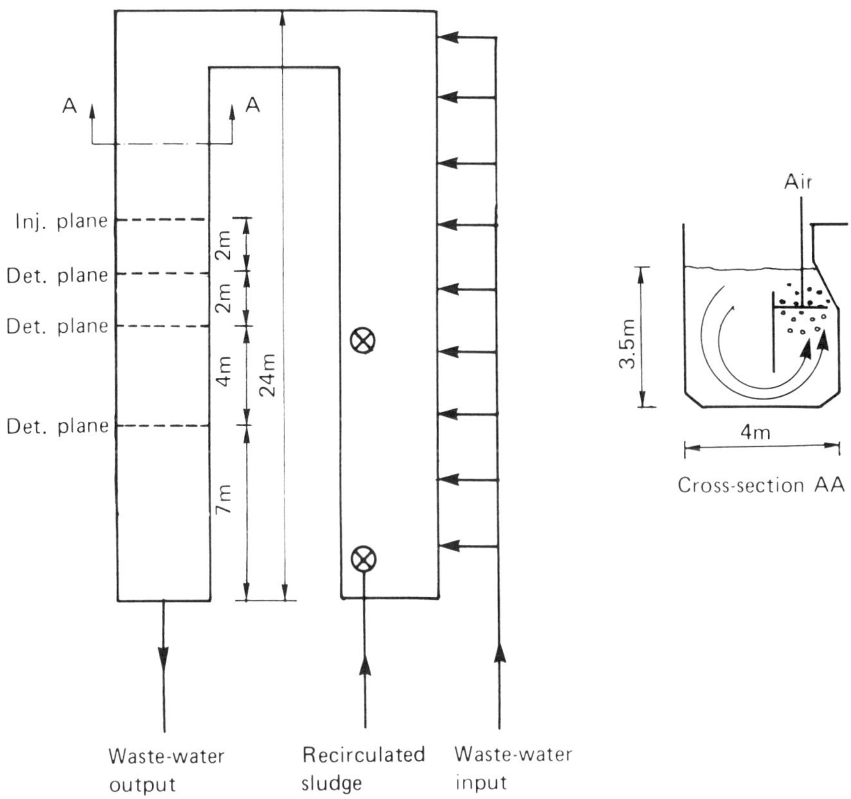

Fig. 5.6 — Experimental set-up of RTD measurement in an Inka aeration basin.

basins in series, each with a volume of about 285 m^3. The normal liquid flow rates were about 260 m^3/h raw wastewater and about 200 m^3/h returned activated sludge. The air-flow rate amounted to about 10 000 m^3/h. In the Inka system aeration takes place through perforated grids set about 0.8 m beneath top water level. To prevent difficulties caused by multiple lateral influent feeds in the first section (the so-called 'step-feed', 'stepped loading' or 'step aeration' mode), measurements were made in the last section.

Tracer experiments consisted of injecting about 150 l of a saturated sodium chloride solution into the basin and determining the electrical conductivity as a function of time at several points and at various distances from the point of injection (Fig. 5.6).

Experiments were carried out at several liquid flow rates, varying from 0 up to about 3 m^3/s. As a considerable amount of backmixing could be measured, the RTD curves were compared with two theoretical models allowing backmixing:

- the continuous backflow model (a turbulent axial diffusion mechanism superimposed upon plug flow); and
- the stagewise backflow model (a cascade of perfect mixers with internal recirculation).

It appeared experimentally that the measured RTDs were best described by the stagewise backflow model, which is shown schematically in Fig. 5.7. Some measured

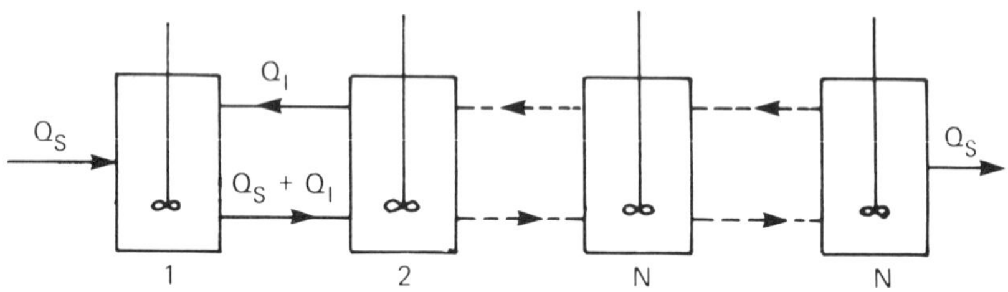

Fig. 5.7 — Stagewise backflow model.

and historical RTD responses, according to this model at various liquid-flow rates, are shown in Fig. 5.8.

However, due to its simpler character the continuous backflow model is used preferably in RTD descriptions. The model lends itself better to a physical–mathematical description, which simplifies the modelling of scale-up factors. Furthermore it may be shown that both models converge towards each other.

The stagewise backflow model is described by two parameters (Fig. 5.7):

N = the number of mixing stages

$$\beta = \frac{Q_i}{Q_s} = \text{the internal recirculation ratio}$$

As the exchange between mixing stages can be considered to be effected by a transfer mechanism of fluid elements (Section 5.3.2), it is more correct from the viewpoint of process engineering to describe the backmixing by a transfer coefficient. Hence;

$$\beta = \frac{Q_i}{Q_s} = \frac{kA}{Q_s}$$

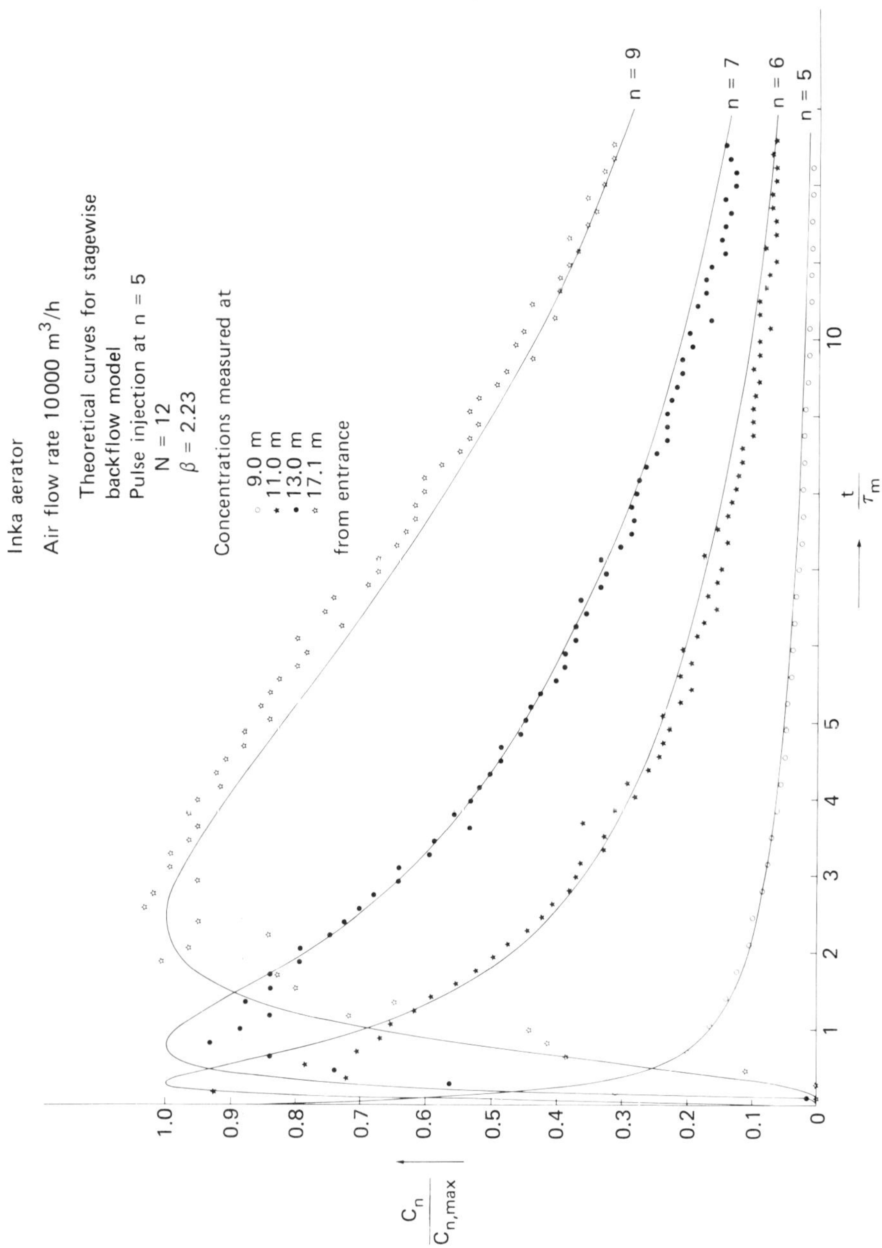

Fig. 5.8 — (a) Experimental and theoretical determined residence-time distribution curves in an Inka system.

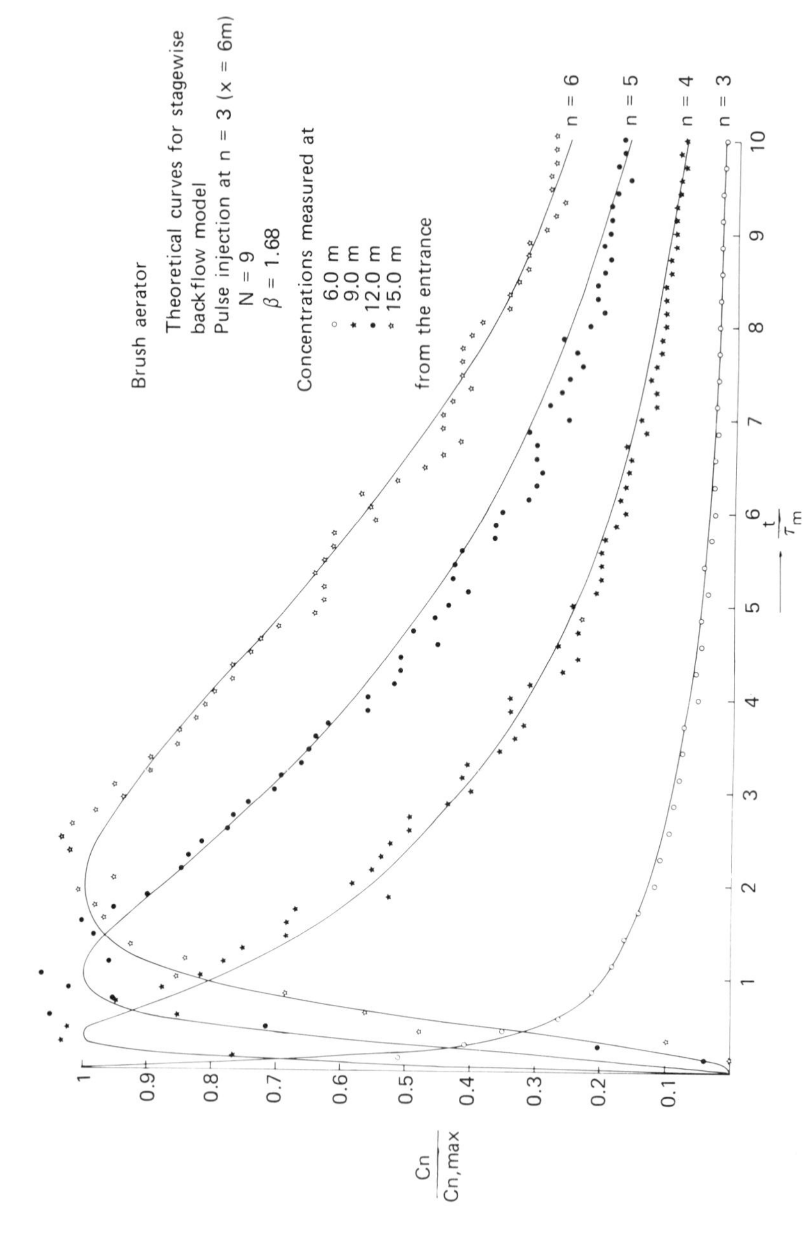

Fig. 5.8 — (b) Experimental and theoretical determined residence-time distribution curves in a Kessener brush system.

where k is the transfer coefficient and A is the cross-sectional area of the basin.

With a pulse-function (or delta Dirac function) as input to the first mixing stage the variation coefficient of the RTD curve for the stagewise backflow model [13–15] is:

$$\left(\frac{\sigma}{\mu}\right)^2 = \frac{N(1-\gamma^2) - 2\gamma(1-\gamma^N)}{N^2(1-\gamma)^2} \tag{6}$$

where

$$\gamma = \frac{\beta}{1+\beta} = \frac{Q_i}{Q_i + Q_s}$$

is the ratio of the internal flow rates.

The variation coefficient for the RTD curve according to the continuous backflow model is given by Van der Laan [16]:

$$\left(\frac{\sigma}{\mu}\right)^2 = \frac{2}{\mathrm{Pe}^2}(\mathrm{Pe} - 1 + e^{-\mathrm{Pe}}) \tag{7}$$

where $\mathrm{Pe} = (U_0 H)/E$ is the Peclet number, U_0 the axial liquid velocity, H the length of the basin and E the turbulent, longitudinal mixing or dispersion coefficient.

At sufficiently high values of N and Pe the two variation coefficients approach respectively:

$$\left(\frac{\sigma}{\mu}\right)^2 = \frac{1+\gamma}{N(1-\gamma)} \quad \text{and} \quad \left(\frac{\sigma}{\mu}\right)^2 = \frac{2}{\mathrm{Pe}} - \frac{2}{\mathrm{Pe}^2}$$

If the stagewise and continuous-backflow models may be assumed equal for the same values of the variation coefficients, it follows that:

$$\mathrm{Pe} = \frac{2N}{1+2\beta} - 1 \tag{8}$$

According to the continuous backflow model the longitudinal mixing is described by a turbulent, longitudinal mixing or dispersion coefficient. Kolmogorov [17] and later Hinze [18] described in some detail the situation when the turbulence intensity of a fluid is uniform and acts equally in any direction. The longitudinal turbulent diffusion is the integral effect of all eddies, which contribute to a transport in this direction. Although the turbulent eddy spectrum extends to a very small scale, the majority of this transport is done by the larger eddies [19]. The largest eddies are generated by an energy source, for example rotating brushes, or diffused air bubbles, and they break down to smaller eddies which eventually are smoothed out by viscosity effects.

The isotropic turbulence model has proved useful in correlating data for process modelling.

A considerable amount of data has been collected from scale-model studies as well as from commercial plants, in order to develop a relationship which gives a reasonable prediction of the rate of longitudinal mixing. The correlation thus obtained, which describes the longitudinal diffusion coefficient [3], is:

$$E = a_2\left(v_0 g\frac{H^*}{H}\right)^{1/3} R_H (H^{*\,1/3})\left(\frac{B}{H}\right)^n \tag{9}$$

with

$$n = +1 \quad \text{if} \quad B \geqslant H$$
$$n = -1 \quad \text{if} \quad B \leqslant H$$

In Eqn. (9) a_2 is a constant, v_0 the superficial gas velocity, g the gravity acceleration, H^* the depth of submergence of the aeration device, and B and H the width and height of the aeration basin. R_H is the hydraulic radius of the cross-section defined by:

$$R_H = \frac{2BH}{2H + B} \tag{10}$$

Eqn. (9) can be transformed into an equation of dimensionless numbers:

$$\mathrm{Pc}^* = a_3 \mathrm{Fr}^{*\,-1/3}\left(\frac{H}{H^*}\right)^{1/3}\left(\frac{H}{B}\right)^n \tag{11}$$

where

$$\mathrm{Pe}^* = \frac{v_0 R_\mathrm{H}}{E} \quad \text{(modified Peclet number)}$$

$$\mathrm{Fr}^* = \frac{gH^*}{v_0^2} \quad \text{(modified Froude number)}$$

A plot of observed data according to Eqn. (11) is shown in Fig. 5.9.

To support turbulent motion, energy has to be supplied continuously to make up for viscosity losses. Via a wide range of eddies with decreasing length scales, this energy is transferred and is eventually dissipated into heat by the small eddies. The small eddy scale is referred to as the Kolmogorov microscale or ‘inner’ scale of the turbulence field.

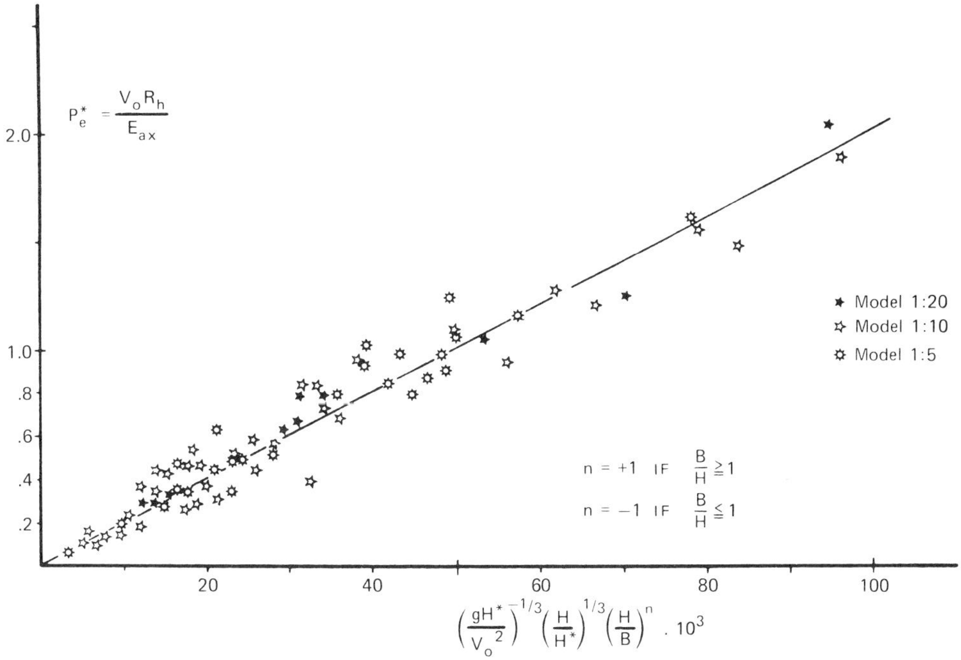

Fig. 5.9 — Plot of observed data according to Eqn. (11).

Let the eddies which contribute to the longitudinal diffusive transport have a size λ and a velocity, v_λ, then the rate of transfer of energy of these eddies to smaller eddies is proportional to $(v_\lambda^3)/\lambda$.

This energy is eventually dissipated at a rate ε, which should be equal to the rate of supply in the steady state. Hence:

$$\varepsilon \sim \frac{v_\lambda^3}{\lambda}$$

In the case of eddy diffusivity, it can be shown by dimensional analysis that

$$E = a_1(\varepsilon^{1/3})(\lambda^{-4/3}) \tag{12}$$

ε can be calculated from the volumetric air-flow rate Q_g to the aeration basin and the hydrostatic pressure drop Δp of the diffused air bubbles. As Δp is given by $\Delta p = \rho_c g H^*$ it follows for the energy dissipation rate ε per unit of mass of liquid:

$$\varepsilon = \frac{Q_g \Delta p}{V_c \rho_c} = v_0 g \frac{H^*}{H} \tag{13}$$

where V_c is the liquid volume of the basin and ρ_c the liquid density. Substituting Eqn. (13) in Eqn. (12) yields:

$$E = a_1\left(v_0 g \frac{H^*}{H}\right)^{1/3} \bar{\lambda}^{4/3} \tag{14}$$

It may be expected that the influence of the size $\bar{\lambda}^{4/3}$ of the eddies on E must be given by a function containing the geometrical parameters of the basin. Since the turbulent diffusion coefficient is strongly related to the transverse circulating flow (Section 5.3.2), the hydraulic radius $R_H = (2BH)/(2H+B)$ of the cross-section can be expected to play a role in this function.

From many experiments it was concluded that the relationship

$$\bar{\lambda}^{4/3} = R_H (H^{*1/3}) \left(\frac{B}{H}\right)^n \tag{15}$$

with

$$n = +1 \quad \text{for} \quad B \geqslant H$$
$$n = -1 \quad \text{for} \quad B \leqslant H$$

describes reasonably well the influence of the geometry of the basin on E in Eqn. (14).

The combination of Eqn. (14) and (15) yields Eqn. (9).

5.3.2 Transverse mixing phenomena and circulating flows

Bubble aeration devices are usually situated along one side of an aeration basin in order to introduce rolling flow by the lift of the air bubbles (Fig. 5.10). In this way agitation is supplied, which is necessary to keep the activated-sludge flocs in suspension. Even in plug-flow processes, transverse homogeneity is desirable. If the agitation is insufficient to keep the sludge flocs in suspension and well distributed throughout the liquid, the reduced contact between micro-organisms and nutrients will slow down the rate of nutrient removal. Moreover, these mixing phenomena are required to ensure that sufficient dissolved oxygen is supplied throughout the basin so that certain regions of the basin do not become anoxic.

Streamline profiles of transverse circulating flows in scale models of aeration basins were demonstrated visually by suspending polystyrene particles in the liquid. These particles were illuminated by intensive light sources located behind a narrow slot perpendicular to the longitudinal axis of the basin. This resulted in an illuminated cross-section in which the movement of the particles was observed from a direction perpendicular to it.

From photographs it has been concluded that the circulating flow generally has its centre in the middle of the cross-section. However, at low depth : width ratios of the basin flow profiles are no longer rotationally symmetrical at the circulating flow rates (Fig. 5.11).

Transverse circulating flows have been shown experimentally to influence longitudinal mixing phenomena considerably [3]. From experimental investigations it has

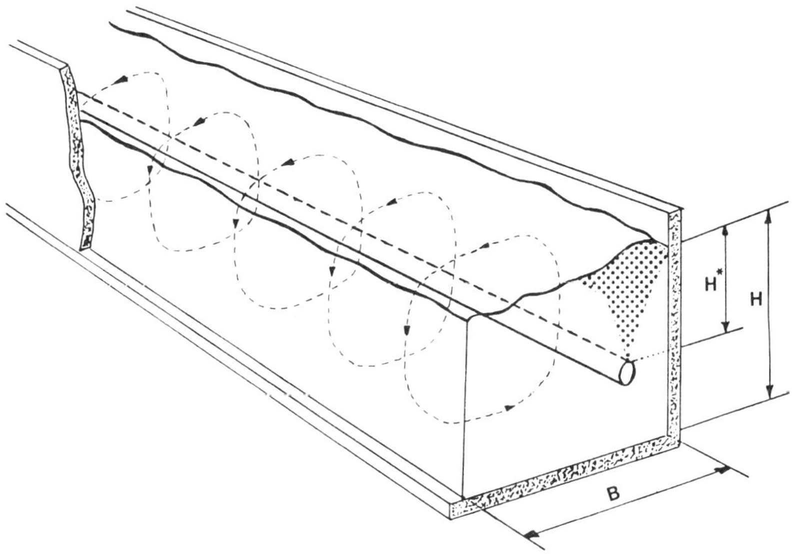

Fig. 5.10 — Schematic diagram of a scale model of an oblong aeration basin.

been concluded that at constant geometrical sizes of the basin the influence of the gas-flow rate and the height of submergence of the aeration device on the longitudinal dispersion coefficient can be fully characterized by the circulation time of the transverse circulating flow.

Is has been pointed out in Section 5.3.1 that in full-scale oblong aeration basins the longitudinal mixing regime is achieved by a series of ideally mixed stages, even without the presence of discrete partitions in the basin. This phenomenon can also be explained from the viewpoint of transverse circulating flow. To understand this, part of a schematic longitudinal section of an Inka basin is shown Fig. 5.12 at the position of the aeration devices. In zones 3–4–6–7 an upward liquid flow, together with a highly turbulent mixing, is caused by the diffused air bubbles. The upward flow is counterbalanced by a downward flow on both sides of the aeration devices A and B, and a transverse circulating flow perpendicular to the plane. Since the circulation velocities are so much larger than the superficial throughput velocity (by a factor of about 50) the volume 1–3–8–9 behaves more or less as a perfectly mixed stage. An indication of the validity of this mixing mechanism is the shape of a foam layer that is consistent with the circulation described as shown in Figs 5.12 and 5.13.

5.4 MACRO-KINETICS: THE INFLUENCE OF MIXING ON THE RATE OF CONVERSION

The removal of pollutants from a wastewater by biological processes is due to several mechanisms. In sewage-treatment processes part of the oxygen-demanding substances are present in the form of suspended and colloidal materials. Whilst these

Fig. 5.11 — Streamline profile of the transversal circulating flow in a scale model of an oblong aeration brain (H = 30 cm, B = 40 cm, H^* = 10 cm, circulating time τ_c = 7.3 s).

materials are removed rapidly from the liquor by enmeshment or physicochemical adsorption in the biological flocs, complete removal is a much slower process. Soluble organic matter is removed by biosorption by the micro-organisms and partly degraded to mineral oxidation products (Section 5.1.2).

In idealizing the engineering aspects of the macro-kinetics of the process, this section will start from the concept of a homogeneous reaction according to the rate expressions given in Section 5.2. Moreover, for this application the following additional assumptions are made:

- no physical transport limitations for oxygen or substrate occur, neither in the activated sludge floc nor in the liquid;
- the removal of substrate in the settling tank may be neglected;
- the activated sludge is present freely dispersed in the aeration basin and completely separated in the settling tank; and
- the oxygen concentration in the aeration basin is sufficiently high (>1 mg/l) to have no influence on the substrate removal rate.

In this section two mixing regimes will be considered, the completely mixed and the

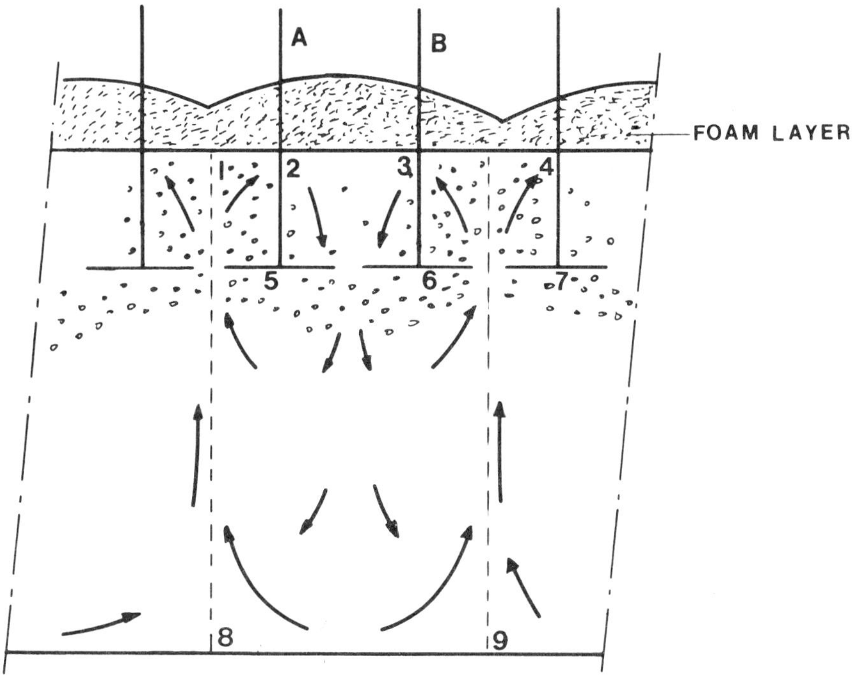

Fig. 5.12 — Mechanism affecting mixing stages.

perfect plug-flow system; although the latter is hardly ever encountered in practice (Section 5.3.1), the analytical expressions resulting from both models have the advantage of providing insight. Moreover, from a viewpoint of residence time distribution, both mixing regimes refer to systems with extreme values of the variation coefficient. Hence any other mixing regime will yield a rate of conversion which is within these two extremes. Fig. 5.14 shows a flow sheet of the biological treatment stage, including both the aeration basin and the sludge settling tank. In the figure liquid-flow rates are indicated by Q, substrate and organisms concentrations by L and X, respectively. Influent and effluent concentrations are indicated by the subscript i and e, respectively. The various flow rates given in the figure, which result from mass balances on the separate process units, are self-evident.

5.4.1 The completely mixed system

In a completely mixed system, the substrate and sludge concentrations in the effluent stream equal the respective concentrations in the aeration basin. If the system is in a steady state a material balance of sludge yields is according to rate expression, Eqn. (5):

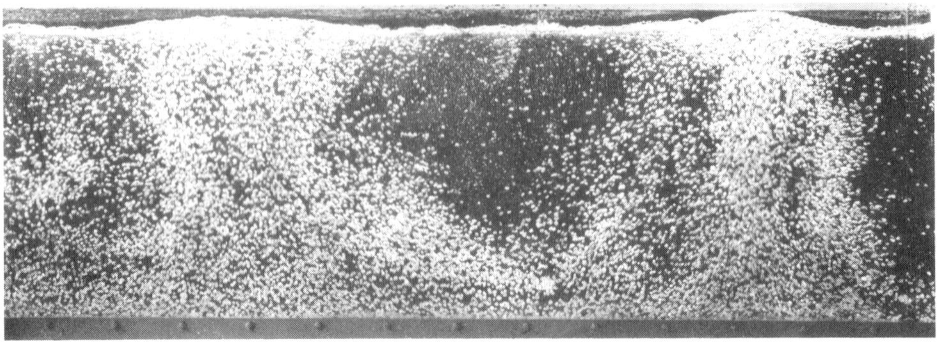

(a)

(b)

Fig. 5.13 (a) Bubble stream formation in a scale model of an oblong aeration basin. (b) Foam waves in an Inka aeration basin.

$$(1-r)(Q_r+Q_s)X_e = V\mu_m\frac{\text{Le}}{\text{Le}+K_s}X_\text{e} - VK_2X_e \qquad (16)$$

net sludge removal — sludge production — auto-oxidation

where V is the aeration tank volume.

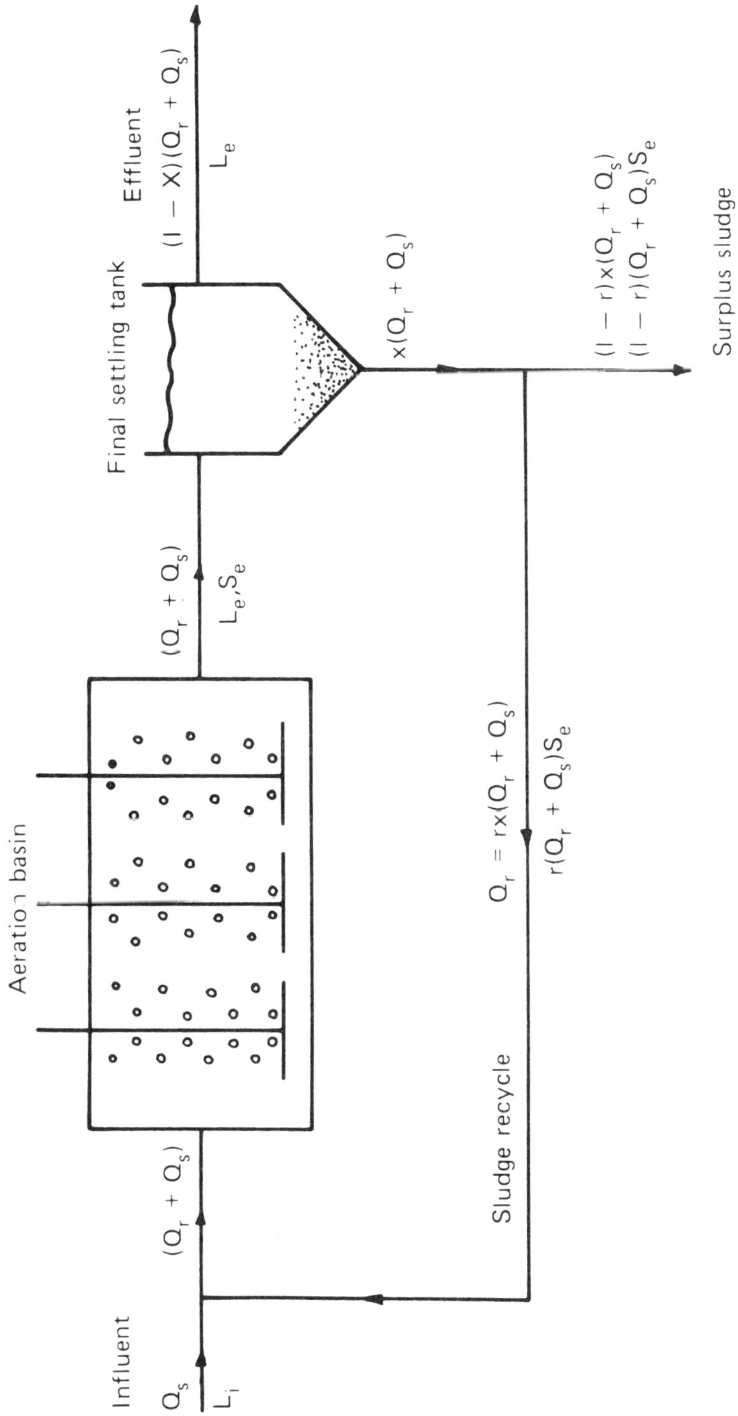

Fig. 5.14 — Flow sheet of the biological stage.

Eqn. (16) allows the effluent substrate concentration to be calculated according to:

$$\text{Le} \; \frac{K_s}{\dfrac{\mu_m \tau_0}{(1-r)(1+\alpha)+K_2\tau_0} - 1} \qquad (17)$$

where $\tau_0 = V/Q_s$, the average residence time in the aeration basin, and $\alpha = Q_r/Q_s$, the sludge recirculation ratio.

From material balances of sludge and substrate and Eqn. (2), the sludge concentration in the aeration basin can be calculated:

$$YQ_s(\text{Li}-\text{Le}) = (1-r)(Q_r+Q_s)X_e + VK_2X_e$$

assimilated substrate	sludge production	auto-oxidation

or

$$X_e = \frac{Y(\text{Li–Le})}{(1-r)(1+\alpha)+K_2\tau_o} \qquad (18)$$

From Eqn. (17) several interesting conclusions can be drawn:

- The effluent concentration of substrate is independent of the influent concentration. Of course this statement holds only as long a the system is in a steady state. If the influent substrate concentration is increased, for example by a step function, this will result in an increase of the sludge concentration level according to Eqn. (18). The effluent substrate concentration will only temporarily increase and will reach the old level if new steady-state conditions have set in.
- In a completely mixed system the effluent stream always contains some substrate. The minimal effluent substrate concentration

$$\text{Le}_{\text{min}} = \frac{K_s}{\dfrac{\mu_m}{K_2} - 1}$$

can be achieved if $\tau_0 \rightarrow \infty$ or $r \rightarrow 1$ (no sludge removal from the system).
- There is a minimal residence time in the aeration basin below which no substrate degradation occurs. This phenomenon is physically explained by the fact that the wash-out rate of the micro-organisms exceeds the net growth rate. Substituting Le = Li in Eqn. (17) it follows for this critical residence time τ_{0c} that:

$$\tau_{0c} = \frac{(1-r)(1+\alpha)}{\dfrac{\mu_m}{(1+K_s/Li)} - K_2}$$

The path of the dimensionless concentration Le/Li as a function of $\mu_m \tau_0$ according to Eqn. (17) is graphically shown in Fig. 5.15.

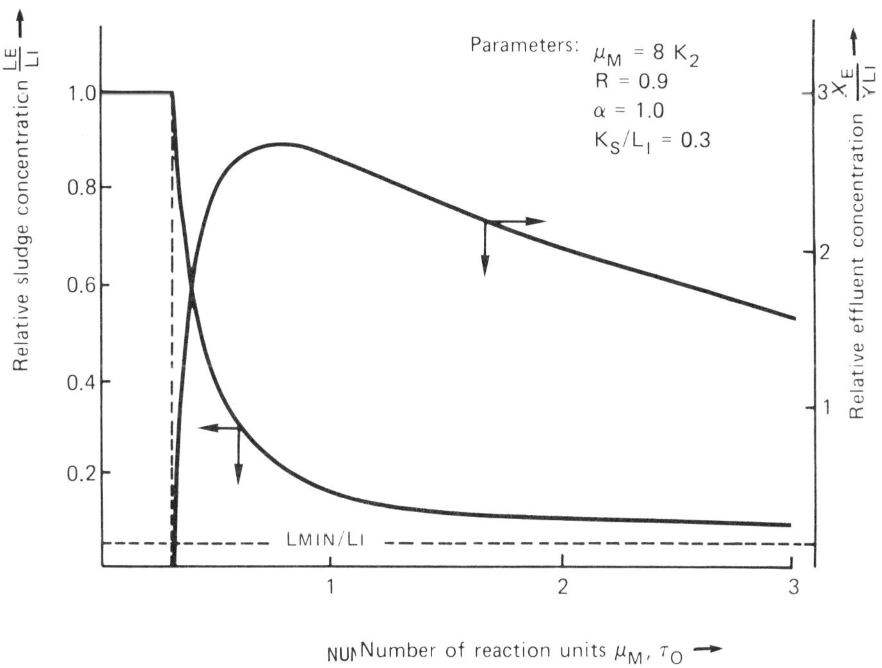

Fig. 5.15 — The effluent substrate and sludge concentration as a function of the number of reaction units in a perfectly mixed tank.

In wastewater treatment plants the mean sludge-residence time is an important design parameter. This quantity is defined as the total amount of activated sludge in the system, divided by the total rate of sludge removal. It should be borne in mind that sludge removal from the system is effected by the withdrawal of surplus sludge as well as by the auto-oxidation of the sludge. As in well-working plants the amount of sludge in the settling tank is relatively small, the amount of sludge is frequently related to the mass of sludge in the aeration basin. In this way it follows for the mean sludge-residence time τ_s in a completely mixed system that:

$$\tau_s = \frac{VX_e}{(1-r)(Q_r+Q_s)X_e + VK_2X_e} = \frac{\tau_0}{(1-r)(1+\alpha)+K_2\tau_0} \quad (19)$$

In combining Eqns. (17) and (19) the effluent substrate concentration can be related to the average sludge age according to:

$$\mathrm{Le} = \frac{K_s}{\mu_m \tau_s - 1} \tag{20}$$

Analogue relations are described in the literature where other, different-order, kinetic models are used instead of the Monod equation, e.g. first-order kinetics [9].

The given relationships are found to correlate quite well with experimental data.

5.4.2 The perfect plug-flow system

In a plug-flow system the concentration of substrate, as well as that of sludge, varies as a function of the distance y in the basin. Hence material balances have been made for a differential element with thickness Δy. With the assumptions given above a material balance of sludge yields in the steady state are:

$$(Q_r + Q_s)X_y + \frac{\mu_m L X}{(L + K_s)} A\Delta y = (Q_r + Q_s)X_{y+\Delta y} + AK_2 X\Delta y$$

sludge input	sludge production	sludge output	auto-oxidation

where A is the cross-sectional area of the basin. By rearranging the different terms, dividing by Δy and taking the limit for $\Delta y \rightarrow 0$ a differential equation has been obtained, which describes the sludge concentration X as a function of the dimensionless distance $\sigma = y/H$ in the reactor:

$$\frac{1}{X}\frac{\mathrm{d}X}{\mathrm{d}\sigma} = \frac{\tau_0}{(1+\alpha)}\left(\mu_\mathrm{m}\frac{L}{(L+K_s)} - K_2\right) \tag{21}$$

The boundary condition for this differential equation is:

$$\sigma = 0; \qquad X_0 = rX_e \tag{22}$$

In the same way the differential equation describing the substrate concentration can be derived:

$$\frac{1}{X}\frac{\mathrm{d}L}{\mathrm{d}\sigma} = -\frac{\mu_m \tau_0}{(1+\alpha)Y}\frac{L}{(L+K_s)} \tag{23}$$

with boundary condition (Fig. 5.14):

$$\sigma = 0; \qquad \text{Lo} = \frac{\text{Li} + \alpha\text{Le}}{(1+\alpha)} \tag{24}$$

From Eqn. (23) the sludge concentration X can be expressed as a function of the substrate concentration L and substituted in Eqn. (21). In this way a non-linear differential equation is obtained, which cannot be easily solved by analytical means. Hence a solution has been made by digital or analogue computer techniques. Fig. 5.16 shows, as an example, the computed concentration profiles in the basin at given

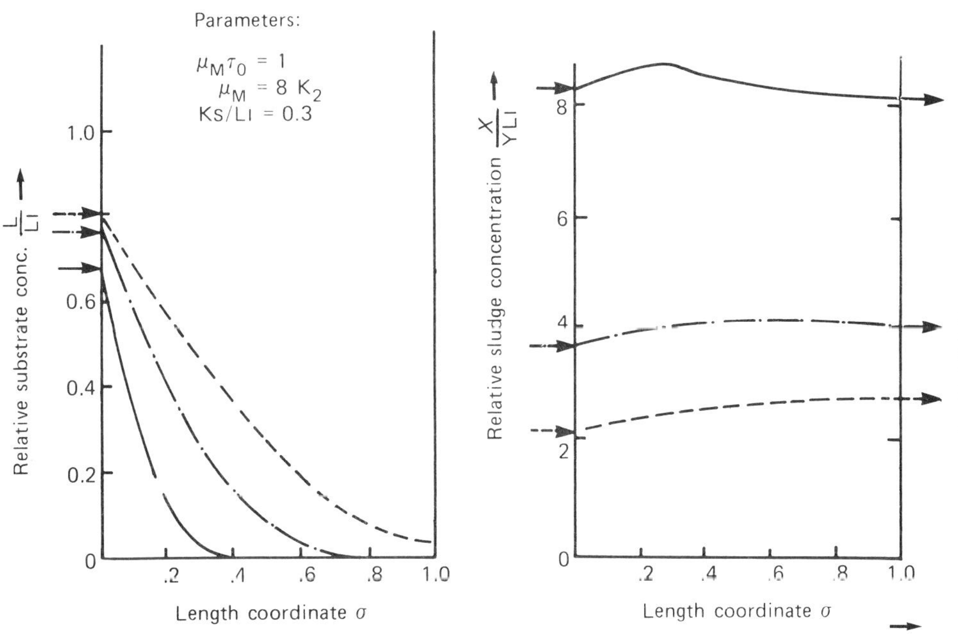

Fig. 5.16 — Substrate and sludge concentration profiles in a plug-flow basin.
Key: $R = 1.0, \alpha = 0.33$ (——);
$R = 0.9, \alpha = 0.29$ (—ß—);
P $= 0.8, \alpha = 0.25$ (---).

values of the process parameters.

From these concentration profiles it may be concluded that it is a good approximation to suppose that the sludge concentration is constant throughout the whole basin at sufficiently high concentration levels. With this assumption (X = constant) Eqn. (23) can be solved easily in an analytical way. Together with a total material balance of sludge according to Eqn. (18) the solution becomes:

$$\frac{(\text{Li} - \text{Le})}{(1+\alpha)}(1 - \mu_m \tau_s) + K_s \ln\left[\frac{\text{Li} + \alpha\text{Le}}{(1+\alpha)\text{Le}}\right] = 0 \tag{25}$$

where τ_s is given by Eqn. (19).

Eqn. (25) allows the effluent substrate concentration to be calculated for a perfect plug-flow system. This approximation method has proved also to be in good accordance with experimental data for such flow systems.

5.5 REFERENCES

[1] Ardern, E. and Lockett, W. T. (1914). Experiments on the oxidation of sewage without the aid of filters. *J. Soc. Chem. Ind.*, **33**, 523.

[2] Murphy, K. L. and Timpany, P. L. (1967). *J. Sanit. Eng. Div. ASCE SAS*, **93**, 1.

[3] Ottengraf, S. P. P. (1980). Longitudinal dispersion in oblong aerated systems. *Chem. Eng. Sci.*, **35**, 687.

[4] Chudoba, J., Ottova, V. and Madera, V. (1973). Control of activated sludge filamentous bulking I. Effect of the hydraulic regime on degree of mixing in an aeration tank. *Water Res.*, **7**, 1163.

[5] Michaelis, L. and Menten, H. (1913). Die Kinetik der Invertinwirkung. *Biochem. Z.*, **49**, 33.

[6] Briggs, G. E. and Haldane, J. B. S. (1925). A note on the kinetics of enzyme action. *Biochem. J.*, **19**, 338.

[7] Monod, J. (1941). Recherches sur la croissance des cultures bacteriennes. Thèse Université de Paris.

[8] Monod, J. (1949). The growth of bacterial cultures. *Ann. Rev. Microbiol.*, **3**, 371.

[9] Eckenfelder, W. W. (1966). *Industrial Water Pollution Control*, McGraw-Hill, New York.

[10] Winkler, M. A. (1981). *Biological Treatment of Wastewater*, Ellis Horwood, Chichester.

[11] Wuhrmann, K. (1956). *Biological Treatment of Sewage and Industrial Wastes*, Vol. I, Reinhold, New York.

[12] Ottengraf, S. P. P. and Rietema, K. (1969). The influence of mixing on the activated sludge process in industrial aeration basins. *J. Water Pollut. Contr. Fed.*, **37**, R282.

[13] Klinkenberg, A. (1966). Distribution of residence times in a cascade of mixed vessels with backmixing. *Ind. Eng. Chem. Fund.*, **5**, 283.

[14] Klinkenberg, A. (1968). Moments of residence-time distributions for cascades of stirred vessels with backmixing. *Chem. Eng. Sci.*, **23**, 175.

[15] Roemer, M. H. and Durbin, L. D. (1967). Transient response and moments analysis of backflow cell model for flow systems with longitudinal mixing. *Ind. Eng. Chem. Fund.*, **6**, 120.

[16] Van der Laan, E. T. (1958). Notes on the diffusion type model for the longitudinal mixing in flow. *Chem. Eng. Sci.*, **7**, 187.

[17] Kolmogorov, A. N. (1941). *CR Akad. Nauk. USSR*, **30**, 301; **31**, 538; **32**, 16.

[18] Hinze, J. O. (1975). Turbulence, McGraw-Hill, New York.

[19] Tennekes, H. and Lumley, J. L. (1972). *A First Course in Turbulence*, MIT Press, Boston.

6

Biomethanation

H. Sixt and **H. Sahm**
Consultants, Institute fur Biotechologie der Kernforschungsanlage, Julich, GmbH, West Germany

6.1 INTRODUCTION

The anaerobic treatment of liquid wastes is the oldest method of wastewater purification known. It was applied in the Middle East many centuries before Christ. Anaerobic wastewater treatment fell into oblivion with the invention of aerobic processes such as biofiltration and activated-sludge treatment, since these involved substantially shorter reaction times.

Increased environmental consciousness has called for enhanced industrial wastewater purification in the past few years. Anaerobic methods are increasingly being considered for industrial wastewaters, particularly those of higher organic strength, largely because of the cost of energy to run aerobic processes.

Anaerobic processes are suitable for the treatment of highly polluted organic wastewaters. Buswell [1] specifies 1200 to 2000 mg/l BOD_5 as the minimum pollution strength. This is an economic rather than a process-engineering limit. The upper limit is currently estimated to be about 100000 mg/l COD [2].

The following are among the industries that produce wastewater which can be partially treated anaerobically:

the manufacture of	
sugar	ice cream
starch	chewing gum
yeast	olive oil
pectin	cardboard and chipboard
cellulose	palm oil
the processing of	
potatoes	meat
fruit and vegetables	fish
as well as	
distilleries	breweries
abattoirs	dairies
the fermentation industry	the pharmaceutical industry

The biomethanation of sewage sludge produced in connection with municipal wastewater treatment will not be described here in detail, but reference is made to relevant technical literature [3,4,5].

In addition to the degree of pollution, of decisive importance in the successful application of anaerobic processes is also the specific composition and origin of the wastewater.

In the past, the aim was to treat highly polluted wastewater as fully as possible using anaerobic processes, i.e. to attain ultimate BOD_5 values of less than 30 mg/l. In order to achieve this goal, while maintaining the operational safety required, very long digestion times were selected, often exceeding 20 days. Retention time was determined empirically. The objective today is to eliminate a substantial part of the pollution load using anaerobic processes and to accept ultimate BOD_5 values of a few hundred milligrams per litre. In this respect, anaerobic processes can only be regarded as a primary treatment stage and it is necessary to have a subsequent secondary stage. However, partial anaerobic treatment can only be economical if, using recent microbiological findings, the process is intensified and stabilized so that most of the pollution load can be degraded in short reaction times equivalent to those needed for the equivalent degree of aerobic treatment for similar wastewaters [6]. The higher the pollution load of wastewater the more efficient will be the process in terms of retention time (reactor volume), capital investments and methane production.

In anaerobic wastewater treatment processes, methane (digester gas or biogas) is produced. An average of 0.3–0.5 m^3 of biogas is produced per kilogram of organic matter destroyed, measured as COD; but much depends on the nature of the wastewater and process technology [7]. This equates to a specific energy production of 1.9–3.2 kWh/kg COD destroyed, based on an average energy equivalent of 6.4 kWh/m^3 of biogas. In addition, anaerobic processes offer the advantage of very low bacterial growth, which means that the production of sludge is relatively low.

6.2 MICROBIOLOGICAL FUNDAMENTALS

6.2.1 Anaerobic biodegradation

The degradation of organic substances in an anaerobic environment takes place in several steps, in each of which particular metabolic processes are performed by specific micro-organisms: this is shown schematically in Fig. 6.1.

Undissolved organic substances are broken down by hydrolytic bacteria with the aid of exoenzymes and converted into dissolved substrates. Anaerobic bacteria convert carbohydrates, for example, into fermentation products such as low-chain fatty acids, alcohols, hydrogen and carbon dioxide (acidification phase). Exoenzymes hydrolyse cellulose, for example, to glucose which is then converted, as shown in Fig. 6.2, into different fermentation products.

Fats are split into long-chain fatty acids and glycerol by lipases (lipolysis). Glycerol is closely related to the carbohydrates and is degraded to pyruvate [8]. The fatty acid chains are degraded by so-called β-oxidation, splitting off units of acetic acid [9].

Proteins are degraded extracellularly to amino acids by enzymes (proteases).

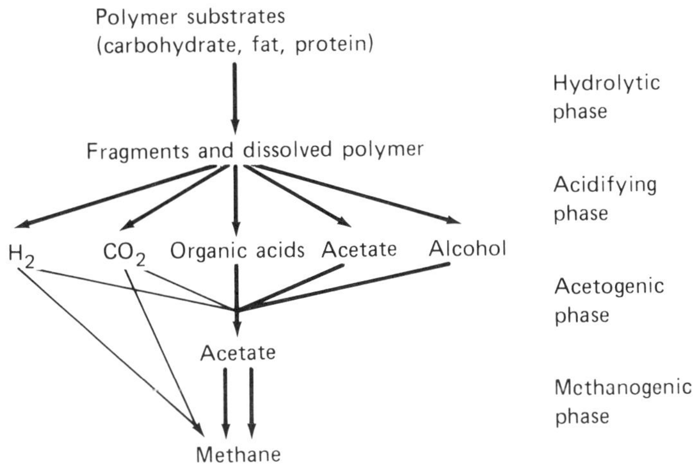

Fig. 6.1 — Anaerobic metabolism.

These are degraded intracellularly while the amino nitrogen is set free as ammonium NH_3. Certain bacteria of the genus *Clostridium* are capable of degrading amino acids by coupled oxidation–reduction reactions (Stickland reaction). The classical demonstration model is the decomposition of the amino acid combination of alanine and glycine, where alanine acts as the H-donor and glycine as the H-acceptor [10], as shown in Fig. 6.3.

6.2.2 Methanogenesis and acetogenesis

As described, the metabolism of the main substrates — carbohydrate, fat and protein — leads, in the hydrolysis and acidification phase, to organic compounds which can be further degraded. Formerly, it was assumed that the acid intermediates could be directly processed by the methane bacteria [11]. However, it was demonstrated in 1967 [12], by means of the symbiotic reaction of *Methanobacterium omelianskii*, that methane bacteria need a substrate preparation and can only process a few of the acidification intermediates directly. In the acetogenic phase [6], alcohols and higher-chain fatty acids are rebuilt to acetate, hydrogen and carbon dioxide which then constitute methanogenic substrates. This substrate preparation and transfer can take place in a close symbiosis, as is shown by the example in Fig. 6.4.

For thermodynamic reasons, the conversion of ethanol into acetate can only take place at a low hydrogen partial pressure. This is ensured by the direct processing of hydrogen by methane bacteria which, on the other hand, depend on the availability of substrates [13]. The hydrogen produced must be consumed at its place of origin in the immediate vicinity of the acetogenic bacteria. For this reason, intimate cell contact is required between acetogenic and methanogenic bacteria since the necessarily low hydrogen partial pressure cannot be maintained by diffusion of the hydrogen alone [14]. In practical anaerobic wastewater treatment, it is therefore necessary to pay particular attention to the maintenance of a close association of cells.

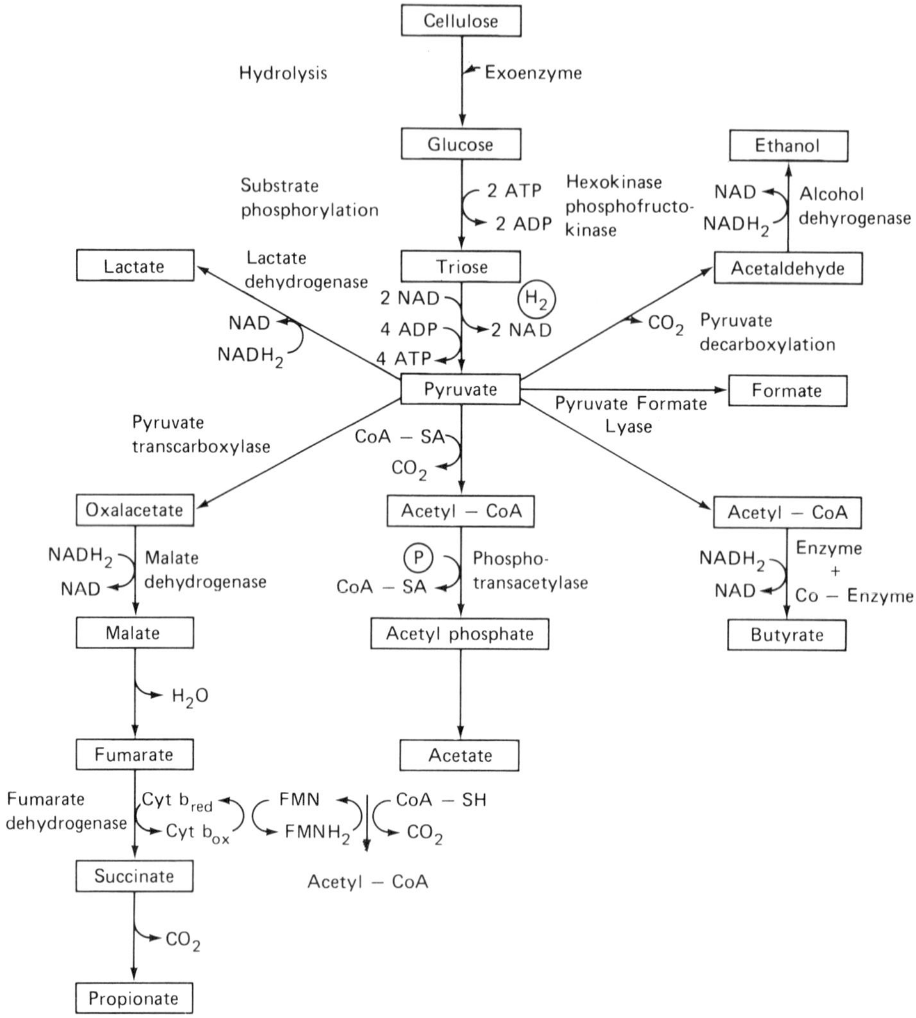

Fig. 6.2 — Fermentation and intermediates.

6.2.3 Desulphurication

Sulphate can present a problem in practical wastewater treatment, since many production processes also use sulphuric acid, sulphates passing into the wastewater. Bacteria capable of reducing sulphate can also grow in the absence of sulphate [15]; they then act as acetogenic bacteria. For example, *Desulfovibrio desulfuricans* can oxidize ethanol or lactic acid to acetic acid in the absence of sulphate, or at very low sulphate concentrations, if the methane bacteria process the hydrogen directly. In this case, methanation is not impaired. At higher sulphate concentrations, however, sulphate is reduced primarily to hydrogen sulphide (Fig. 6.5) because, in this case, more energy can be produced biochemically [16]. The desulphurizers then interfere

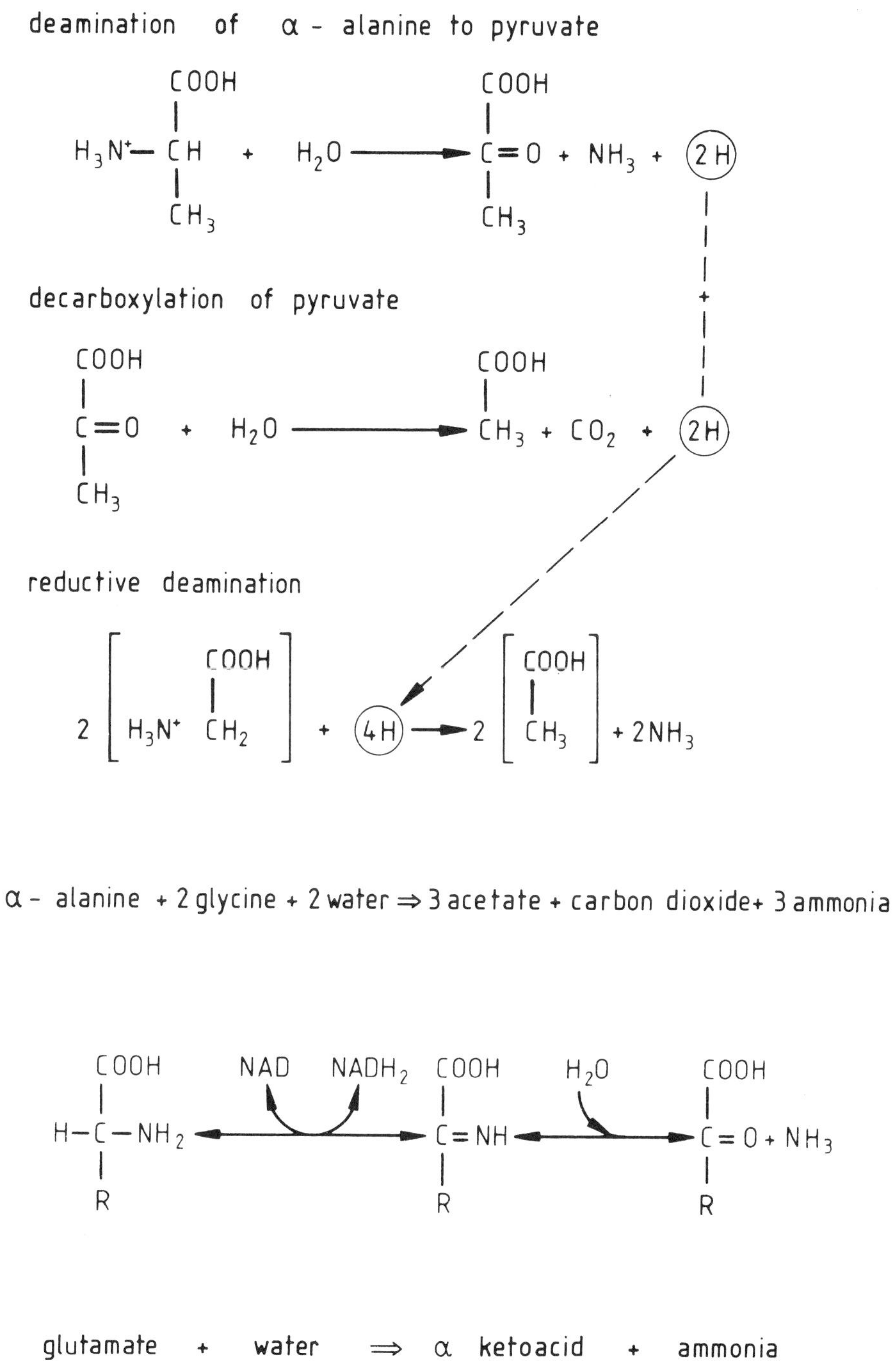

Fig. 6.3 — Protein decomposition.

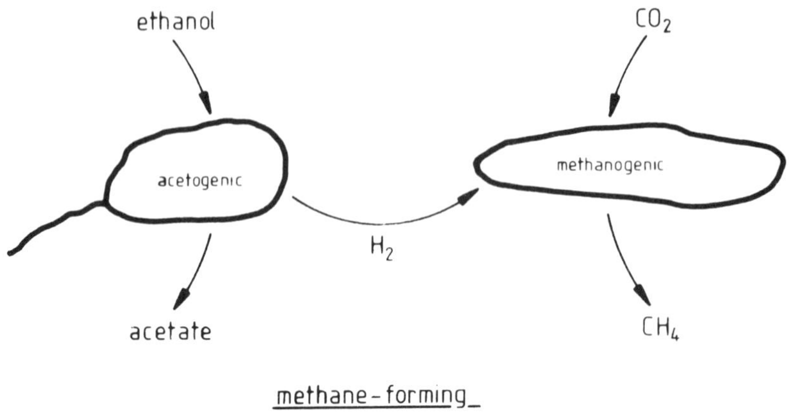

Fig. 6.4 — Hydrogen interspecies transfer.

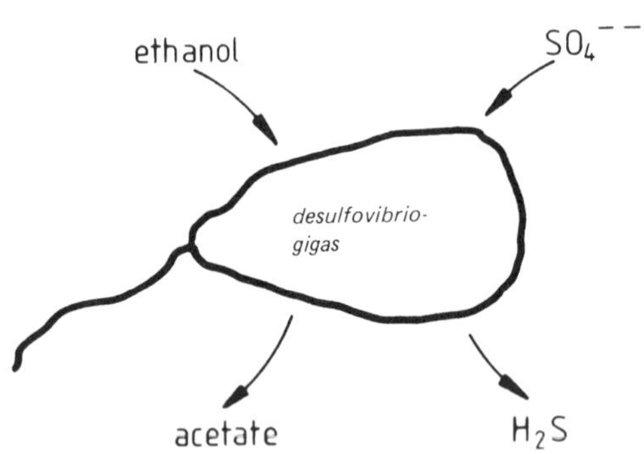

Fig. 6.5 — Desulphurication.

directly with the symbiosis of acetogenic bacteria, consuming hydrogen. The formation of methane is then impeded by the lack of hydrogen; moreover, H_2S has a toxic effect at elevated concentrations [17,18].

This has been confirmed experimentally using pure cultures of *Methanosarcina barkeri* [19]. As is shown in Fig. 6.6, small amounts of sodium sulphide enhance biomethanation, whereas higher concentrations, for example, 12 mmol, fully inhibit biomethanation.

6.2.4 Biomethanation

Approximately 20 different methane-forming bacteria have been isolated to date. They are sensitive to the presence of oxygen and have a narrow substrate spectrum. All of the methane bacteria can process hydrogen, some of them formate, and

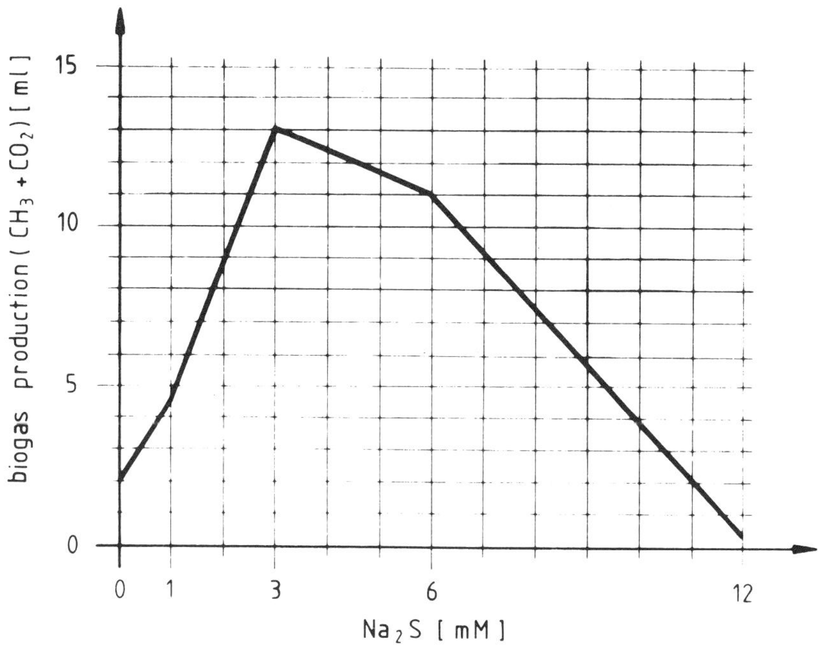

Fig. 6.6 — Relation between biogas production and Na_2S concentration.

Methanosarcina barkeri can process methanol, methylamine and acetate. Sarcines are especially likely to play a particular role during methanation since about 70 per cent of the methane is formed from acetate [20].

Although some of the intermediate steps in methane formation are still unclarified, the Barker scheme [21] (Fig. 6.7) is regarded as generally valid. The coenzyme M plays an important role in this process, acting as an intermediate carrier in the last step of the reduction of CO_2 to methane. The chemical structure of this coenzyme is $HS—CH_2—CH_3—SO_4$ (2-mercaptoethansulphonic acid).

The mercapto group, HS, acts as the acceptor for the methyl group [22,23]. The electron flux of the HS coenzyme M proceeds, among other things, via F_{420} and NAD. F_{420} represents a coenzyme found exclusively in methane bacteria. F_{420} is a deazoriboflavin derivative which flouresces at a wavelength of 420 nm. Thus methane bacteria can be identified specifically by fluorescence microscopy.

6.3 PROCESS CONDITIONS

6.3.1 Microbiological requirements

The technical utilization of microbiological processes involves a number of special boundary and environmental conditions. Of particular influence are:

- substances contained in the liquid wastewater;
- temperature;
- pH value;

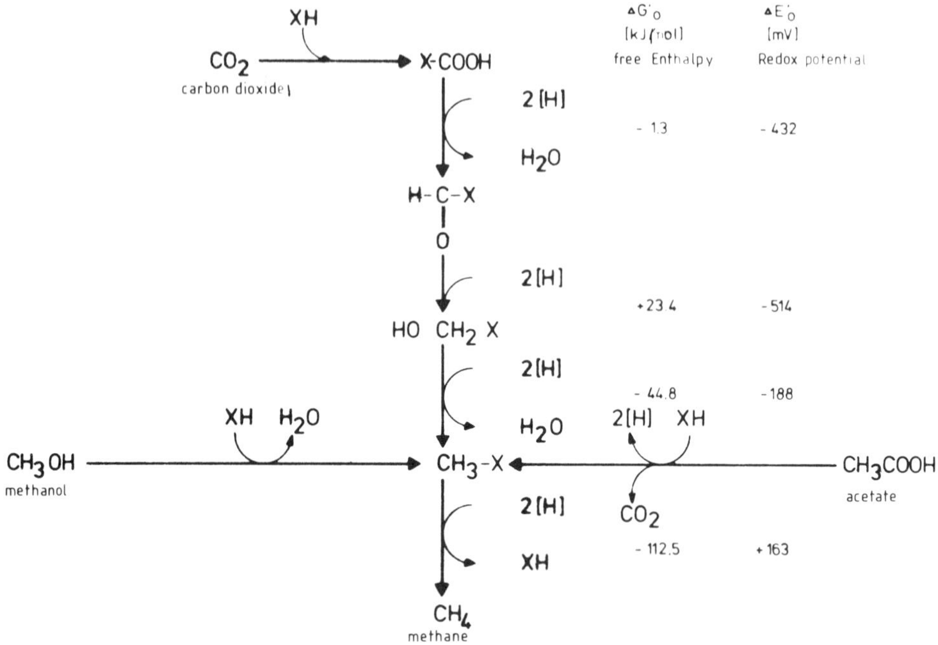

Fig. 6.7 — Biomethanization—Barker scheme.

– treatment plant dimensions and loading.

Theoretically, all organic carbon compounds can be degraded to methane and carbon dioxide, but there are some organic compounds such as hydrocarbons, lignin, ether and certain plastics which cannot be degraded anaerobically [14,24]. Different substances are metabolized by the anaerobic micro-organisms at different rates [14]. Anaerobic bacteria processing carbohydrate and protein grow with generation times of less than one day. On the other hand, bacteria degrading fatty acids grow slowly with generation times of about five days, so that the fatty acid degradation is rather slow. This is usually the rate-limiting factor in biomethanation.

Anaerobic micro-organisms need the following nutrients in addition to organic carbon sources: nitrogen, sulphur, phosphorus, potassium, calcium, magnesium; and the following trace elements: iron, manganese, molybdenum, zinc, copper, cobalt, selenium, tungsten and nickel.

Halogenated hydrocarbons, cyanides and heavy metals in elevated concentration have a toxic effect on anaerobic processes [5]; heavy metals can be bound and precipitated by sulphide.

Current practice is limited to mesophilic and thermophilic anaerobic treatment. The temperature for mesophilic anaerobic processes ranges between 30 and 37°C, the optimum being 37°C [25]. It is not absolutely necessary to select the optimum temperature. However, it should be ensured that the temperature selected is maintained with only minor deviations, since significant variations reduce the rate of degradation. Most treatment plants are operated in the mesophilic range, since the thermophilic reaction does not offer any significant advantages in terms of reaction kinetics [26]. With the exception of wastewater produced with temperatures exceeding 40°C, more process-sustaining energy is required for the thermophilic reaction than for the mesophilic process. Furthermore, reactors operated thermophilically may impose more stringent design constraints, particularly with regard to statics, reinforcement and thermal insulation.

Methane bacteria are very sensitive to pH value. They need a pH range between 6.5 and 7.8. In a single-stage reactor in equilibrium, the amount of acid produced just about equals that which can be processed in the methane phase. Inhibition of the activity of the methane bacteria must be expected if acid production increases to such an extent that the pH value falls below 6. pH values above 8, which may result, for example, from ammonia production during protein degradation, also have an inhibiting effect: this is discussed later.

In addition to the effect on pH values of the metabolism of substances contained in the wastewater, the acidity or alkalinity of the wastewaters themselves, or of substances contained in them, is also of significance. It is, for example, necessary to neutralize mineral acids or alkaline detergents to prevent changes in the environmental conditions. On the other hand, acidity caused by degradable organic acids in the wastewater does not require neutralization.

In practice wastewater is usually produced with a constantly changing composition. Strictly controlled chemostat conditions are normally not achievable so biomass recycling must be employed. For this reason, the theoretical approaches based on reaction kinetics (Monod kinetics) are seldom helpful for dimensioning and loading considerations.

6.3.2 Process design

Designers working in the field of aerobic wastewater treatment are familiar with such parameters as sludge loading, space loading, retention time, sludge age and others. In particular the parameter of sludge loading is only valid as a design parameter for aerobic systems because, as a rule, a mixed population working on the single-phase principle ensures degradation from the initial substrate through to the final products of carbon dioxide and water [18]. As has been described, anaerobic degradation proceeds in a more complicated manner, the individual metabolic steps being governed by different bacteria with different reaction kinetics and growth so that, depending on the substances contained in the wastewater, different degradation phases may separately govern the overall reaction rate of the process.

This demonstrates that the dimensioning parameter of sludge load is potentially unreliable and, indeed, is only valid for anaerobic treatment for a specific type of liquid wastewater. This has been confirmed by different workers [27,28]. It is not possible, for example, to forecast probable process characteristics on the basis of the types and numbers of substrate and reaction-specific micro-organisms present in an anaerobic reactor [29]. Even if this were possible there would still remain uncertainty, since the distribution of intermediates in the acidification phase changes under different loads and pH values [15,30,31].

In connection with the unregulated hydrolysis and acidification of starch and pectin it was found that these are hydrolysed and acidified at a constant conversion rate of approx. 85–99 per cent within large loading rate ranges of B_R = 0.7–8.5 kg COD/m^3. The percentage distribution of the intermediates shows an interesting development as a function of the load and associated pH values of 5.0–3.2 (Fig. 6.8).

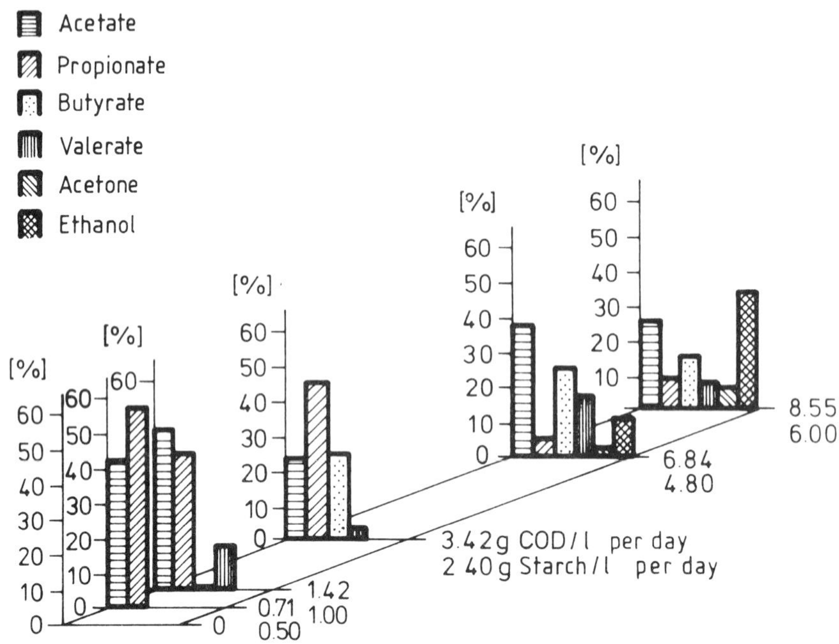

Fig. 6.8 — Distribution of intermediate acids according to space load (kg COD/l per day).

While acetate and propionate are formed almost exclusively at low loading rates, an increasing production of butyric and valeric acid, as well as acetone and ethanol, is observed with rising load and simultaneously decreasing pH value. A similar result is shown in Fig. 6.9 for the acidification of a 1 per cent solution of glucose in the approximate pH range 5–8.

The distribution of the intermediates remains stable in the range pH 6–6.5 but changes considerably in neutral to weakly alkaline environments. Because substrate specificity and the possible adaptation of acetogenic bacteria to special intermediates may be expected, it is generally not possible to forecast whether the mixed culture present also contains bacteria in sufficient quantity to biodegrade the particular intermediates that may be formed. In practice a regime will be established in practice with regard to the intermediates in the acidification process arising from unavoidable changes in feed conditions. In spite of the fact that more information is available today about the growth periods of micro-organisms, reactor design based on retention time or sludge age is potentially dangerous because the phenomena referred to above also must be taken into account. The most appropriate procedure is therefore to determine, for example, the digestion time, sludge loading and sludge age by carrying out a series of pilot tests.

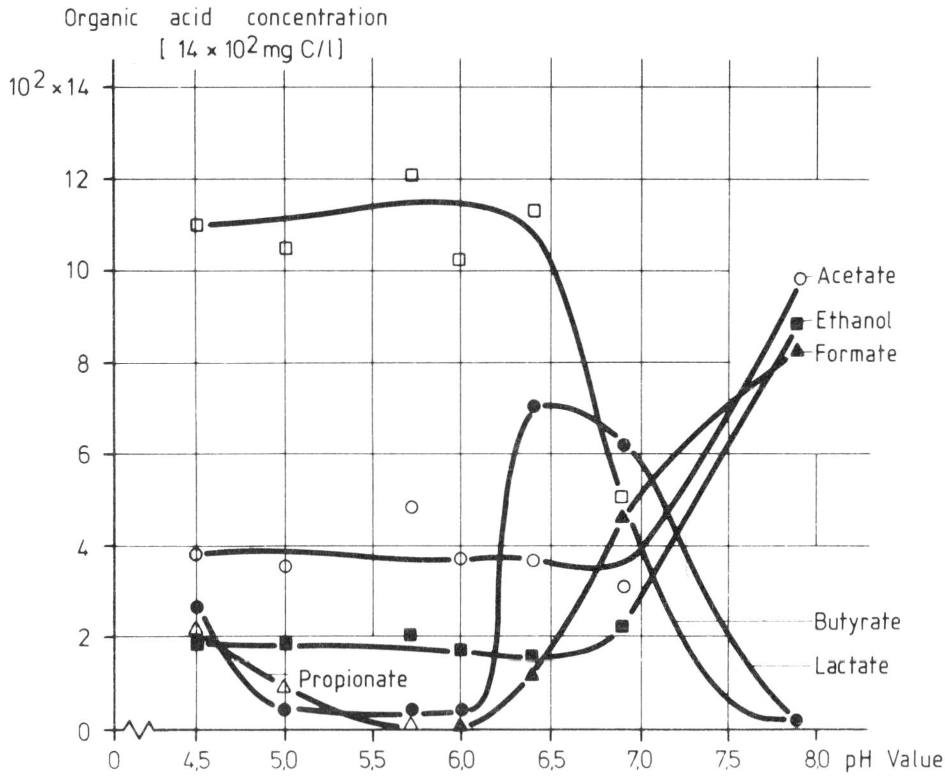

Fig. 6.9 — Acid distribution according to pH value.

6.4 PROCESS ENGINEERING AND REACTOR TECHNOLOGY

6.4.1 Basic needs

The degradation rate and efficiency are significantly influenced by process and reactor technology. This differs considerably from conventional sludge digesters used for municipal wastewater treatment. Of particular significance [32] are:

- preserving and concentrating the active biomass in the reactor;
- preserving the bacterial symbioses (acetogenic/methanogenic);
- optimizing the reaction process, possibly by separating it into a two-stage substrate-specific process flow.

Since most of the bacteria living under anaerobic conditions grow relatively slowly there is normally the danger that they may be quickly flushed out of the reactor owing to the hydraulic conditions. As a rule, it is therefore necessary to concentrate the bacteria by immobilization or recycling. By analogy to the aerobic activated-sludge method, an anaerobic activated-sludge process was developed — the anaerobic contact process [33].

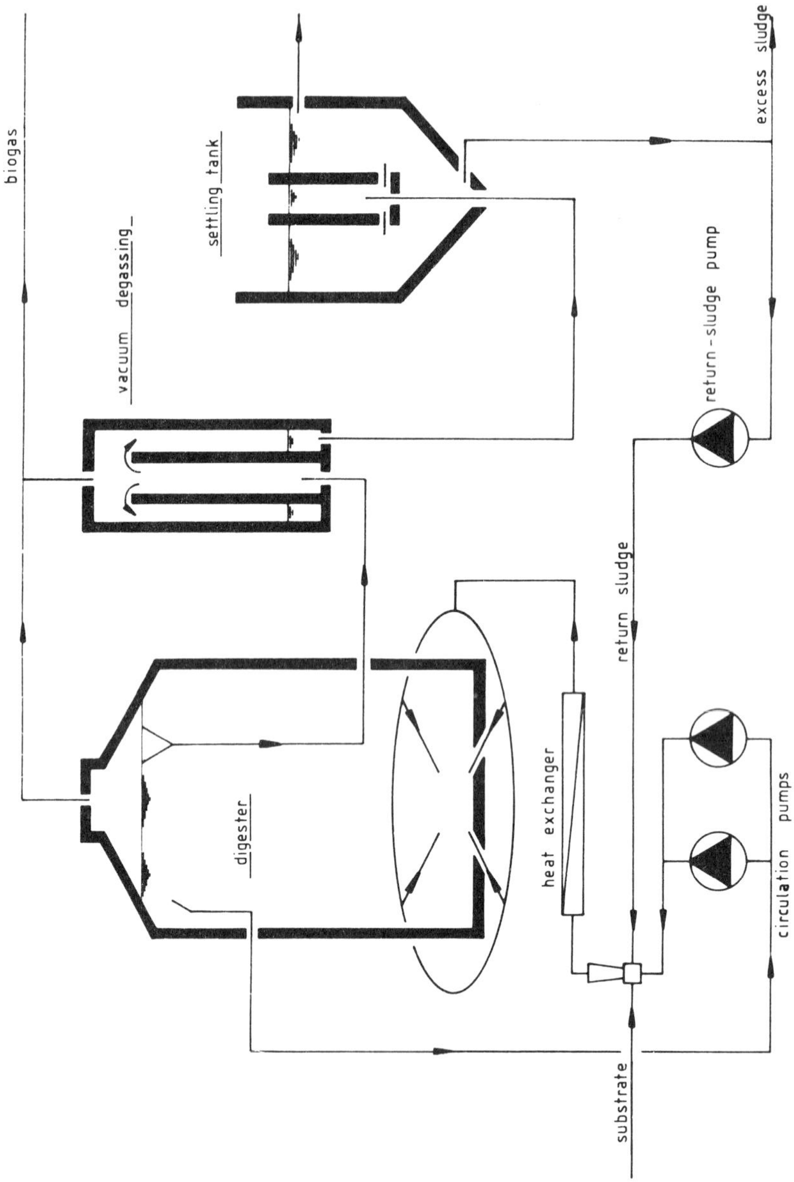

Fig. 6.10 — Anaerobic activated-sludge process.

6.4.2 Reactor design

Ideally the anaerobic activated-sludge reactor should be completely mixed. There are, however, a number of factors in conflict with this aim, so compromise must inevitably be made. The sensitive symbiosis of acetogenic and methanogenic bacteria described above permits only low shear stresses, so that mechanical stressing caused by, for example, mechanical mixing should be avoided. On the other hand, thorough mixing is necessary for the nutrients and bacteria to come into contact with each other [34].

In the case of long reaction times, heat losses through the reactor wall are generally compensated for by heat supplied through external heat exchangers in a recirculation process. A certain turbulence is required in the medium to be heated for interface renewal in order to achieve an adequate heat transfer. If solids are contained in the wastewater, a minimum turbulence is needed to avoid the deposition of solids and the build-up of dead zones. Slow-running centrifugal pumps, internal mixers with speeds below 750 r.p.m. or gas injection have proved to be efficient for this purpose.

The recirculating process for anaerobic activated-sludge reactors must be adapted for each type of liquid waste, to the reactor design, temperature conditions, solids concentration, etc., in order to be economically efficient. Experience gained from conventional sludge digestion can only serve as a starting point [35]. This applies, in particular, to the energy density. The kinetic viscosity of anaerobic activated sludges in the digestion of highly polluted liquid wastewaters containing small amounts of solids generally requires a lower energy density than municipal sludge digestion [4].

6.4.3 Solid separation

The separation and deposition of the sludge may be effected and carried out in:

- settling or sedimentation tanks;
- lamella separators; and
- flotation units.

The use of mechanical dewatering using, for example, decanting centrifuges, belt presses and filter plate presses has not been reported to date except for one case in the potato-processing industry [36]. Possibly their use has not been considered because of the need for gentle separation. Settling tank design is currently based upon municipal wastewater tank practice. In the absence of more relevant dimensioning data, surface loading is mainly used, although anaerobic sludges can be very different from municipal wastewater activated sludges. It has been reported, however, [28,37,38], that good settling performances have been achieved with surface loadings of approx. 0.20 m^3/m^2 per hour. A degassing [39] or cooling [32] stage may be included in the reactor process prior to separation in order to improve sedimentation.

Lamellar separators have been used in the anaerobic treatment of sugar factory wastewaters by the ANAMET process. Details of their effectiveness are not known. Theoretical considerations on utilizing the flotation effect of residual gases in the reactor process led to attempts to enhance this flotation effect using inert gas or biogas. Initial experiments have not yet yielded satisfactory results, since process control is relatively difficult.

In all external settling or separation processes, anaerobic micro-organisms are exposed, more or less extensively, to alien environmental conditions for short periods of time, and negative effects must be expected. In order to avoid this and, moreover, further to preserve bacterial symbiosis, the upflow reactor or UASB (upflow anaerobic sludge-blanket) process was developed [40].

6.4.4 Upflow reactor

The upflow reactor is characterized by an upward flow regime. A first-phase

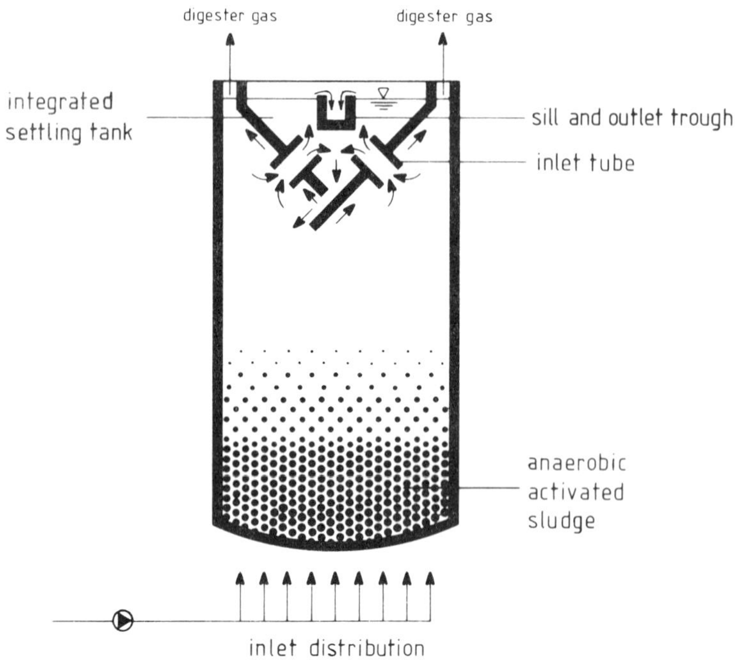

Fig. 6.11 — Upflow reactor.

separation of sludge–water and gas takes place at the bottom of the main reactor section. The sludge–water mixture is passed through slots or tubes into the integrated settling section in which the phase separation between sludge and water takes place. The wastewater is introduced and distributed at the bottom of the reactor, where the sludge bed is located, so that the main nutrient supply immediately contacts the highest concentration of sludge (micro-organisms). The upflow reactor is intimately mixed by the incoming wastewater and by the production of biogas. Heavier sludge particles can settle against the upflow so that only the lighter fractions remain to be settled in the settling section. These constant environmental conditions and the extremely gentle treatment of the symbioses of acetogenic and methanogenic bacteria lead to the formation of small pellet-like clumps of bacteria which have particularly good settling properties [41]. The presence of numerous methane bacteria in sludge from UASB process has been detected using fluorescence microscopy [24].

It has been reported that the UASB process has been applied successfully on numerous occasions [42]. The loading rates are relatively high, with average removal efficiencies of 80 per cent or more for wastewaters with a low solids content. Removal efficiency decreases with wastewaters high in suspended solids such as those from slaughterhouses. This is attributable to the sensitivity of the upflow reactor to blocking due to solids in the inlet [43]. Other workers have ascertained that periodic sludge wash-out in the UASB process leads to considerable operational disturbance [44]. Both the anaerobic activated-sludge process and the UASB process are likely to be applied in practice, selection depending on local conditions [34]. Neither process is to be preferred for all possible applications, but a consideration in selection may be the fact that the bacteria encounter more favourable conditions for aggregation into stable flocs in the case of the UASB process.

6.4.5 Anaerobic fixed-film reactor

In order to ensure the necessary contact between substrate and bacteria on the one hand, without destroying the agglomerations of acetogenic and methanogenic bacteria on the other hand, anaerobic processes were developed in which anaerobic bacteria are immobilized. These are anaerobic fixed-bed or filter reactors or fluidized-bed reactors. Initial tests were carried out by Young and McCarthy [45] as well as Lovan and Foree [46]. The first plant of this type was probably commissioned in 1972 [47]. An inventory of the results and experience gathered with anaerobic fixed-film reactors was taken in 1982 within the scope of an IAWPRC workshop [48]. According to Aivasidis and Wandrey [49] this type of reactor will prevail in the future.

As shown in Fig. 6.12, the reactor contains a fixed medium upon which the bacteria become immobilized. Porous materials such as plastics, gravel and glass granules are used with a large internal surface area of, for example, 200 to 300 m^2/m^3 of contact material. The reactors can be operated both in the upflow and in the downflow modes. Special boundary conditions must be taken into account in each case. Immobilization leads to a high bacterial density with, consequently, a high sludge age; the separation and recycling of bacteria essential in the alternative processes described above are unnecessary [50].

Systematic comparisons of intimately mixed reactors with upflow and fixed-bed reactors, with and without recycle, have been reported [44]. According to these studies, the fixed-bed reactor, with immobilization of bacteria, offers advantages over the other two reactor types with regard to both efficiency and reliability. Although sludge wash-out was occasionally observed, an adequate level of bacterial growth was always maintained in the contact beds. The fixed bed, with a large surface area in comparison to the unit volume, allows a significant concentration of the anaerobes with reduced cell wash-out. Furthermore, cell groupings of acetogenic

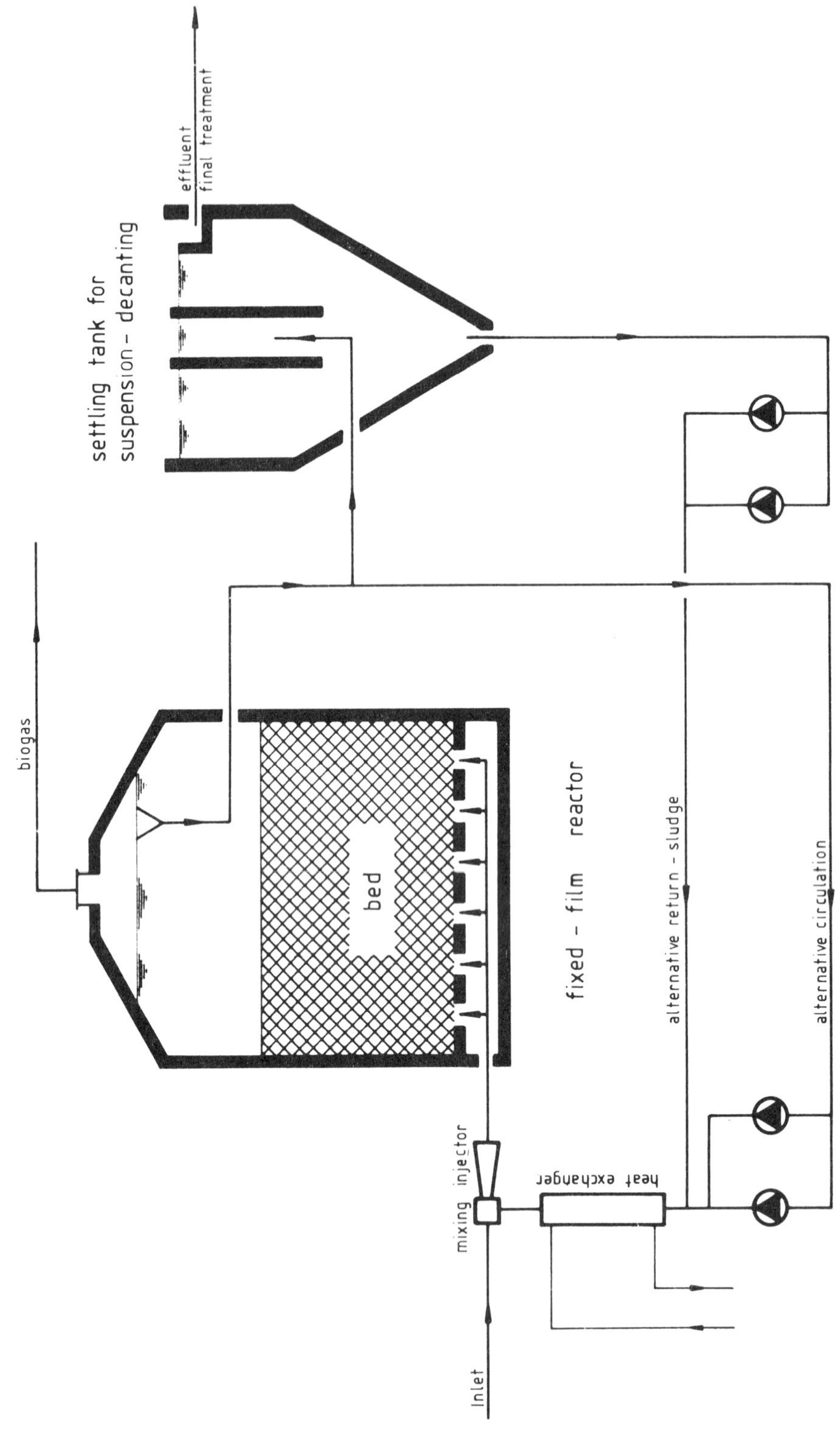

Fig. 6.12 — Anaerobic fixed-film reactor.

methanogenic bacteria can form without any disturbance, so ensuring a rapid and stable metabolism. Contact beds with larger free passages are recommended for higher solids content wastewaters to prevent blockage.

6.4.6 Anaerobic fluidized-bed reactor

Fluidized-bed reactors were developed in order to benefit from the advantages of a fixed-bed reactor (Fig. 6.12) with regard to immobilization without the potential penalty of blockage [51–53]. In a fluidized-bed reactor (Fig. 6.13), the filter material—generally quartz sand—is suspended in the upflow; this requires additional energy. The ANITRON fluidized-bed reactor has external biomass/sand separation [53]. Good results have also been achieved in a large-scale plant with internal sand separation as in the upflow reactor [51].

6.5 MULTI-STAGE AND COMBINED PROCESSES

Basic research into anaerobic degradation has shown that the different stages of degradation have different environmental optima and technical boundary conditions [15, 54]. For example, the optimum growth rate of acidifying bacteria is achieved at pH 6 and not in the neutral to alkaline range; furthermore, strong turbulence should prevail in acidification reactors to ensure rapid mass transfer. Fixed-bed reactors also seem to be suitable for acidification, provided that they have a large internal surface area [44,55]. It has been proved that different intermediates are formed in the acidification process depending on the pH value and load and are again methanized at different rates [30]. In the case of difficult and complex substrates, the aim of complete anaerobic degradation can only be achieved by uncoupling the acidification phase. A division of the anaerobic degradation process into two stages appears advantageous from a microbiological point of view [56], since this will permit optimum environmental and boundary conditions to be maintained in each specific case. On the other hand, two-stage treatment requires greater expenditure on instrumentation and also increases the effort required for maintenance and operation. In addition, it has been demonstrated that a two-stage process does not offer any advantages for the anaerobic treatment of certain wastewaters containing fat and protein, although acidification is the limiting metabolic step for these types of wastewater [55].

In many cases, the volume of organic, highly polluted industrial wastewater is not large enough to justify the construction of an anaerobic treatment stage. In such cases the capacity of the sludge digesters in any nearby sewage treatment works should be established to see if they could also accommodate the additional industrial wastewater load. In the case of very small volumes of wastewater, which do not significantly reduce the digestion time for the sewage sludge, the wastewater can be added without difficulty, possibly after flow balancing [57]. This method is used, for example, at three sewage treatment plants in the Federal Republic of Germany:

- Buehl: distillery slop;
- Lahr: chemical wastes;
- Nienburg: pharmaceutical wastes.

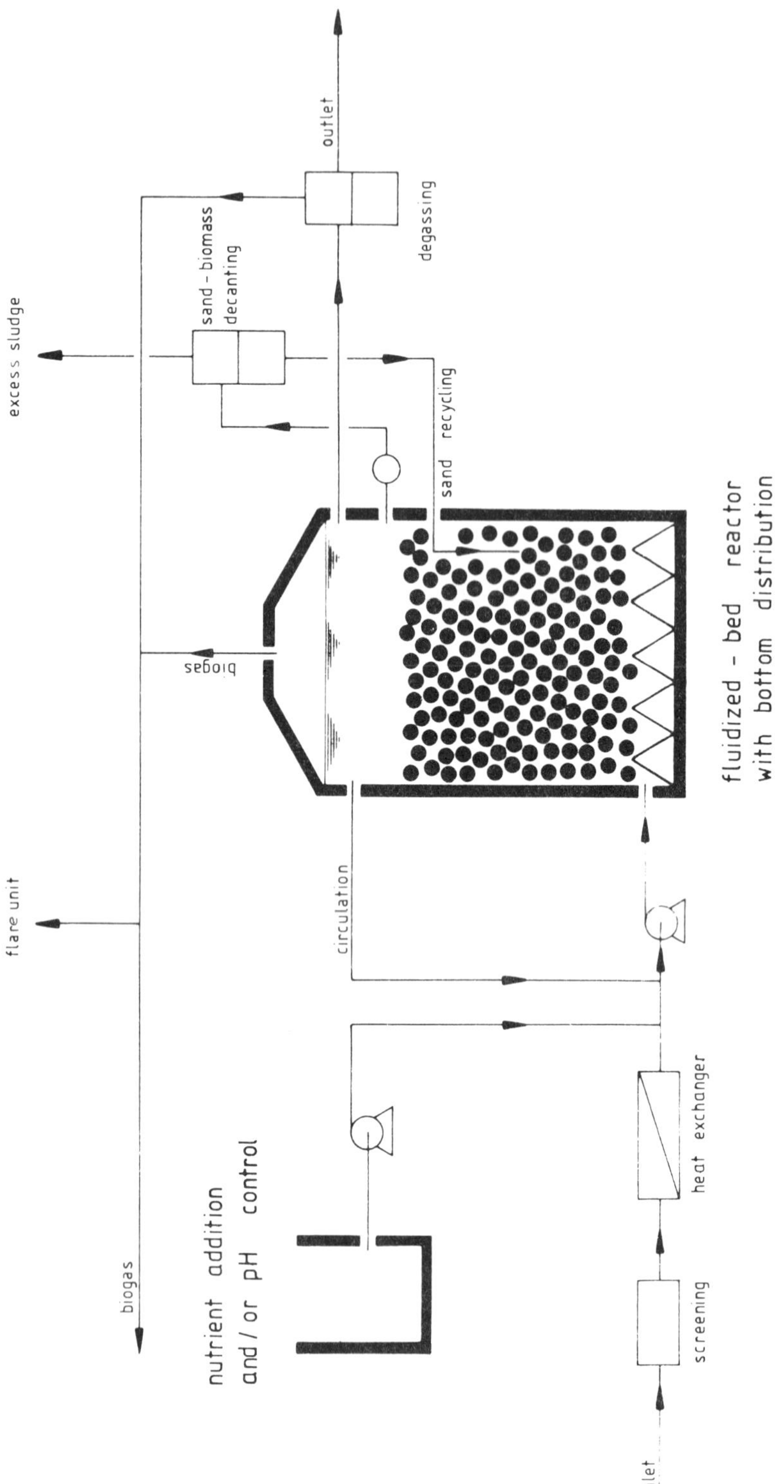

Fig. 6.13 — Anaerobic fluidized-bed reactor.

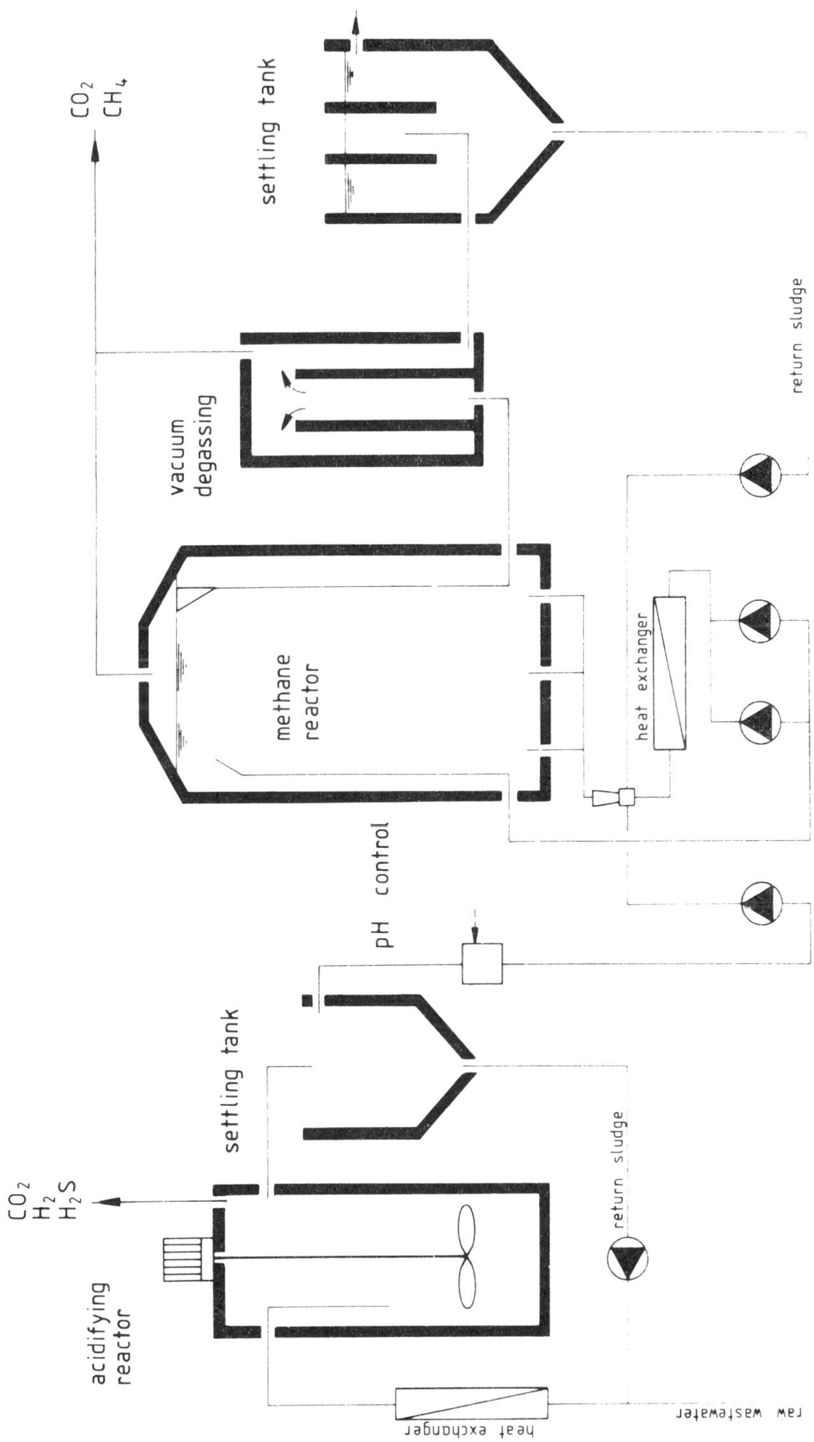

Fig. 6.14 — Two-stage anaerobic process.

If the wastewater volumes are too high to allow co-digestion with the sewage sludge without plant modifications, a careful separation and recycling of sewage sludge and anaerobic activated sludge is required. In this way, the solids retention time (SRT) can be extended adequately by loop-reactor operation [58]. Good results are obtained with this technology at a municipal sewage treatment plant in northern Germany for wastewater from a pickle-canning factory. This plant is to be extended using the same process to allow for increased factory production.

6.6 LOAD AND PURIFICATION CAPACITY

The application of anaerobic process techniques has only recently become accepted practice and statistical data from practical applications can only be referred to for a few types of industrial wastewater: wastewaters from sugar factories, pectin factories, distilleries and starch factories. However, limited experimental results are available for most of the other wastewaters.

Sixt reports a survey of treatment capacity as a function of the loading rate for different wastewaters [28]. Frostell specifies the same relationship as a function of the process [2]. Both studies are still valid today although they were published in 1979. A common feature of both studies is the wide scatter of load and treatment capacity data; no further differentiations were made. A more detailed consideration and description of all the parameters influencing loading and treatment capacity would be beyond the scope of this chapter.

6.7 CONCLUSIONS

Biomethanation is one of the most important techniques for the biodegradation of organic substances. It can be economically efficient in the field of environmental protection, *inter alia*, stabilizing sewage sludge and treating high-strength organic industrial wastewaters. Although the processes of biomethanation are still not completely understood in every respect, an attempt has been made to outline the current level of basic research and technical application.

The key aspects that have been addressed may be summarized as:

- multi-stage anaerobic biodegradation consisting of hydrolysis and acidification, acetogenic and methanogenic stages;
- degradation pathways of carbohydrates, fats and proteins;
- the influence of special wastewater constituents and nutrients as well as different process conditions such as temperature, pH value and the distribution of intermediates as a function of load;
- the different reactor and process technologies, such as the anaerobic activated-sludge process, UASB process, fixed-film reactors, fluidized-bed reactors and combined processes; and
- loading and dimensioning limits as well as removal efficiencies with respect to the organic content of wastewater.

An internationally valid cost function for anaerobic facilities has not been established because of the variety of local imponderables and the lack of a comparative benchmark (daily pollution load, reactor size, removal rate, etc.).

Biomethanation will become a tried, economically efficient and successful process technology in many more sectors of wastewater treatment in the future in view of ever scarcer energy resources, increased environmental consciousness and detailed cost–benefit analysis.

REFERENCES

[1] Buswell, A. M. and Le Bosquet, M. (1936). Complete treatment of distillery waste. *Industrial and Engineering Chemistry*.

[2] Frostell, B. (1979). Anaerobic wastewater treatment with emphasis on sludge retention. PhD thesis, Stockholm.

[3] Sixt, H. (1981). Anaerobe behandlung von abwasserschlämmen. *Wissenschaft und Umwelt,* **3**.

[4] Sixt, H. (1985). Schlammstabilisierung—rückblick und perspektiven. *Umwelt,* **2**.

[5] Awassertechnische Vereinigung (1978). *Lehr- und handbuch der abwassertechnik*, Vol. III (2nd edn), Wilhelm Ernst, Berlin.

[6] Sixt, H., Wernecke, S. and Mudrack, K. (1980). Neuere entwicklungen auf dem gebiet der anaeroben abwasserbehandlung. *Korrespondenz Abwasser,* **27** (1).

[7] Sixt, H. (1982). *Treatment of concentrated wastewater from food industry by anaerobic processes and use of digester gas as an energy source.* 1st German–Japanese Workshop, Tokyo.

[8] Crowther, R. F. and Harkness, N. (1975). *Anaerobic bacteria in aspects of used-water treatment,* Vol. 1, Academic Press, London.

[9] Sanzin, W. J. (1968). Biochemische reaktionsmechanismen bei der anaeroben schlammfaulung. *Wasser- und Abwasserforschung,* **6**.

[10] Kotze, I. P., Thiel, P. G. and Hattingh, W. H. J. (1969). Anaerobic digestion. II. The characterization and control of anaerobic digestion. *Water Research,* **3**.

[11] Roediger, H. (1962). *Die anaerobe alkalische schlammfaulung* (2nd edn), R. Oldenbourg, München.

[12] Bryant, M. P., Wolin, E. A. and Wolfe, R. S. (1967). *Methanobacillus omelianskii.* A symbiotic association of two species of bacteria. *Archives of Microbiology,* **59**.

[13] Thauer, R. K. and Jungermann, K. (1977). Energy conversion in chemotrophic anaerobic bacteria. *Bacterial Review,* **41**.

[14] Sahm, H. (1982). Umweltbiotechnologie: abwasserreinigung mit anaeroben verfahren. *Handbuch der Biotechnologie,* Akademische Verlagsgesellschaft, Wiesbaden.

[15] Kunst, S. (1982). Untersuchungen zum anaeroben abbau polymerer kohlenhydrate zur optimierung der versäuerungsstufe bei anaeroben abwasserreinigungsanlagen. Publications of the Institutes für Siedlungswasserwirtschaft der Universität Hannover, No. 54.

[16] Winfrey, M. R. and Zeikus, J. G. (1977). Effect of sulphate on carbon and

electron flow during microbial methanogenesis in fresh water sediments. *Applied and Environmental Microbiology*, **2**.
[17] Sahm, H. (1982). Mikrobiologische und biotechnologische vorgänge bei der biogasgewinnung. *Biogas aus Abfall und Abwasser, Abfallwirtschaft*, **11**.
[18] Seyfried, C. F. and Sixt, H. (1981). Betriebserfahrungen mit der anaeroben reinigung hochverschmutzter abwässer—folgerungen für bemessung und installation. *Wasser und Boden*, **33** (5).
[19] Scherer, P. and Sahm, H. (1981). Influence of sulphur-containing compounds on the growth of *Methanosarcina barkeri* in a defined medium. *Applied Microbiology and Biotechnology*, **12**.
[20] Mah, R. H., Hungate, P. E. and Ohwaki, H. (1976). Acetate: a key intermediate in methanogenesis. *Microbial Energy Conversion*, Göttingen.
[21] Barker, H. A. (1956). *Bacterial fermentation*, Wiley, New York.
[22] Weimer, P. J. and Zeikus, J. G. (1978). Acetate metabolism in *Methanosarcina barkeri*. *Archives of Microbiology*, **119**.
[23] Weimer, P. J. and Zeikus, J. G. (1978). One-carbon metabolism in methanogenic bacteria. Cellular characterization and growth of *Methanosarcina*. *Archives of Microbiology*, **119**.
[24] Schobert, S. M. (1978). *Mikrobielle methanisierung von klärschlamm biologische abfallbehandlung klärschlamm–stand und aussichten*. BMFT-Expertengespräch, Jülich.
[25] Stander, G. J. (1967). Treatment of wine distillery wastes by anaerobic treatment. *Proceedings of the 22nd Industrial Waste Conference* Purdue University.
[26] Winter, J., Temper, U. and Steiner, A. (1981). *Thermophile methangärung—stand und aussichten*. Mikrobiologische und verfahrenstechnische Optimierung biologischer Abbauprozesse, BMFT.
[27] Schlegel, S. (1974). Die anaerobe behandlung von filtratwässern thermisch konditionierter schlämme. Publications of the Institutes für Siedlungswasserwirtschaft der Universität Hannover, No. 39.
[28] Sixt, H. (1979). Reinigung organisch hochverschmutzter abwässer mit dem anaeroben belebungsverfahren am beispiel von abwässern der nahrungsmittelherstellung. Publications of the Institutes für Siedlungswasserwirtschaft der Universität Hannover, No. 50.
[29] Sixt, H. (1981). *Die problematik der bemessung und belastung anaerober abwasserreinigungsanlagen*. Mikrobiologische und verfahrenstechnische Optimierung biologischer Abbauprozesse, BMFT.
[30] Kunst, S. and Mudrack, K. (1982). Untersuchungen zum anaeroben abbau von stärke unter besonderer berücksichtigung einer optimierung der hydrolyse- und versäuerungsstufe. *gwf-wasser/abwasser*, **124**.
[31] Cohen, A., Zoetemeyer, R. J. and van Andel, J. G. (1977). Anaerobe zuivering van glucose bevattend water met separate zuurvormende en methaanvormende reaktoren. *H_2O*, **10**.
[32] Seyfried, C. F. and Saake, M. (1983). Entwicklungen in der prozeßtechnik zur anaerobven abwasser- und schlammbehandlung. *Gewässerschutz Wasser Abwasser, Aachen*, No. 59.
[33] Schroepfer, G. J., Fullen, W. J., Johnson, A. S., Ziemke, N. R. and Anderson,

J. J. (1955). The anaerobic contact process as applied to packing-house wastes. *Industrial Wastes, Sewage and Industrial Wastes,* **27**,
[34] Sixt, H. (1984). *Anaerobic treatment of wastewater from palm oil mills.* University of North Sumatra, Indonesia.
[35] Sixt, H., Mortola, G. and Costadura, M. (1982). *Techniche di processo nella digestione dei fanghi.* Disinquinamento–Antinquinamento, Milan.
[36] Lok, H. G. (1978). Twee traps anaerobe zuivering van het afval water van een aardapelverwerkende bedrijf. *De Ingenieur,* **40**, 90.
[37] Schlegel, S. and Kalbskopf, K. H. (1981). Treatment of liquors from heat-treated sludge using the anaerobic contact process. *Anaerobic Digestion,* Elsevier Biomedical Press, Amsterdam.
[38] Morfaux, J. N. and Touzel, J. P. (1981). Anaerobic treatment of canning wastewaters. *Anaerobic Digestion,* Elsevier Biomedical Press, Amsterdam.
[39] Sixt, H. (1985). *Pektinfabriken; Lehr- und handbuch der abwassertechnik,*, Vol. V, Wilhelm Ernst, Berlin.
[40] Lettinga, G., van der Sar, J. and van der Ben, J. (1976). Anaerobe zuivering van het afvalwater van de bietsuikerindustrie. *H_2O,* **9**.
[41] Lettinga, G. (1978). *Feasibility of anaerobic digestion for the purification of industrial wastewaters.* EAS, Munich.
[42] Lettinga, G., Hulshoff Pol, L. W., Koster, I. W., Wiegant, W. M., de Zeeuw, W. J., Rinzema, A., Grin, P. C., Roersma, R. E. and Hobma, S. W. (1984). High-rate anaerobic wastewater treatment using the UASB reactor under a wide range of temperature. *Biotechnology and Genetic Engineering Reviews,* **2**.
[43] Tschersich, J. and Mansky, H. (1982). Biothane—Verfahren. *Biogaserzeugung und -verwertung. Folgerungen für die Praxis.* FGU, Berlin.
[44] Seyfried, C. F., Mudrack, K., Kunst, S. and Saake, M. (1983). Untersuchungen zur anaeroben reinigung des abwassers der stärkeindustrie. BMFT-Forschungsbericht.
[45] Young, J. C. and McCarthy, P. L. (1969). The anaerobic filter for waste treatment. *JWPCF,* **5**.
[46] Lovan, C. R. and Foree, E. G. (1971). The anaerobic filter for the treatment of brewery press liquor wastes, *Proceedings of the 26th Industrial Waste Conference*, Purdue University.
[47] Taylor, D. W. (1972). Full-scale anaerobic filter treatment of wheat starch plant wastes. *Proceedings of the 3rd National Symposium of Food Processing Wastes.*
[48] Henze, M. (1983). Anaerobic treatment of wastewater in fixed film reactors. *Proceedings of a specialized seminar of the IAWPRC*, Copenhagen, Vol. 15, Pergamon Press.
[49] Aivasidis, A. and Wandrey, Ch. (1985). Biomassentrennung in der anaeroben abwasserreinigung. *gwf-wasser/abwasser,* **126** (2).
[50] Sahm, H. (1984). Anaerobic wastewater treatment. *Advances in Biochemical Engineering/Biotechnology,* **29**.
[51] Heijnen, J. J., Enger, W. A., Mulder, A., Lourens, P. A., Keijzers, A. A. and Hoeks, F. W. J. (1985). Anwendung der anaeroben wirbelschichttechnik in der biologischen abwasserreinigung. *gwf-wasser/abwasser,* **126** (2).

[52] Sutton, P. M. (1979). Oxytron fluidized bed wastewater treatment system: application to high-strength industrial wastewater. *Proceedings of the 34th Industrial Waste Conference*, Purdue University.

[53] Sutton, P. M., Li, A., Evans, R. R. and Korchin, S. (1982). Dorr-Oliver's fixed-film and suspended-growth anaerobic system for industrial wastewater treatment and energy recovery. *Proceedings of the 37th Industrial Waste Conference*, Purdue University.

[54] Zoetemeyer, R. L., Mathijren, A. J. C. M., Cohen, A. and Boelhower, C. (1982). Product inhibition in the acid-forming stage of the anaerobic digestion process. *Water Research,* **16** (5).

[55] Kunst, S., Koenemann, W. and Mudrack, K. (1985). Untersuchungen über die anaerobe abbaubarkeit von fett- und eiweißhaltigen abwässern in festbettreaktoren. *gwf-wasser/abwasser,* **126** (2).

[56] Verstraete, W., de Baere, L. and Rozzi, A. (1981). Phase separation in anaerobic digestion; motives and methods. 34. International meeting: Methangewinnung aus organischen Abfällen, Lüttich.

[57] Sixt, H. and Wilderer, P. (1983). Design and performance of egg-shaped digesters for combined sludge and industrial wastewater treatment. *Proceedings of the 38th Industrial Waste Conference*, Purdue University.

[58] Dague, R. R., McKinney, R. E. and Pfeffer, J. T. (1970). Solids retention in anaerobic waste treatment systems. *JWPCF,* **2**.

7

Recovery of by-products and raw materials and wastewater conversion

A. D. Wheatley
Cranfield Biotechnology Centre

7.1 INTRODUCTION

Waste treatment is the largest and one of the most important controlled applications of micro-organisms. Table 7.1 compares the quantity of sewage treated in the UK

Table 7.1 — Quantities of sewage effluent treated annually compared to other common industrial products (UK figures).

Product	Tonnes/a ($\times 10^6$)	Price (£/t)
Water as sewage	6500	0.10
Milk	16	25
Steel	12	300
Beer	6.6	280
Inorganic fertilizer	3.3	200
Sugar	1	350
Cheese	0.2	1300
Baker's yeast	0.1	460
Citric acid	0.015	700
Penicillin	0.003	45000

with other common industrial products. The cost of this treatment in 1982/83 was £1100 million [1]. There is also 4000 Mt/a of domestic and industrial solid refuse: 60 per cent of this is treated biologically in landfills [2].

In the USA a total of $40 000 million per year is spent on pollution control [3]. Currently the chemical industry estimates that pollution control, environmental impact and toxicity testing can account for between 10 and 20 per cent of the production costs of new products [4]. There is no doubt that these costs will increase in real terms owing to popular demand for a better environment. The size of this pollution control or environmental-management market is, in consequence, enormous and only small improvements in technology could result in significant savings. It is predicted that biological waste treatment should be comparable in size financially to the market for biologically produced fine and pharmaceutical chemicals in the foreseeable future [5].

The recent discoveries of how to increase the efficiency of microbial and biochemical conversions offer new opportunities for waste treatment. Traditionally biological waste treatment has been used to render waste inoffensive and non-pathogenic. It now includes the conservation of resources and by-product recovery. The available technologies will be reviewed in this chapter. Unfortunately, recovery of materials from waste is rarely the first approach to waste treatment. This is partly because of the complex heterogeneous nature of the wastes, but the poor value of many of the recovered by-products is also an important factor. Thus, with the exception of some simple processes for water and fertilizer recovery, much of this chapter is speculative. Even the medium-value by-products which have shown great promise technically have not been as successful economically as may have been expected on the basis of the amount of research and development that has been carried out. Thus, much of the technology is only available at the laboratory, pilot or demonstration scale.

This chapter is divided into three sections:

- low-value, high-volume by-products using simple mixed cultures and biochemical conversions, such as to fertilizer and water;
- more valuable by-products such as methane and protein; and
- complex conversions using monocultures to yield valuable by-products such as polymers and metals.

7.2 LOW-VALUE HIGH-VOLUME BY-PRODUCTS

7.2.1 Water recovery and reuse

If wastewater is not suitably treated before it is returned to the natural environment then it becomes a nuisance. Polluted water destroys aquatic life, reduces land values, can cause an offensive smell and is almost certain to be associated with disease by the general public. Treated or restored water, on the other hand, can be considered as an additional resource for reuse. In practice there is no economic method of treatment which will remove all the impurities present and water reclamation to drinking-water standards is very expensive. Planned reuse of polluted water for purposes other than drinking can easily be justified economically and can produce significant savings.

7.2.1.1 Drinking water

Whilst it might be desirable from a health and an economic point of view to obtain raw drinking water from upland sources free from both natural and urban contaminants, this is becoming increasingly difficult and is virtually impossible in arid climates.

Thus rivers and lakes have become aqueducts for both water supply and the disposal of wastewater (Fig. 7.1). For example, in its lower reaches the Rhine is commonly 50 per cent sewage effluent [6] and provides drinking water for six million people. Similarly the rivers Thames and Lee in the UK are frequently 90 per cent sewage effluent under dry conditions and typically supply over 30 per cent of London's drinking water [7]. This practice is quite common and has continued for many years without any ill effects but there are potential health risks of breakdown, human error and the long-term effects of trace chemicals that may remain in the wastewater. Much has to be learned about the removal of pathogenic micro-organisms, particularly viruses. Considerable research has recently been undertaken to refine and scientifically confirm that the procedures identified by experience are safe. The establishment, and the imposition of controls, will influence the quantity of recycled water and the technology of wastewater treatment.

Some published work from the United States and Europe has demonstrated an association between ill health and reused drinking water [8,9]. One study on drinking water taken from the Mississippi indicated a 15 per cent increase in statistically corrected mortality from cancer in certain sections of the population. The organic derivatives of chlorination, particularly those derived from humic and fulvic acids, were implicated. The results were ambiguous because not all groups in the population were affected. The Water Research Centre and Royal Free Hospital recently undertook a full epidemiological study to take into account socio-economic factors and the degree of reuse. The first study [10] on the London area, where water supplies have for many years contained the highest proportion of recycled water in the UK, showed no correlation between water reuse and disease. Socio-economic factors were more important and strongly correlated to health. A later study [11] showed some slight adverse effects from recycled water. Stomach and urinary-tract cancer in women, together with still births, were marginally higher in areas with extensive reuse. The results were complicated by an increase in stomach cancer, also in women, but associated with fresh upland water. This may have been related to the natural acids present but more research is indicated to unravel these complications.

Until recently water quality has been checked routinely by simple chemical and bacteriological tests such as total organic carbon, turbidity and coliform tests [12]. Newer analytical tests such as mass spectrometry and high-pressure liquid chromatography can now be used to detect minute concentrations of organic materials from sewage, agricultural and industrial wastes. A recent survey using these techniques detected 700 organic compounds in tap water; just over half were identifiable [13]. Attempts are now being made by a number of national and international authorities to set new standards for drinking and raw water. The establishment of these new standards is restrained by a lack of toxicity data. An EEC Directive has set standards for 39 different parameters, including 18 metals and 7 organic materials [14]. Judgement has been reserved on a further 7 metals and 2 organic substances. An additional Directive sets out the analytical methods and the minimum frequency of sampling.

7.2.1.2 Treatment techniques

All raw waters are treated by a combination of physicochemical and biological processes. Solids are removed by chemically assisted precipitation and sand filtration. The sand filtration includes a biologically active immobilized layer of bios.

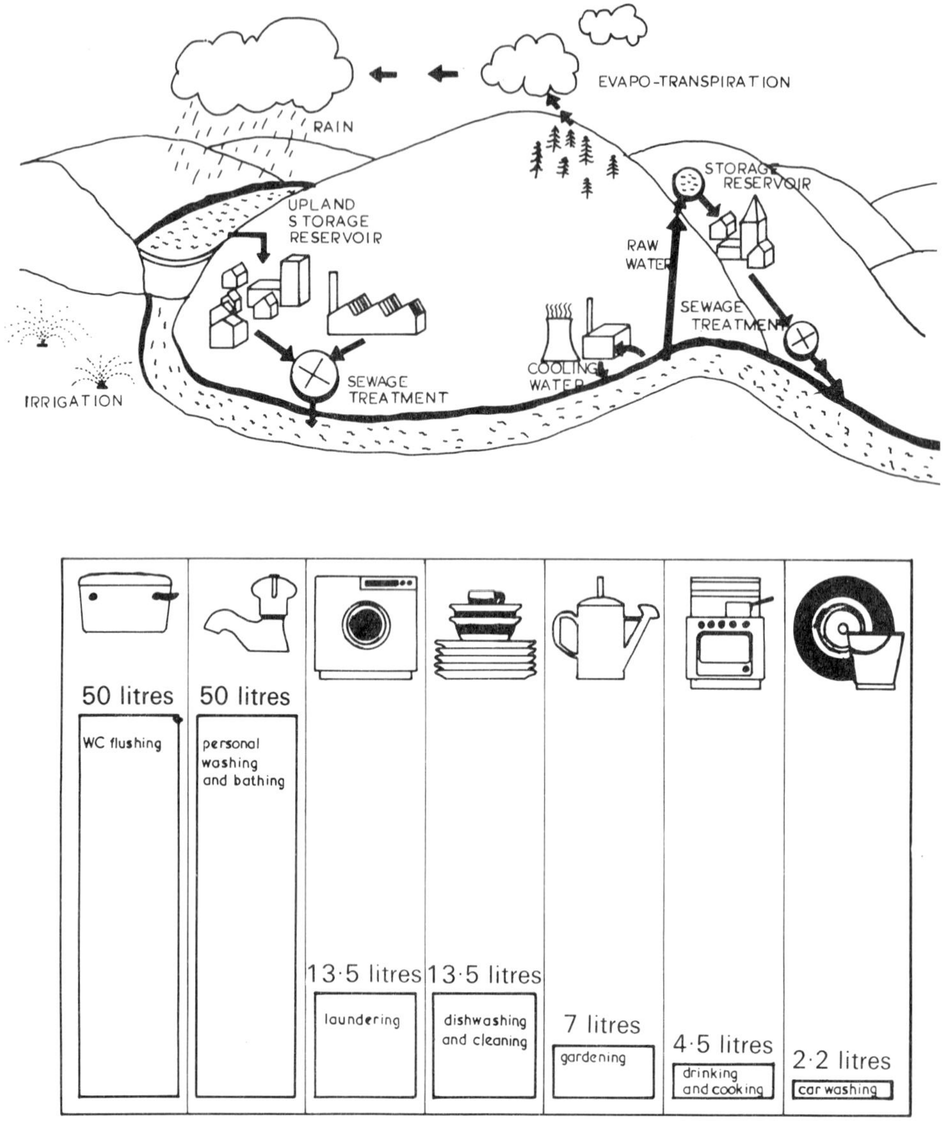

Fig. 7.1

Additional treatment with activated carbon, membrane filtration or deionization is necessary with recycled water. Table 7.2 shows the likely removals of known toxins by conventional means and with additional treatment by adsorption and filtration. Unfortunately there is as yet little information on the organochlorine compounds formed as a result of the disinfection process, but the concentration of residual organical carbon is quite critical. Activated carbon is quite versatile and is able to adsorb a very wide range of organic materials. Many existing drinking-water plants

Table 7.2 — The efficiency of removal of known toxins by standard water treatment units

Substance	Coagulation and sand filtration		Powdered activated carbon		Granular		Ozone		Other types	
	a	b	a	b	a	b	a	b	a	b
Organohalogens										
Chloroform					<0.04	100			16 days storage gives 80% removal	
Lindane		<10	0.01	90						
Dieldrin	4.5	55	<1.0	99	<0.1	99				
Endrin	6.5	35			<0.1	99				
DDT	0.2	98			<0.1	99			Reverse osmosis gives 50% removal	
Organophosphorus										
Parathion	2.0	80	<0.1	99	<0.1	99				
Carcinogens										
PAH	0.013	90	0.0006	99	0.0005	99	0.007	75	21 days storage and slow sand	
Benzopyrene	1.0	98	1.0	99			0.0002	85	<0.006	97
Metals										
Mercury (inorganic)	2.0	80	2.5	70					Lime pH 9.5	
(methyl)			3.5	30		100			1.5	35
Cadmium (inorganic)	7.0	80	1.5		1.5	95				
Hydrocarbons										
Oils		75			0.1				16 days storage 80% removal	

Column (a) lowest concentration achieved (b) percentage removal of substance.
DDT, 1,1,1-trichloro 2,2 bis(*p*-chlorophenyl)ethane (common name dichlorodiphenylethane).
PAH, polynuclear aromatic hydrocarbons (e.g. benzidine, β-naphthylamine).

utilizing upland water as raw water have periodically used activated carbon to overcome occasional problems associated with taste and odour.

The simplest technique is to add the powdered carbon directly into the distribution main after treatment. This avoids the construction of a separate stage. The disadvantages are that the carbon cannot be recovered and the mixing and adsorption are less than perfect. The alternative is to use columns of granular activated carbon. The granular carbon can then be thermally regenerated, although there is a 5–10 per cent loss of activity. Such a plant has recently been built at Nottingham to restore River Trent water to drinking-water standards [15].

Dissolved salts may also accumulate and deionization may be necessary. Nitrate, for example, can combine with the haemoglobin in blood causing a serious condition in infants known as methaemoglobinaemia. The WHO has set a maximum limit of 10 mg/l, etc. (for NO_3) [16]. There is also evidence that it may be reduced in the gut to nitrite, which can then form nitrosamines, which are carcinogens.

Published work from the UK, USA, Israel and South Africa indicates that technically, with a combination of these treatment techniques, it is possible to produce a water nearly free of dissolved and suspended contaminants. Activated carbon can reduce the total organic carbon to 1–2 mg/l and disinfection with 0.5 mg/l free chlorine for a contact time of one hour should be sufficient to eliminate the coliforms and enteric viruses. Thus, the main limit on the recycling of wastewater is the cost of the alternatives. In many arid parts of the world the cost of desalination sets this limit.

7.2.1.3 Industrial and domestic recovery

In the UK mains water costs about £1 per tonne and effluent disposal between £1 and £3 per tonne. Table 7.3 shows some likely capital and running costs of an effluent

Table 7.3 — Costs for wastewater-treatment plant with a capacity of 3 800 m^3/d (estimated for 1985).

	Costs	
	Capital ($\$ \times 10^3$)	Operating ($\$/m^3$)
Settlement and activated sludge	4 800	0.054
Secondary biological filters	2 060	0.022
Sand filtration	1 020	0.020
Activated-carbon treatment	3 200	0.050
Chlorination (to 15 mg/l)	160	0.006
Ion exchange (40% t.d.s. removal)	2 400	0.068
Total	13 640	0.242

Cost of water treatment: $1.75 million per year. Cost of effluent treatment $3.51 million per year.

treatment/advanced water-treatment plant.

At these costs recycling industrial water is only beneficial if there is a large-scale use for water of a lower quality than that available from supply. Thus, water recycling is normal practice in heavy industries such as power generation, steel making and coal preparation, where relatively low water quality is sufficient and water treatment can be kept to a minimum: usually settlement and/or cooling. In some cases where effluent discharge has been prevented, or where local capacity is insufficient, manufacturers have been faced with no alternative but to treat and recycle [17,18]. Usually this takes the form of the establishment of several grades of water within the process. The higher grades of water quality from, for example, cooling, sterilizing and food preparation are recycled with a minimum of treatment for a lower grade use such as vegetable cleaning [19]. Biologically treated effluent, after solids removal and sterilization, can also be used; for example, for washing vehicles and yards. Such simple reuse can be justified economically. Similar schemes have also been considered for recycling domestic wastewaters in arid areas. Used water from bathing, dishwashers and washing machines can be reused for flushing toilets following settlement and mild sterilization with, for example, hypochlorite solution [20].

Consideration must also be given to the number of times the water is to be recycled. Dissolved salts such as sodium chloride and calcium bicarbonate are always present in natural waters. In wastewaters the concentrations of dissolved salts are increased by biological oxidation, particularly nitrate, sulphate, phosphate and chloride. Dissolved salts can exceed 1000 mg/l in wastewater. If the water is recycled in a closed system then this concentration will increase and cause scaling, corrosion and toxicity. These inorganic salts are commonly removed by ultrafiltration, reverse osmosis or ion exchange. Ultrafiltration uses selective membranes which allow charged ions to pass into a concentrating stream while retaining non-polar materials. Reverse osmosis is an extension of conventional filtration: the membrane retains salts, organic materials and any fine solids. A pressure of 20–50 kgf/cm^2 is used to counteract the osmotic pressure. Membrane fouling is a common problem with both of these techniques. Ion exchange utilizes a standard granular column of ion-collecting resin. The resin can be periodically regenerated with strong acids or alkalis.

7.2.1.4 Reclamation by ground-water recharge

Reclamation of used water by ground-water recharge is aesthetically often more acceptable than direct reuse. It also has the benefit of a further filtering action through soil and is able to equalize particular depressions in the water table by transport through the aquifers. There are also cost advantages in storing water underground; aquifer recharge is cheaper than using surface reservoirs and distribution.

Normally recharging is by surface spreading but injection is also carried out where the aquifer is very deep or the topography or existing land-use prevents spreading. Injection is particularly effective in replenishing freshwater aquifers against intrusion of saltwater in coastal regions.

7.2.1.5 Agricultural reuse of effluents

The reuse of wastewater for irrigation in agriculture is one of the oldest forms of water reclamation. Effluents contain a wide range of inorganic plant nutrients although in a lower concentration than in an ideal nutrient solution (Table 7.4).

Some materials in effluents, such as metals, ammonia and boron, however, can be toxic to plants. Boron, for example, is a common component of many detergents and is not removed by conventional biological treatment. It is toxic to citrus crops. There is also a potential hazard from contamination by pathogenic organisms. Codes of practice for safe irrigation and cropping have been drawn up by the WHO [21] and in the UK by the Ministry of Agriculture [22]. In some countries untreated sewage is used for irrigation but this practice is discouraged. Some care is required to select crops which are not prone to accumulate toxins or to ensure that the edible portion is not immersed in the effluent. Table 7.5 shows the heavy-metal content of tomatoes grown on treated sewage effluent compared to those grown by conventional irrigation [23].

The origin and quality of the wastewaters can be monitored by simple analysis and crops selected by reference to the literature and to advisory services. If the use of sewage effluent is not to be restricted to particular crops then disinfection is required. The WHO has recommended a standard for uncontrolled irrigation that the effluent

Table 7.4 — Concentrations of inorganic nutrients in sewage effluent compared to ideal nutrient solutions (in mg/l).

Nutrient	Treated domestic effluent sewage	Ideal nutrient solution
Nitrate (as N)	20–25	40–45
Ammoniacal nitrogen (as N)	0.1–5.0	0.1
Phosphorus (as P)	5–12	90–100
Potassium	10–18	90–100
Calcium	80–90	125
Magnesium	5–9	85
Iron	0.01–0.1	8–12
Manganese	0.1	1
Sodium	70–90	60
Chloride	60–100	50
Boron	1–2	–

Table 7.5 — Heavy-metal content of tomatoes grown on treated sewage compared to conventional irrigation

	Sewage-effluent-grown (mg/kg)	Conventional irrigation (mg/kg)
Iron	34	29
Manganese	9	20
Zinc	34	32
Copper	12	11
Nickel	6	4
Chromium	1	1
Lead	3	3

does not contain more than 100 coliforms per 100 ml in 80 per cent of the samples tested.

This can be achieved by chlorinating a biologically treated effluent with 15–20 mg/l of chlorine for 1–2 h [6]. Many other species of pathogenic bacteria are more sensitive to chlorine than the coliforms and the treatment has some effect against amoebic cysts [24]. The viruses, however, are not affected to the same extent and further work is required to evaluate their epidemiological significance.

The WHO [24] has reviewed over a 100 references where wastewater has been used for crop irrigation. The survey concluded that there were very few adverse comments and that crop yields were often increased with no loss in quality in the crop. In tests at Labbock, Texas [6], for example the yields of three crops—sorghum, wheat and cotton—were compared. The crops were grown under three sets of conditions: one group without irrigation, one group with fertilizer and well water, and one group with wastewater. The results are shown in Table 7.6. In the UK and

Table 7.6 — Yield of common crops irrigated with wastewater compared to synthetic fertilizer and no irrigation (kg/ha).

Crop	No irrigation	Irrigation with well water and fertilizer	Irrigation with wastewater
Sorghum	150–180	730–920	1200
Wheat	110–132	330–440[a]	880
Lint cotton	27–41	110–147	230

[a]Note that the yield of wheat seems low compared to UK expectations of 3–4000 kg/ha with about 100 kg N applied per hectare.

most of Europe, where irrigation of crops is unnecessary except in the dryest season, effluent is too dilute to use as a plant nutrient. In arid climates wastewater should be an essential source of both nutrient and water. Costs published by the United Nations [25] predict a doubling of the needs for fertilizer between 1990 and 2000 (see

Table 7.7 — Estimated cost inputs to agriculture in developing countries.

	1980	1990	2000
Water ($\$ \times 10^9$)	8.3	10.3	12.1
NPK fertilizer ($\$ \times 10^9$)	21.3	52.7	104.0
Pesticides ($\$ \times 10^9$)	2.0	3.3	5.1

Source: Food and Agriculture Organization (FAO) of the United Nations.

Table 7.7). It has been estimated that 15 large-scale chemical plants will be required between now and the end of the century to supply this demand for fertilizer. Much of this demand for water and fertilizer could be provided by recycling treated wastewater. Estimates from the USA show it could be between 10 and 40 per cent cheaper than other sources of water and fertilizer. Plants are efficient at removing these inorganic nutrients when they are applied at the right time in the growing cycle.

Table 7.8 shows the uptake of inorganic salts by sugar-beet and tomatoes grown

Table 7.8 — Removal of inorganic nutrients from treated sewage effluent by sugar-beet and tomatoes.

	Biologically treated effluent (mg/l)	Percentage removal, sugar-beet	Percentage removal, tomatoes
Nitrate (as N)	22	52	50
Ammoniacal nitrogen (as N)	3	90	95
Phosphate (as P)	10	20	52
Potassium (as K)	15	38	89

hydroponically with treated sewage effluent in a single-pass system [23]. An ideal application of inorganic fertilizer can result in better than a 90 per cent uptake of nitrogen.

Plants are therefore a useful method of preventing inorganic enrichment of natural waters by biologically treated wastewaters. Eutrophication (excessive algal growth in natural waters) could then also be reduced.

Recent work on using activated sludge as a feed supplement for animals (discussed in Section 7.3) has been extended to include tests on the possible use of sewage effluents as a source of water and minerals [26] for animals. Separate groups of chickens were given tap water, biologically treated effluent and alum-flocculated raw sewage to drink. The two wastewaters were treated with calcium hypochlorite to leave a residual chlorine concentration of 3 mg/l. The results of the 12-week study are shown in Table 7.9.

Table 7.9 — Body weight and water consumption of chickens drinking sewage effluent compared to tap water.

	Month 1		Month 2		Month 3	
	Body weight (kg)	Water consumption (l/wk)	Body weight (kg)	Water consumption (l/wk)	Body weight (kg)	Water consumption (l/wk)
Tap water	1.48	1.5	1.51	1.4	1.56	1.5
Alum-flocculated raw sewage	1.49	1.5	1.57	1.4	1.62	1.4
Biologically treated sewage effluent	1.57	1.5	1.66	1.6	1.67	1.6

Both the sewage effluents were clear in appearance and no preferences for the type of water were obvious from the results. The alum-flocculated sewage did, however, reduce feed consumption and egg-laying, although the weight of the birds did not seem to be affected adversely. There was no apparent affect on the group fed with biologically treated effluent. Further research was recommended, particularly on the significance of the mineral content of the treated wastewaters, which was very much higher than that of the tap water.

7.3 SLUDGE AS FERTILIZER

Most wastewater-treatment processes generate surplus solids in the form of very dilute suspensions. There are two important sources of these sludges. One type of sludge is generated in the early stages of wastewater treatment by the simple settlement of the effluents. About 30 per cent of the total organic matter and about 60 per cent of the suspended matter can be removed from domestic sewage by quiescent settlement for a few hours. This is known as primary sludge. The second source of sludge is surplus biomass from the multiplication and growth of the micro-organisms treating and utilizing the waste. Biological treatment converts the soluble and colloidal materials present in the waste into separable biomass. Large volumes of dilute sludge are therefore formed with a solids content of between 1 and 4 per cent. These sludges are, in general, difficult to dewater and the biological sludges particularly so, since they contain large quantities of bound water. The disposal of this sludge is one of the major problems of wastewater treatment and frequently accounts for half of the costs of treatment. The sludges are putrescible and offensive and are the source of most of the complaints by the public about wastewater-treatment plants. Seventy per cent of the sludge generated undergoes some form of treatment before disposal. The sludges also usually collect any pathogens or toxic materials present in the wastewater. Anaerobic digestion is the most common type of treatment (see also Section 7.4.4 and Chapter 6). Anaerobic treatment reduces sludge volume and pathogens, and generates methane, a valuable by-product.

There are also various methods of aerobic composting and this method of sludge treatment is popular in the United States [27]. Some sludge is composted with domestic refuse; the product is similar to peat [28].

About 1.2 mt/a of dry solids are produced as sludges from wastewater treatment in the UK; 67 per cent of this sludge is ultimately disposed of to land and 29 per cent to sea; the small remainder is incinerated. Of the sludge disposed of to land, about 68 per cent is spread on agricultural land as fertilizer [29]. The rest is used for landfill. Table 7.10 shows the quantities and types of sludge applied to various types of land.

Of the sludge applied to land 46 per cent is treated anaerobically and 51 per cent is disposed of in liquid form. Sludge can be used to condition soil by providing both nutrients and humus. Table 7.11 shows the N:P:K ratios of some typical sludges. Experimental work reported by the Ministry of Agriculture, Fisheries and Food has shown that 85 per cent of the total nitrogen and 50 per cent of the phosphate can be taken up from digested sludge when applied during the spring [22].

Only small quantities of potassium and magnesium are present in sludge and these have to be supplemented. Much of the nitrogen in digested sludge is in the form of ammonia which, because of its solubility, can be lost during sludge dewatering. Thus it is the water content of the sludge which governs its rate of application. Leaching losses in wet weather can be 75 per cent of the nutrient content. The run-off, or drainage through cracks in the soil in summer, can be a source of significant

Table 7.10 — Sewage sludge disposed of to land in the UK (percentage of total disposed) [29].

	Sludge type					
Land type	Untreated, fresh	Untreated, stored < 6 months	Chemically treated, de-watered, stored < 12 months	Chemically treated, de-watered, stored > 12 months	Digested cold	Digested warm
Grassland:						
temporary	0.73	1.15	1.18	0.15	0.32	7.50
permanent	0.74	2.21	0.92	0.04	0.49	5.08
General arable	3.39	5.51	12.61	1.04	0.52	13.16
Horticultural	0	0	0	0	0	1.03
Forestry	0	0	0	0	0	0.10
Landscaping	0	0	0.68	0.09	0	1.20
Fertilizer manufacture	0	0	0	0	0	0.52
Landfill: on site	1.63	0.19	3.60	2.07	0.84	3.93
off site	0.25	0.03	6.07	0.63	0.01	3.08
Land reclamation	0.20	0. 07	1.71	0.39	0	2.22

Table 7.11 — Nutrient content of various types of sludge.

Type of sludge	Nitrogen (% as N)	Phosphate (% as P_2O_5)	Potassium (% as K_2O)
Digested liquid sludge	0.2	0.2	0.010
Raw sludge (4% dry solids)	0.15	0.15	0.012
Sludge cake (20–40% dry solids)	1–1.4	1–2.0	0.09

pollution. Most reports indicate that improvements in growth are in proportion to the nitrogen content of the sludge at the time of application [30]. Applied after the growing season much of the nutrient was lost. Sludge is a useful addition of organic matter at any time.

In 1980 in the UK the equivalent savings in inorganic fertilizer were 21 000 t of nitrogen, 16 000 t of phosphorus (as P_2O_5) and 1500 t of potassium (as K_2O). Based on a discounted price of £500/t for 19 per cent nitrogen fertilizer this was worth about £52.5 million. This compares with the £2000 million spent on inorganic fertilizers each year.

7.3.1 The metals content of sludges

A disadvantage of sewage sludge is that it may contain appreciable concentrations of potentially toxic materials. The best-documented toxins are the heavy metals. Since the new Water Act of 1973 [31], more rigorous consent conditions have been imposed by the water authorities on industrial discharges to sewer and in many cases the concentrations of metals in sludges has fallen by over 50 per cent. Additional improvements have been brought about by the recession of old heavy industry. There is, therefore, greater potential for the reuse of sludge as a fertilizer. At present it is used on only 1.25 per cent of the land used for agricultural purposes in the UK.

Most data on phytotoxicity relate to zinc, copper and nickel; their effects seem to be additive. To cater for the most sensitive crops it is assumed that copper is twice as toxic as zinc, nickel eight times as toxic and boron 150 times more toxic than zinc. Cadmium, lead and chromium cause problems for the consumer rather than having a direct effect on plant growth. Cadmium accumulates in the leaves of plants and additions are restricted to 5 kg/ha per year. Lead and chromium are less toxic since they are not taken into the edible part of the plant. Normally, totally domestic sewages have low concentrations of heavy metals, but they may contain appreciable quantities of zinc from cosmetics and pipework. Table 7.12 shows the metal content of some typical wastewater sludges.

Table 7.12 — Metals in domestic sewage sludge (mg/kg dry solids).

Type of sludge	Dry solids (%)	Cd	Cr	Cu	Fe	Pb	Ni	Zn
Raw sludge Ex. 1	1.9	20	90	315	13814	300	15	871
Raw sludge Ex. 2	4.9	20	42	169	6651	206	15	568
Digested sludge	2.7	20	403	605	19355	454	81	1411

Fortunately zinc is not highly toxic and work by the Agricultural Advisory Service has shown that up to 20 kg/ha (or zinc equivalent) may be added annually for 30 years [32]. If the application is to grassland where it is not intended to grow arable crops for many years, or if the soil is calcarious with a pH above 7.0, then 37 kg/ha per year may be added.

There are local variations and complexities depending on the soil characteristics. Soil pH, organic content, proximity of the water table, rainfall and normal background element concentrations are variables which affect the mobility of metals in soil. Often metals added with sludge become fixed by organic material and are not easily taken up during plant growth. Work is in progress to devise a standard test for extractable metals for comparison with crop uptake and to provide a better assessment of toxic effects [29].

At the moment the presence of cadmium arouses the most concern because it is so readily absorbed by plants, enters the food chain and accumulates in mammals. The other elements which could be present in sludge and pose a potential risk are lead, mercury, molybdenum, arsenic, fluorine and selenium. Most of these elements are also derived from aerial deposition and great care is recommended to ensure that total quantities are kept within safe limits (Table 7.13).

Table 7.13 — Recommended maximum additions of elements to uncontaminated non calcareous soils over a period of 30 years.

Element	Likely background concentration (mg/l)	Maximum addition (kg/ha)
	Extractable	Total
Zinc	2.5	560
Copper	5	280
Nickel	1	70
Boron	1	4.5 1st year 3.5 subsequent years
	Total	Total
Chromium	100	1000
Cadmium	1	5
Lead	50	1000
Mercury	<0.1	2
Molybdenum	2	4
Arsenic	5	10
Fluorine	200	600
Selenium	0.5	5

The additions of zinc, copper and nickel are subject to the overriding total zinc equivalent. The annual addition is normally one-thirtieth of the maximum but up to one-fifth of the maximum is permitted. Extractable metals are measured using EDTA; boron is extracted by hot water. Total metals are measured following treatment with a strong acid, fluorine by fusion and an ion-selective electrode. If analysis of the soil shows the existing concentrations to be higher than the uncontaminated values suggested in the table then the additions have to be reduced by a corresponding amount.

7.3.2 Pathogens in sludge

Assessing the actual health risk of pathogens present in soils is difficult. There are no reliable data on the infective doses of pathogens nor is there an easy method of determining the viability of cysts, spores or eggs. Standard culture techniques are not usually suitable indicators of the potential for infection. Further difficulties arise because both wild and domesticated animals are often infected with potential pathogens without showing symptoms of disease. There is an important epidemiological study currently in progress within the European community which will attempt to quantify these risks [33]. Many years of experience of sewage sludge application to land has, however, evolved a code of practice in the UK and there have been no infections attributed to sewage sludge. Much research has recently been conducted to corroborate these empirical methods.

The two most important factors controlling the survival of micro-organisms are time and temperature. A 90 per cent loss of viability is common within a hour after a change from the natural environment and substrate. A 10°C increase in temperature can accelerate this loss of viability by a factor of between 2 and 20. Most of the experimental work in the UK has been with *Salmonella* sp. Results show that the numbers of *Salmonella* fell rapidly a few days after the application when the weather was dry and the sludge spread thinly. More time was required when the sludge did not dry and the recommendations include a safety margin (Table 7.14). Between 1 and 6 months are therefore allowed before normal grazing is resumed, depending on the condition of the sludge. It was shown that very large numbers and a prolonged exposure were necessary to induce disease [34]. Less is known about the viability of parasite eggs [35]. The parasites of most concern are the tapeworms *Taenia* and *Talnia*: the eggs can be viable for up to 6 months. In the case of raw vegetables 12 months are allowed before the soil may be used again for this type of crop.

Virtually unrestricted use of sludge may be practised following chemical or heat treatment. Pasteurization at 70°C for 30 minutes, thermophilic composting, or heat-drying are all reported to be more effective at destroying pathogens than anaerobic digestion. Types of disinfection such as these are only justified to avoid even more expensive incineration or dumping. They may become mandatory in a few countries but it is an unnecessary use of resources.

One or two log reductions in pathogens were apparent from lime treatment [36]. The pH achieved is critical: a pH of 11.0 stops all bacterial activity and kills the vegetative forms. Many spores, cysts and eggs are protected by a wax coat which may help them to survive. Research work is continuing to determine the mobility of metals and on the survival of parasite eggs. Little is yet known about persistent trace organics in sludge, partly because they are so variable, and partly due to the comparatively recent development of suitable analytical techniques. Their presence is due to contamination by industrial or agricultural wastewaters and, if present, steps should be taken to prevent them entering the sewage system. A survey is being carried out on the concentrations of polychlorinated biphenyls (PCB) and the chlorinated aryl pesticides (aldrin, dieldrin, endrin) in sludges in the UK. There are no reports of either infection or metal toxicity and very few of water contamination by sewage sludge. Most complaints arise from the unpleasant smells associated with untreated sludge spreading.

7.4 MEDIUM-VALUE BY-PRODUCTS

7.4 Protein

The recovery of biomass, and particularly protein, is one of the best documented areas of biotechnology and by-product recovery. It is the subject of several reviews and two books (Table 7.15).

The nutritional value of micro-organisms is similar to other forms of biomass but their growth rate is much higher than other sources of protein. The attraction from a waste-treatment point of view is also that the micro-organisms will grow readily on a wide variety of substrates, including wastes. There is a long history of fermented foods such as sour vegetables and milk products produced by mixed cultures, but normally the micro-organisms involved are only a small part of the final food and many years of use have established that there are no serious toxicology problems. If the foodstuff is entirely microbial, or to be a large part of the diet of animals, then a well-defined, consistent product is likely to be required. This usually means pure-culture fermentation of a standard substrate. If the organism used has no history of usage, a great deal of product testing is necessary. There is a further problem in that

Table 7.14 — Recommended uses of sewage sludge according to treatment available.

Sludge type	Crops to be eaten raw	Crops to be cooked	Grazed crops	Forestry, landfill
(1) Mesophilic anaerobic digestion or heat treatment	12 months required before growing	May be sown after application	One month if >40% reduction in organic content of sludge, otherwise 6 months	Not necessary
Lagooned for 2 years or 1 year cold digestion and storage				
(2) Aerobic treat ment, lime-sta bilized or con ditioned	12 months required	May be sown after application	No pigs or cattle for 6 months	Not necessary
(3) Other sludges stored for a minimum of 2 weeks	Not recommended	May be sown after application	No grazing for 6 months	Not necessary
(4) Raw sludge un treated	Not recommended	May be sown after application	No grazing for 6 months	Not necessary

Table 7.15 — SCP review papers.

Author	Ref.	Date published	Subject area
Prescott and Dunn	[37]	1959	Mostly food residues
Peppler	[38]	1968	Included some waste materials
James and Addyman	[39]	1974	Dedicated to wastes
Samaelov	[40]	1983	Includes substantial section on wastes
Goldberg	[41]	1985	Includes some material on wastes

these well-defined substrates are rarely wastes but valuable commodities for direct physical recovery, or as substrates for higher-value microbial single-cell protein.

Wastewaters are not consistent and are multi-carbon substrates. Mixed cultures are necessary if all the carbon sources are to be utilized to give effective pollution

Table 7.16 — Commercial single-cell protein (SCP).

Company	Trade name	Substrate	Organism
ICI	Pruteen	Methanol	Bacterial
RHM	Myco-protein	Starch	Fungal
Finnish Paper	Pekilo	Sulphite waste	Yeast
BP[a]	Topina	Alkanes	Yeast

[a]No longer in production.

control. Thus, there are difficulties in producing a biomass of consistent nutritive value that is free from the toxicological uncertainties of microbial contamination. The uncontaminated wastes from the food, drinks and fermentation industries are therefore preferable. Technically SCP production from wastewater is relatively simple, but none of the laboratory and demonstration schemes reported have been commercially successful. The value of the protein recovered is low (£100 to £500/t) and the cost of producing it over and above effluent treatment costs (sterilization and drying) cannot be justified at present. Table 7.17 lists some of the work on the recovery of SCP from wastewaters carried out so far.

There is one full-scale SCP plant in the UK. It treats confectionery wastewater from Bassetts in Sheffield. The process uses batch fermentation following the heat-sterilization of the effluent [51]. A pure culture of *Candida* is grown on the waste, which is recovered by centrifuging and drying. It is bagged and sold as a high-protein additive to be blended with animal feed. The plant produces about 140 t/a and removes about 50 per cent of the applied COD. Further plants of this type are unlikely to be commissioned until protein increases in value (Fig. 7.2). Bacteria are the easiest and quickest to grow but are less acceptable historically than yeasts, which have the advantage of containing less nucleic acid, a possible toxin in large quantities. The filamentous fungi are easier to separate and dry than the yeasts; they also have a better food texture than other micro-organisms (Fig. 7.3).

There are economic possibilities for SCP recovery from effluents if the emphasis is on pollution control, with protein recovery as a by-product to offset wastewater treatment and sludge-disposal costs. To reduce costs associated with special equipment, sterilization should be avoided and contamination controlled by using a high inoculum concentration, cell recycling or a low pH. Expensive methods of recovery such as centrifuging, filtration and spray-drying could be omitted and flocculation, flotation and screening considered as alternatives. The preparation of a liquid end product, using the whole fermentation broth after pasteurization as a protein supplement to an animal feed, would also be an important saving. Development costs could be reduced by using micro-organisms which have already been approved for food use, such as *Candida, Saccharomyces* and *Fusarium*.

7.4.2 Oils and fats

Compared to protein there has been less interest in microbially recovered oils. The main reason seems to be the relatively small world market for oils and fats. All of the present 60 Mt of non-dairy oils consumed per year, and any expansion, are likely to

Table 7.17 — Research on SCP from waste.

Organism	Substrate	Author	Ref.
Yeast	Paper-mill waste	Holderby and Moggio	[42]
	General food waste	Righelato *et al.*	*[43]*
	General food waste	Tomlinson	[44]
	Milk waste	Wasserman *et al.*	[45]
	Coconut	Smith and Bull	[46]
	Citric acid	Braun *et al.*	[47]
	Pineapple	Prior	[48]
	Alcohol vinasse	Tauk	[49]
	Sewage	Thanh and Simard	[50]
	Confectionery	Forage	[51]
Fungi	Starch	Munden and King	[52]
	Distillery	Quinn and Marchant	[53]
	Milk	Wheatley *et al.*	[54]
	Fruit and vegetables	Davy	[55]
	Fruit and vegetables	Church *et al.*	[56]
Bacteria	Sewage	Grau	[57]
	Sewage	Beszechits and Lugowski	[58]
Algae	Sewage	McGarry	[59]
Water hyacinths	Sewage	Cornwell *et al.*	[60]

be met easily from increases in supply from traditional plant sources. The cheaper oils have about the same value as protein, i.e. about £300 to £500/t.

This overall price has been static for about 30 years, despite modest increases in consumption. However, some instability in prices during 1973–1975, and the general interest in biotechnology, have maintained research; and steady progress on the understanding of the formation of microbial oils has been made. Further impetus has recently been generated by the possibility that some special oils may have a much higher value because of their potential use in health care. In this respect microbially derived oils grown on waste materials may become much more important. At present most of the information available is based on laboratory work and extrapolated economics, but it is widely assumed that the substrate will have to be a waste material if the process is to have any chance of economic success.

Domestic and animal wastes are unlikely to be suitable for either SCP or single-cell oil (SCO) because of potential pathogens and toxins in the original waste. Food, drinks and fermentation-industry wastes, on the other hand, should be suitable. Table 7.18 indicates some of the possible substrates.

Some of the organisms noted are reported as giving good results [61]. Thirty-one

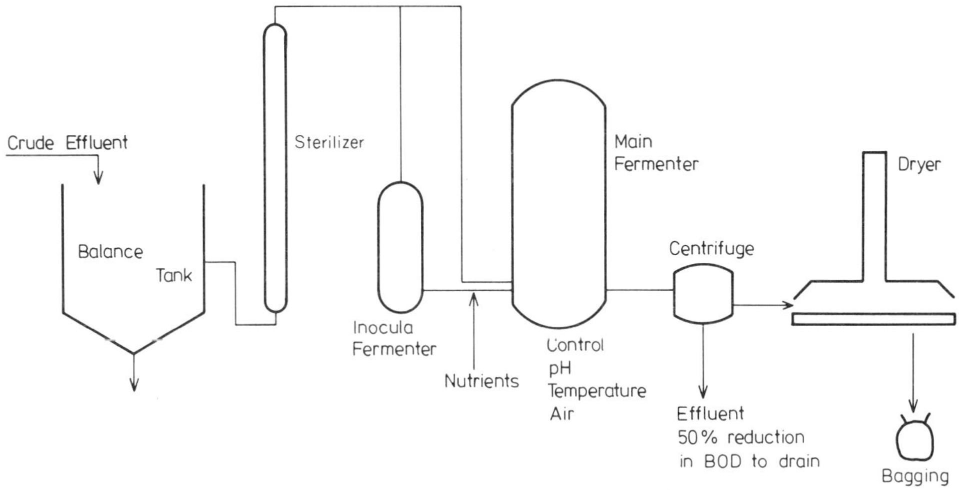

Fig. 7.2 — SCP from confectionery effluent (*Candida*).

species of algae have been found to accumulate oils, including the very fast-growing *Chlorella*. *Chlorella* is the most common algae found growing in polluted water and is an important constituent of the biomass in oxidation ponds and percolating filters, even in the UK. *Chlorella* can contain 30–50 per cent by weight of oil [62]. The yeasts, probably because of their common role in other areas of biotechnology, have attracted most attention as potential oleaginous micro-organisms. The yeasts are not, however, successful in standard waste-treatment processes. It is possible to isolate *Candida, Rhodotorula* and *Trichosporon* from effluent treatment and they will grow on wastes in pure culture. The fungi *Fusarium* and *Geotrichum* are the two most common fungi in polluted waters and they grow very well in competition with other organisms. At present, although not commercially viable, technically microbial oils are an alternative source of supply.

In the case of very specific oils such as γ-linoleic, prospects of early demonstration schemes look more promising than those for the polypeptides. This will be considered again in section 7.5.

7.4.3 Carbohydrates

A large number of microbially produced polysaccharides have now become important industrial gums. Many are already grown on waste materials such as whey, distillers' solubles, molasses, and corn-steep liquor. There are no reports of the use of the more dilute wastes, although in principle they could be used, particularly where the gum produced was not to be used in the food or pharmaceutical industries. There are additional applications in drilling and paper and textile manufacture. Yields and quality would be inferior, but substrate costs would be negligible. Further research on the extracellular polymers of waste-treatment organisms is a priority since the polymer has also important binding functions. This is discussed in Section

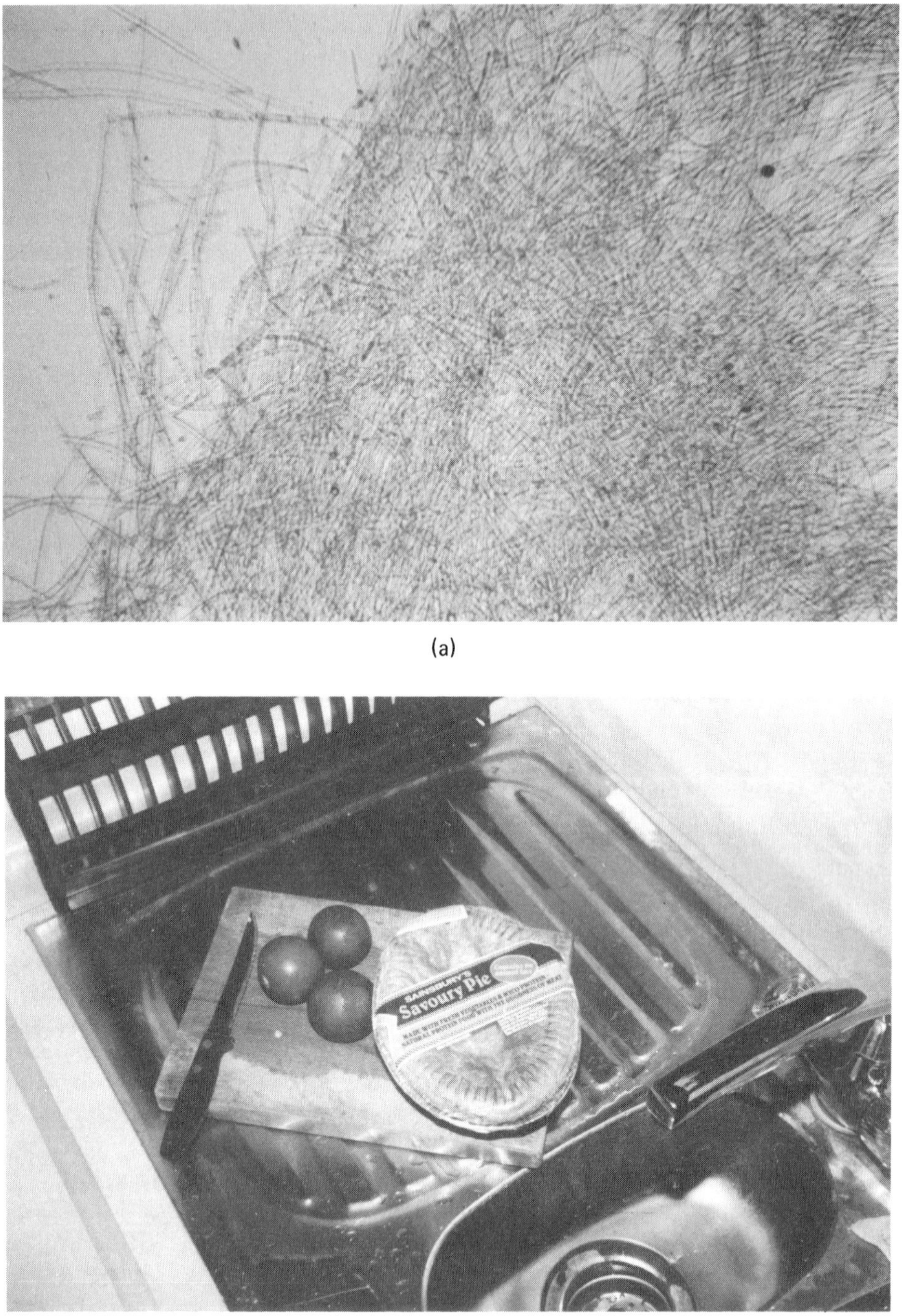

(a)

(b)

Fig. 7.3 — (a) *Fusarium* grown on dairy waste. (b) Savoury pie containing mycoprotein *Fusarium graminearum*.

Table 7.18 — Potential oleaginous micro-organisms.

	Oil content (% w/w)	Substrate
Algae		
Chlorella vulgaris	30	lakewater
Chlorella pyrenoidosa	72	lakewater
Spirulina maxima	11	lakewater
Botryococcus braunii	53	lakewater
Sceredesmus acutus	25	lakewater
Yeasts		
Candida curvata	58	Whey
Lipomyces sp.	60	Molasses and other wastes
Rhodotorula sp.	50	Corn-steep liquor
Rhodotorula sp.	40	Molasses
Trichosporon	45	Whey
Fungi		
Fusarium	40	Whey
Geotrichum candidum	45	Various wastes
Penicillium sp.	23	Date extract

7.5. Laboratory work and desk studies have been carried out in three other areas: Amberg *et al.* [63] have conducted work on producing aldehydes and ketones; Coombs [64] and Compare and Griffith [65] on the alcohols and acids.

7.4.4 Biomass for energy

There is also interest at present in the possibility of general biomass production for energy recovery. Several papers have been published in the last two years on growing water hyacinths, algae, grasses and reeds on effluents (Table 7.19). Treatment systems are very simple, needing little energy or maintenance. They are ideal where land is not expensive (see Ch. 12). The recovered biomass can be burnt directly, converted to methane by anaerobic digestion, or catalytically hydrogenated to produce fuel oil [76,77].

7.4.5 Biogas

Biomethanation from waste is discussed in detail in Chapter 6. For this reason only a brief outline relating to the extent of the application for waste treatment is discussed here.

Biogas recovery from the anaerobic digestion of sewage sludge is very common (05.Mt/a as dry solids are anaerobically treated). This process has been successfully applied since 1901, to reduce sludge volume, to eliminate pathogens, to prevent smell nuisance and to generate methane as a by-product. This is well-established

Table 7.19 — Recent work on aquatic biomass grown on effluent.

Author	Ref.	Work carried out
Water hyacinth		
Thyagarajan	[66]	Symposium on all aspects of culture on different types of waste
John	[67]	Rubber wastewaters, palm-oil waste, growth used for compost, biogas and protein
Reddy *et al.*	[68]	On domestic sewage for nutrient removal
Cornwell *et al.*	[60]	Domestic wastes, protein recovery
Algae		
Abbasi and Nipaney	[69]	Domestic and agricultural wastes for biogas generation
Pretorius and Hensman	[70]	Domestic effluents for composting and fertilizer
Oron *et al.*	[71]	Domestic effluents, water recovery and protein
Macrophytes		
Edwards	[72]	Domestic effluents, water recovery and composting
Gersberg *et al.*	[73]	Domestic wastes, water recovery
Gaigher *et al.*	[74]	Sorghum beer-brewery effluent
Toerien and Toerien	[75]	Piggery wastewater

technology and has been widely publicized. There were difficulties, however, which prevented more widespread use and development. The process was reported to be unreliable and susceptible to a wide range of interferences and shock loads. Most of these problems were attributed to the slow growth rate of the obligate anaerobic bacteria. Few new anaerobic digesters were built from 1970 to 1980, but by 1975 the cost of the alternative aerobic, physical or chemical treatment of sludge was an acute problem and attention focused on methods of improving anaerobic technology [78].

Significant advances have been made since then in the development of the anaerobic process to include industrial waste as well as sludges. Process configurations available include the anaerobic contact process, the anaerobic filter (packed-bed reactor) the expanded/fluidized-bed reactor and the upflow sludge blanket reactor (Fig. 7.4). Considerable efforts have been made by a number of companies to commercialize these modern digesters. At the moment there are about 100 large-scale anaerobic digesters treating industrial wastes within the European Community [79]. The most common application is the treatment of wastewaters from the food, drinks and fermentation industries. There are seven in the UK [80]. Most investigators have noted problems associated with control and reliability. Difficulties arise because of the differences in the optimal conditions for growth of the synergistic

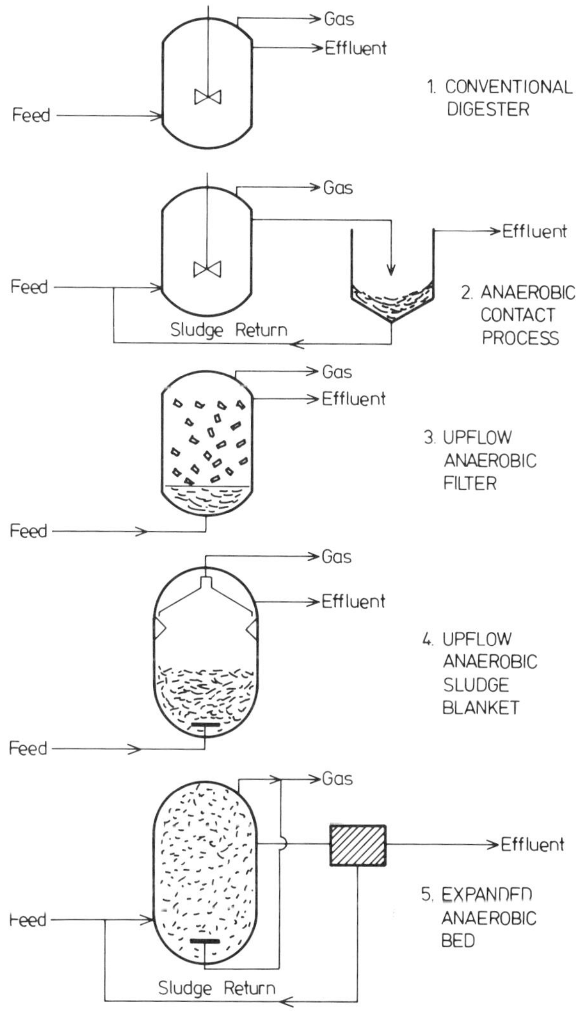

Fig. 7.4 — Schematic diagram of anaerobic reactors.

bacterial populations. High-rate anaerobic digestion of industrial wastes requires careful control of feed rate, balancing and recycle rate, depending on effluent strength, gas flow and quality. The low running costs of anaerobic treatment make the process economically attractive. Increases in water and pollution charges should improve the pay-back and should encourage an expansion of the technology.

7.5 LOW-VOLUME HIGH-VALUE BY-PRODUCTS

7.5.1 Metal recovery

Probably the second most advanced microbial recovery system, after protein, is for the extraction of metals from wastes. Restrictions on the discharge of metals to the environment have become stricter as more evidence about their accumulation and toxicity has been reported. Thus, the role of micro-organisms in metal mobility is the subject of detailed and extensive discussion in the literature. The processes available are described by Ferraiolo and Del Borghi in Chapter 9.

Many bacteria can precipitate metals from solution and, historically, *Sphaerotilus, Gallionella* and *Leptothrix* have been most studied. The reasons why they, in particular, concentrate metals is still the subject of speculation. Anaerobic bacterial cultures cause the precipitation of metals in the form of insoluble sulphides, and a large number of aerobic bacteria can oxidize metals; *Thiobacillus* is the most studied. Micro-organisms play an important part in the precipitation of ocean metallic nodules, corrosion and metal encrustation.

In ore deposits there is a wide range of metallic sulphides which are oxidized and solubilized by a complex microbial community. The process starts with the autotrophic oxidizing activity of *Thiobacillus* on sulphide and reduced iron compounds in the ore. Sulphuric acid is formed, which further accelerates the leaching of the acid-soluble metal salts. The bacteria are able to oxidize both the sulphide ores and the lower oxidation states of the metals [81].

In industrial leaching the low-grade ore and other waste rock are laid on an impermeable base and a mildly acid leach solution is sprayed over the surface of the bed. The solution percolates down through the ore to dissolve metals released by microbial oxidation. Normally there is little advance preparation of aggregate size or segregation of materials other than to ensure that there is sufficient voidage for aeration and drainage. An example is copper, where the solubilized salts may contain 1–2 g/l of copper, which may then be concentrated by electro-precipitation, solvent extraction or conventional precipitation. The leaching solution is recycled after extraction with some additional make-up of water and acid. Copper and uranium are the principal metals extracted commercially by this technique, but the leach solutions usually contain a wide variety of other valuable metals. In the USA 10–15 per cent of copper needs are met by leaching.

Problems can arise because of the size of the fermentation and the consequent lack of control. Compaction, blockage and exothermic reactions are common difficulties. Controlled chemostat fermentation in agitated lagoons can overcome some of these difficulties. The ore can be finely ground and nutrients, pH and dissolved oxygen can be controlled [82]. Some tests are also reported on metal oxidations using bacteria immobilized on plastic.

One interesting new research area of importance in the control of atmospheric pollution is that of biological desulphurization of coal. Similar bacteria to those now used for leaching readily dissolve inorganic or pyritic sulphur from coal. However, this group of bacteria does not readily attack the organic sulphur in coal and further research is underway to find other species capable of removing the organic sulphur [83].

7.5.2 Immobilization of metals by micro-organisms

All micro-organisms accumulate metals because they are often important co-factors in enzyme activity. Research has indicated that some micro-organisms can accumulate large concentrations. Work on an acetate rayon waste, for example, which contained zinc in high concentrations (50–100 mg/l), showed that the biomass could contain up to 12 per cent by weight of zinc without interfering with BOD removal [84].

Conventional biological effluent treatment is known to be quite effective in removing metals from domestic and industrial wastes [85]. The metals are precipitated with the sludge or surplus biomass and can reach a concentration sufficient to interfere with the later processing of the sludge. Selection of micro-organisms with abilities to bind specific metals for use in engineered reactors may prove very useful in the decontamination of a wide range of mining and metal-processing wastes. At present the technology usually consists of a series of lagoons in which algae and micro-organisms are encouraged to develop. The organisms accumulate dissolved and small particulates.

In general, extracellular binding is by electrostatic attraction between the positively charged metals and negatively charged surfaces of the micro-organism. Micro-organisms and their extracellular polymeric secretions are highly charged from the presence of carboxyl, amine and hydroxyl groups that are present in the protein, carbohydrates and phospholipids. This non-specific bio-accumulation is controlled by physicochemical factors such as competing ions and temperature. Specific, active, biological binding sites have not yet been identified. Surface-bound metals follow standard adsorption curves and are easily removed by chelating agents or dilute acids. A possible industrial process has been described [86] to detoxify surplus activated sewage sludge using hydrochloric acid and hydrogen peroxide. A polyelectrolyte was also used to release bound water; metal recovery was between 70 and 90 per cent. It was not an economic method of metal recovery but could be viable when subsidized by the high costs of disposal of contaminated sludge.

7.5.3 Intracellular accumulation

Norris and Kelly [87] investigated metal uptake in a number of organisms: *Saccharomyces*, *Pseudomonas*, *Bacillus*, *Escherichia*, *Rhodotorula* and *Candida*. The yeasts were generally the most effective and accumulation in *Saccharomyces* could be as high as 10–15 per cent of cell weight.

Uptake was thought to be by the pathways for the uptake of necessary metals, although large amounts of non-metabolic metals, such as cobalt, nickel, copper, cadmium and silver, were also taken up. There is considerable interest in the concentration of uranium and work has been published on accumulation in algae, yeast and bacteria [88,89].

Mercury tolerance has been noted in the strain of fungi *Chrysosporium* [90]. The mercury was adsorbed and fixed to the hyphal walls of the fungus. Cadmium accumulation has been observed in *Citrobacter* [91]. Both species might be adapted to detoxify particular types of waste.

Several mechanisms have been suggested as to how micro-organisms might resist metal toxicity, including polymer traps, enzymatic oxidation, methylation, precipitation and efflux pumps [92]. Metals are thought likely to be absorbed by the specific uptake mechanisms in combination with the selected beneficial metals. It should be possible to modify these mechanisms either naturally or by genetic engineering to allow the accumulation of desired metals.

7.6 RECALCITRANT MATERIALS

There are two basic reasons for attempting genetic engineering of micro-organisms used in waste treatment. The first is a potential improvement of overall performance of wastewater treatment plants, particularly their ability to deal with shock loads; this is discussed by Henze in Chapter 2. The second is the acclimatization of micro-organisms to accumulate or degrade persistent (recalcitrant) or toxic materials. The problems associated with the disposal and destruction of new synthetic organic materials (xenobiotics) has stimulated research into techniques for accelerating biodegradation. The high affinity of biological catalysts for their substrates makes biodegradation particularly useful at low concentrations of the xenobiotic. This makes biodegradation complementary to the traditional methods used for disposing of bulk waste products: oxidation, incineration and precipitation. Another advantage is that the xenobiotic is often ultimately converted into natural products.

Most biodegradation research has been classical, investigating the metabolism of pure cultures; this reduces the complexity of the system and ensures reproducible results. In enrichment culture the compound to be degraded is added in progressively larger doses during an acclimatization period until the xenobiotic then becomes a source of essential nutrient.

The wide variety of natural environments provides habitats for the evolution of a large number of micro-organisms with different metabolic capacities. Screening for a starting inoculum can be speeded up by sampling from an area where the organisms are most likely to have evolved: a habitat which has been exposed to the compound of interest. Batch culture is usually used to screen for suitable organisms and continuous culture to exert selective pressure for the desired organisms. Important additional information on the biochemistry of the microbial degradation such as the rate-limiting steps, catabolic sequences and the substrate specificity can also be obtained from these cultures.

Research has frequently shown that an interdependent microbial community [93] is necessary to metabolize the complex sequence of intermediates which results from the breakdown of xenobiotics. Synergistic microbial communities also provide the opportunity for the exchange of genetic information between populations. Transfers of genetic material, such as plasmids, between organisms may be an important evolutionary mechanism. Laboratory research has established such a transfer of plasmids in species of *Pseudomonas* coding for benzene dioxygenase [94]. One of the drawbacks of enrichment culture is that it produces micro-organisms capable of breaking down recalcitrants randomly. Genetic manipulation can also be carried out to select for desired traits. There are six common methods that have been used for the breakdown for xenobiotics (Table 7.20).

The list of xenobiotics and recalcitrants investigated is now a very long one. In the case of some compounds such as the substituted aromatics and lignins, the metabolic pathways are quite well understood. With others, such as the polyaromatics, the surfactants, the pesticides, the azo dyes, stilbenes (optical brighteners), chloroaromatics, *S*-triazines and chlorinated hydrocarbons, they are little understood [106,107]. The straight-chain non-substituted xenobiotics, such as the oils, are comparatively easily broken down by microbial activity, and wastewaters are normally treated biologically after removal of most of the oil by physicochemical

Table 7.20 — Examples of genetically engineered micro-organisms for waste treatment.

Technique	Organism	Use	Author	Ref.
(1) *In vivo/in vitro* recombinant technologies using ligases and endonucleases	*Nocardia*	Polycyclic aromatics and hydrocarbons	Calberg	[95]
DNA phages	*Streptomyces*	Dehalogenation	Chacko *et al.*	[96]
(2) Plasmid exchange	*Pseudomonas*	Aromatic hydrocarbons	Williams	[97]
	Bacillus	Long alkanes	Stewart and Levin	[98]
	Clostridium	Dehalogenation	Li *et al.*	[99]
(3) Transposon mutagenesis	*Pseudomonas*	Aromatics	Chakrabarty	[100]
(4) Protoplast fusion	*Streptomyces*	Aromatics	Gabor and Hotchkiss	[101]
(5) Mutagenesis	*Arthrobacter*	Long alkanes	Timmis	[102]
(6) Sexual transduction, transformation and conjugation	*Achromobacter*	Hydrocarbons	Twarog and	[104]
	Moraxella	Aromatics	Blowse Juni	
	Mycobacteria	Cycloalkanes	Konicek and Konickova-Radochova	[105]

processing. It has been estimated that 50 per cent of the micro-organisms found naturally in seawater are capable of using oil derivatives in metabolism [108]. Similarly the straight-chain detergents introduced in 1955 to overcome the recalcitrance of the branched alkyl surfactants are degraded by β-oxidation of the chain.

Future applications are envisaged to be in three forms [109]:

(1) Controlled degradation of specific wastes with specialized cultures at the source of the waste.
(2) Improvement of waste-treatment systems by inoculation with adapted laboratory strains. Cook [110] reports on commercially available specialized organisms for improving BOD removal, for eliminating filamentous growths in 'bulking', and for improving methane generation in anaerobic treatment.
(3) The clean-up of spills and decontamination of soils using specialized cultures.

Four companies in the UK are actively selling preparations for supplementing existing effluent treatment processes: International Biochemicals (Interbio), London; Bactozyme, Worksop; Bioflow, Stafford; and ABM, Manchester. In the United States there are three major companies: Polybac, Allentown, PA; Sybron, Birmingham, NJ; and Flow Laboratories, Inglewood, CA. They share an annual $5–7 million market for enhanced cultures for pollution control [108].

There are a number of reports in the trade literature detailing the effectiveness of these products but there are as yet no details of controlled experiments in referred publications. Clear descriptions of the derivation of the culture as well as the elimination of uncontrolled factors are required to determine whether they offer any economic advantage.

Specific reactors for the breakdown of recalcitrants would be the easiest to operate and control because the waste stream could be better defined and applied to existing reactor designs. To supplement existing waste-treatment systems, or to be effective on spills, the organisms and their enzymes will have to survive and function in the sub-optimal conditions of a complex ecosystem. It is in this area, however, that enhanced cultures have had their greatest impact so far.

7.7 BIOSCRUBBING

Like the traditional methods of disposing of recalcitrants the usual methods of waste-gas control such as incineration, dispersion, catalytic oxidation, scrubbing and adsorption are best suited to large volumes of well-defined waste gases. Malodour problems, in particular, are normally caused by complex and varying mixtures at very low concentrations: many of the mercaptans, for example, have odour thresholds below 1 p.p.b. Biological control of this type of problem, like that of the recalcitrants, may offer a simpler alternative treatment. Other advantages of the biological nature of the process are that there are no chemical costs and energy requirements are low. Patents for biological control systems were filed in 1930 but there are still few working systems. It seems likely that the idea arose from the observation that biological growths occurred on many water-scrubbing systems. There are two engineering approaches to the problem. One resembles physicochemical scrubbing units combined with a biological filter [111]. The design requirements of these bioscrubbing systems are similar to those of the physicochemical units; the principal requirement is to provide the best surface possible for gas–liquid–biomass interchange. The alternative is percolation through a prepared soil bed [112]. The initial removal mechanism, as in a biological filter, is likely to be biophysical adsorption and solubilization of the material. In this form it will then be available for microbial breakdown. The packed bed serves both to provide a large gas–liquid surface area for adsorption and to immobilize the biomass. Excessive amounts of biomass could occlude some of the surface area and the concentration of organic matter in the effluent should be controlled to maintain optimal efficiency. The prototype bioscrubbing film systems are associated with effluent treatment plants because this is a good source of substrate for biological growth. Completely novel chemicals may require a prolonged acclimatization period, but seeding of subsequent systems handling similar materials would then be simplified. Biological control of gases is as yet an under-researched area, although applications both for oxidizing biofilm (for mercaptans, hydrogen sulphide and cyanide) and for reducing biofilms (for sulphur dioxide and chlorinated hydrocarbons) can be envisaged.

7.8 FUTURE BY-PRODUCTS

The impact of biotechnology on by-product recovery from wastes has so far been slight. There is, however, great potential for the application of biologically engineered ligands for the collection of valuable materials from wastes. The materials would have to be of high value and application is likely to be restricted to recovery within the food, drinks and fermentation industries. Expensive polypeptides, such as enzymes and valuable oils like γ-linoleic, seem the most likely. Some valuable enzymes, such as cholesterol oxidase, are already recovered from animal-processing waste. Other possibilities are optically active, valuable materials such as natural flavours and colours. Further work also seems likely on the extracellular polymers of micro-organisms grown on waste. Microbial surfaces and microbial polymers can supply a very large, active surface area for adsorption more cheaply than chemical surfaces like activated carbon. Such a material would have a role in the recovery of precious materials such as uranium and gold, or the collection of dangerous toxins such as pesticides and radioactive nuclides.

7.9 CONCLUSIONS

Aerobic effluent treatment is the largest controlled use of micro-organisms in industry. The diversity, volume and heterogeneous nature of wastes means that there are few alternatives to this type of treatment for domestic wastewater. The size of this market will continue to stimulate development of more efficient processes. Improved reliability and reduced biomass yields are two areas where progress is expected.

The future of medium-volume by-products from wastes is uncertain. Substrate costs are only a small fraction of the total fermentation costs and it seems likely that other surplus materials or other processes will be more attractive. Even the anaerobic fermentation of waste for pollution control and energy recovery is less attractive economically than expected. However, research and development that has already started should improve the reliability and efficiency of the process to ensure its future. The use of bio-processes for the breakdown of aqueous and atmospheric recalcitrants is yet to be realized and most research is still at a fundamental stage. There is strong competition from the non-biological methods which do not need such large investments in research and development. There are also restrictions in the United States concerning the release of engineered micro-organisms into the environment. Some progress is expected in this area, particularly with complex mixtures of very low concentrations of xenobiotics.

The recovery of more valuable materials such as enzymes, special oils and other materials which are difficult to synthesize will be worthwhile in the long term.

REFERENCES

[1] Water Data Unit (1978). *Department of the Environment Water Data,* Reading, UK.

[2] Rees, J. F. (1983). Landfill technology—prospects for control. *Biotech 83 Proceedings of the International Conference on Applications and Implications of Biotechnology,* Online Publications, Northwood, London, pp. 743–760.

[3] Congressional Office of Technology Assessment (1981). *The impacts of genetics: applications to micro-organisms, animals and plants,* Washington, DC.

[4] Ling, J. T. (1982). *Low or Non pollution Technology through Pollution Prevention: an Overview.* United Nations Environment Programme/3M, St Paul, Minnesota, 35 pp.

[5] Dunnhill, P. and Rudd, M. (1984). *Biotechnology and Industry,* NERC/SERC Publications, Swindon.

[6] World Health Organization (1973). *Reuse of Effluents, Methods of Waste Water Treatment and Health Safeguards: Report of WHO Meeting of Experts,* WHO Technical Report Series, Geneva, No. 517.
[7] Packam, R. F. (1983). Water quality and health. In Harrison, R. M. (ed.) *Pollution: Causes, Effects and Control,* Royal Society of Chemistry, London, pp. 19–32.
[8] Stocks, P. (1973). Mortality from cancer and cardiovascular disease in the county boroughs of England and Wales classified according to the sources and hardness of their water supplies 1958–1967. *J. Hyg. Camb.*, **71**, 237–252.
[9] Page, T., Harris, R. H. and Epstein, S. S. (1976). Drinking water and cancer mortality in Louisiana. *Science,* **193**, 55–57.
[10] Beresford, S. A. A. (1980). *Water Reuse and Health in the London Area.* Water Research Centre Technical Report TR138, Medmenham Laboratory.
[11] Beresford, S. A. A., Carpenter, L. M. and Powell, P. (1984). *Epidemiological Studies of Water Reuse and Type of Water Supply.* Water Research Centre Technical Report TR216, Medmenham Laboratory.
[12] Department of the Environment, National Water Council (1979). *Methods of Examination of Waters and Associated Materials,* HMSO.
[13] Perry, R. and McIntyre, A. E. (1986). Organic micropollutants and the protection of water supplies. *Effluent and Water Treatment Journal,* **26**, 15–18.
[14] Gardiner, J. and Mance, G. (1984). *United Kingdom Water Quality Standards Arising from the European Community Directives.* Water Research Centre Technical Report TR204, Medmenham Laboratory.
[15] Hyde, R. A., Hill, D. G. and Zabel, T. F. (1986). Granular activated carbon as sand replacement in rapid gravity filters. *J. Inst. Wat. Eng. and Scientists,* **40**, 70–80.
[16] World Health Organization (1984). *Guidelines for Drinking Water Quality,* Vol. 1, WHO, Geneva (available HMSO), 55 pp.
[17] McDonald, D. (1974). Water reclamation and effluent treatment in the soft drinks industry. *Symposium on the Treatment of Wastes from the Food and Drink Industry,* Institute of Water Pollution Control, Maidstone, pp. 59–68.
[18] Sidwick, J. M. (1978). The treatment of an industrial effluent from the manufacture of organic chemicals for process reuse. *Progress in Water Technology,* **10**, 443–448.
[19] Shore, M., Broughton, N. W. and Bumstead, N. (1983). Anaerobic treatment of waste waters in the sugar beet industry. *Symposium on the Anaerobic Treatment of Industrial Wastewaters, Coventry,* Institute of Water Pollution Control, Maidstone.
[20] Fewkes, A. and Ferris, F. A. (1982). The recycling of domestic wastewater factors influencing storage capacity. *Building and Environment,* **17**, 209–216.
[21] World Health Organization (1981). *Health Aspects of Treated Sewage Reuse,* Report on a WHO Seminar, Algiers, 1980, WHO, Copenhagen (available HMSO).
[22] National Water Council, Ministry of Agriculture, Fisheries and Foods (1978). *Report of the Working Party on the Disposal of Sewage Sludge to Land National Water Council,* HMSO, London.

[23] Winfield, B. A. and Bone, D. A. (1981). The sewage farm reborn. *Public Health Engineer,* **9**, 185–186.
[24] Shuval, H. I. (1969). Health factors in the re-use of waste water for agricultural, industrial and municipal purposes. In: *Problems in Community Waste Management,* Public Health Paper No. 38, WHO, Geneva, p. 76.
[25] Neison, K. (1983). *Fertilizers,* ICI, London.
[26] Sridhar, M. K. C., Ekpenyony, T. E. and Shoremi, O. I. R. (1985). Sewage effluents as drinking water for Nigerian poultry. *Effluent and Water Treatment Journal,* **25**, 327–330.
[27] Anon. (1985). sludge marketing study surveys 20 cities. *Biocycle,* **26**, 46–47.
[28] Stead, P. A. and Irwin, R. A. (1981). Accelerated aerobic composting of raw sewage sludge and pulverised domestic refuse. *J IWES,* **85**, 230.
[29] Healey, M. G. (1984). Guidelines for the utilisation of sewage sludge on land in the United Kingdom. *Water Science and Technology,* **16**, 461–471.
[30] Hutchings, N. J. (1985). The use of three types of sewage sludge and ammonium nitrate for the nitrogenous fertilization of a grass/white clover sward. *Resources and Conservation,* **11**, 263–272.
[31] HMSO (1974). *Control of Pollution Act,* HMSO, London.
[32] Matthews, P. J. (1984). Control of metal application rates from sewage sludge utilization in agriculture. *CRC in Environmental Control,* **14**, 199–250.
[33] Hermite, P. L. and Oh, H. (1984). Processing and use of sewage sludge. *Proceedings of the 3rd International Symposium,* Brighton Reidel, Dordrecht.
[34] Argent, V. A., Bell, J. C. and Emslie-Smith, M. (1977). Animal disease hazards of sludge disposal to land occurrence of pathogenic organisms. *Wat. Pollut. Contr.,* **74**, 511–516.
[35] Pike, E. B., Morris, D. L. and Carrington, E. G. (1983). Inactivation of ova of the parasites *Taenia Saginata* and *Ascaris Suum* during heated anaerobic digestion. *Water Pollut. Contr.,* **82**, 501–509.
[36] Godfree, A. F. and Jones, F. (1983). The destruction of pathogens and parasites in sewage sludge by chemical means. *Wat. Pollut. Contr.,* **82**, 471–478.
[37] Prescott, S. C. and Dunn, G. G. (1959). *The Yeasts and the Propagation of Yeasts* (3rd ed), McGraw Hill, London.
[38] Peppler, H. J. (1968). Industrial production of single cell protein on carbohydrates. In: Mateles, R. I. and Tannenbaum, S. R. (eds) *Single Cell Protein,* MIT Press, London.
[39] James, A. and Addyman, C. L. (1974). By product recovery from food wastes by microbial protein production. *Symposium on Treatment of Wastes from the Food and Drink Industry,* University of Newcastle, 8–10th January, Institute of Water Pollution, Maidstone.
[40] Samaelov, N. S. (1983). Single cell protein production: review of alternatives. In: Mizraki, A. and van Wezel, A. L. (eds) *Advances in Biotechnological Processes,* Vol. 1, Liss, New York, pp. 293–335.
[41] Goldberg, I. (1985). *Single Cell Protein,* Springer-Verlag, Berlin.
[42] Holderby, J. M. and Moggio, W. A. (1960). Utilization of spent sulphite liquor. *J. Wat. Pollut. Control Fed.* **32**, 171–181.

[43] Righelato, R. C., Imrie, F. K. E. and Vlitos, A. J. (1976). Production of single cell protein from agricultural and food processing wastes. *Resource Recovery and Conservation,* **1**, 257–269.

[44] Tomlinson, E. J. (1976). 1. The production of single cell protein from strong organic waste waters from the food and drink processing industries. Laboratory cultures. *Water Research,* **10** 367–371.
2. The practical and economic feasibility of a non-aseptic batch culture. *Water Research,* **45** 674–680.

[45] Wasserman, A. E., Hampson, J. W. and Alvare, N. F. (1961). Large scale production of yeast in whey. *J. Wat. Pollut. Contr. Fed.,* **33**, 1090–1094.

[46] Smith, M. E. and Bull, A. T. (1976). Studies on the utilisation of coconut water waste for the production of the food yeast *Saccharomyces fragilis. J. Applied Bacteriology,* **41**, 81–95.

[47] Braun, R., Meyrath, J., Staparek, W. and Zerlauth, G. (1979). Feed yeast production from citric acid waste. *Process Biochemistry,* **14**, 16–18 and 20.

[48] Prior, B. A. (1984). Continuous growth kinetics of *Candida utilus* in pineapple cannery effluent. *Biotech. Bioeng.,* **26**, 748–752.

[49] Tauk, S. M. (1982). Culture of *Candida* in vinasse and molasses: effect of acid and salt addition on biomass and raw protein production. *Eur. J. Appl. Microbiology and Biotechnology,* **16**, 223–227.

[50] Thanh, N. C. and Simard, R. E. (1973). Biological treatment of waste water by yeasts. *J. Wat. Pollut. Contr. Fed.,* **45**, 674–680.

[51] Forage, A. J. (1978). Recovery of yeast from confectionery effluent. *Process Biochemistry,* **13**, 8–11.

[52] Munden, J. E. and King, R. W. (1973). High rate biofiltration system for food pilot plants. *Effluent and Water Treatment Journal,* **13**, 159–165.

[53] Quinn, J. P. and Marchant, R. (1980). The treatment of malt whiskey distillery waste using the fungus *Geotrichum candidum. Water Research,* **14**, 545–551.

[54] Wheatley, A. D., Mitre, R. I. and Hawkes, H. A. (1982). Protein recovery from dairy industry wastes with aerobic biofiltration. *Chem. Tech. and Biotechnol.,* **32**, 203–212.

[55] Davy, C. A. E. (1981). In: Herzka, A. and Booth, R. G. (eds) *Recovery of Fruit and Vegetable Waste in Food Industry Wastes: Disposal and Recovery,* Applied Science, London, pp. 219–230.

[56] Church, B. D., Erikson, E. E. and Vidmer, C. M. (1973). *Fungal Digestion of Food Processing Wastes, Food Technology,* **2**, 36–42.

[57] Grau, P. (1980). Utilisation of activated sludge as fodder supplement. *Env. Technology Letters,* **1**, 557–570.

[58] Beszechits, S. and Lugowski, A. (1983). Waste activated sludge: a potential new livestock feed ingredient. *Process Biochemistry,* **18**, 35–37.

[59] McGarry, M. G. (1971). Water and protein reclamation from sewage. *Process Biochemistry,* **6**, 50.

[60] Cornwell, D. A., Zoltek, J., Jr, Patrinely, C. D., Furman, des. T. and Kim, J. I. (1977). Nutrient removal by water-hyacinth. *J. Water Pollut. Control Fed.,* **49**, 57–65.

[61] Ratledge, C. (1982). In: Bull, M. J. (ed.) Microbial oils and fats: an assessment

of their commercial potential, *Progress in Industrial Microbiology,* **16**, 119–206.

[62] Howell, J. (1983). Algae for oil production. *Biotechnology,* **1**, 24.

[63] Amberg, H. R., Aspitate, T. R. and Cormack, J. F. (1969). Fermentation of spent sulphite liquor for the production of volatile acids. *J. Wat. Pollut. Control. Fed.,* **41**, R419–430.

[64] Coombs, J. (1981). Biogas and power alcohol. *Chemistry and Industry,* **4**, 223–229.

[65] Compare, A. L. and Griffith, W. L. (1976). Fermentation of waste materials to produce industrial intermediates. *Dev. in Industrial Microbiol.,* **17**, 247–252.

[66] Thyagarajan, G. (1985). *Proceedings of the International Conference on Water Hyacinth,* HMSO, 1005 pp.

[67] John, C. K. (1985). Treatment of agro-industrial wastes using water hyacinth. *Water Science and Technology,* **17**, 781–790.

[68] Reddy, K. R., Hueston, F. M. and McKim, T. (1983). Water-hyacinth production in sewage effluent, *Symposium on Energy from Biomass and Wastes VII,* Lake Buena Vista, Florida, 24–28th January, Institute of Gas Technology, Chicago.

[69] Abbasi, S. A. and Nipaney, P. C. (1984). Generation of biogas from *Salvina molesta* (Mitchell) on a commercial biogas digester. *Environmental Technology Letters,* **5**, 75–80.

[70] Pretorius, W. A. and Hensman, L. C. (1985). The selective cultivation of easily harvestable algae using crossflow microscreening. *Water Science and Technology,* **17**, 791–802.

[71] Oron, G., Wildschut, L. R. and Porath (1985). Wastewater recycling by duckweed for protein production and renovation. *Water Science and Technology,* **17**, 803–817.

[72] Edwards, P. (1985). Aquaculture: a component of low cost sanitation technology, World Bank, Washington, DC, Technical Paper 36, 45 pp.

[73] Gersberg, R. M., Elkins, B. V. and Goldman, C. R. (1985). Wastewater treatment by artificial wetlands. *Water Science and Technology,* **17**, 443–450.

[74] Gaigher, I. G., Toerien, D. F. and Grobbelaar, J. U. (1985). Preliminary studies on the treatment of sorghum beer brewery effluent in an integrated bacterial/algal/fish/macrophyte culture system. *Agricultural Wastes,* **12**, 207–224.

[75] Toerien, D. F. and Toerien, M. C. (1985). Microbial heterotrophy in an effluent treatment system using macrophytes. *Agricultural Wastes,* **12**, 287–312.

[76] Zlokarnik, M. (1983). Bioengineering aspects of aerobic wastewater purification. Developments and trends. *German Chemical Engineering,* **6**, 183–197.

[77] Benn, F. R. and McAuliffe, C. A. (1980). Conversion of municipal waste into fuel, UK Patent No. 2089831.

[78] Swanwick, J. D., Shurben, D. G. and Jackson, S. (1969). A survey of the performance of sewage sludge digestion in Great Britain. *Wat. Pollut. Control,* **68**, 639–661.

[79] Demuynck, M., Nyns, E. J. and Palz, W. (1984). *Biogas Plants in Europe, A Practical Handbook,* Solar Energy R & D in the European Community Series E, Energy from Biomass Vol. 6, D. Reidel, Lancaster.

[80] Wheatley, A. D. and Winstanley, C. I. (1985). Anaerobic digester systems for waste treatment. *Chemical Engineer,* **416**, 42–46.

[81] Kelly, D. P., Norris, P. R. and Brierley, C. L. (1979). Microbiological methods for the extraction and recovery of metals. In: Bull, A. T., Ellwood, D. C. and Ratledge, C. (eds) *Microbial Technology: Current State, Future Prospects,* Symposium of the Society of General Microbiology, Cambridge University Press.

[82] Lundgren, D. G. and Malouf, E. E. (1983). Microbial Extraction of Metals. In: *Advances in Biotechnological Processes.* A. L. Liss, New York, pp. 223–249.

[83] Brierley, C. L., Kelly, D. P., Seal, K. J. and Best, D. J. (1985). Materials and biotechnology. In: Higgins, I. J., Best, D. J. and Jones, J. (eds) *Biotechnology Principles and Applications,* Blackwell, London.

[84] Kiff, R. J. and Brown, S. (1981). The development of the oxidative acid hydrolysis process for sewage sludge detoxification, *International Conference on Heavy Metals on the Environment,* Amsterdam, September.

[85] Brown, M. J. and Lester, J. N. (1979). Metal removal in activated sludge: the role of bacteria extra cellular polymers *Water Research,* **13**, 817–837.

[86] Abson, J. W. (1980). Detoxification of sewage sludge, *Symposium of Practical Solid Waste Disposal,* Institution of Chemical Engineers, Rugby.

[87] Norris, P. R. and Kelly, D. P. (1979). Accumulation of metals by bacteria and yeast. *Developments in Industrial Microbiology,* **20**, 299–308.

[88] Strandberg, G. W., Shumate, S. I. and Parrot, J. R. (1981). Microbial cells as biosorbents for heavy metals, accumulation of uranium by *Saccharomyces cerevisiae* and *Pseudomonas aeruginosa. Appl. Environmental Microbiology,* **41**, 237–245.

[89] Beveridge, T. J. and Murray, R. G. E. (1976). Uptake and retention of metals by cell walls of *Bacillus subtilis. J. Bacteriol.,* 127, 1502–1510.

[90] Williams, J. I. and Pugh, G. J. F. (1975). Resistance of *Chrysosporium pannorum* to an organomercury fungicide. *Trans. Br. Mycol. Soc.,* **64**, 255–262.

[91] Macaskie, L. E. and Dean, A. C. R. (1984). Cadmium accumulation by immobilised cells of a *Citrobacter* sp. *Env. Tech. Letters,* **5**, 177–186.

[92] Wood, J. M. and Wang, H. K. (1983). Microbial resistance to heavy metals. *Env. Science and Technology,* **17**, 582R–590A.

[93] Harder, W. (1981). Enrichment and characterisation of degrading microbes. In: Leisinger, T., Hutter, R., Cook, A. M. and Nuesch, J. (eds) *Microbial Degradation of Xenobiotics and Recalcitrant Compounds,* Academic Press, London.

[94] Best, D. J., Jones, J. and Stafford, D. (1985). The environment and biotechnology. In: Higgins, I. J., Best, D. J. and Jones, J. (eds) *Biotechnology Principles and Applications,* Blackwell, pp. 213–256.

[95] Calberg, S. R. (1980). Oil pollution of the marine environment with an emphasis on estuarine studies. In: Olausson, E. and Cato, I. (eds) *Chemistry and Biogeochemistry of Estuarines,* Wiley, New York, pp. 367–402.

[96] Chacko, C. I., Lockwood, J. L. and Zabik, M. (1966). Chlorinated hydrocarbon pesticides: degradation by microbes. *Science,* **154**, 893–895.
[97] Williams, P. A. (1981). The genetics of biodegradation. In: Leisinger, T., Hutter, R., Cooke, A. M. and Nuesch, J. (eds) *Microbial Degradation of Xenobiotic and Recalcitrant Compounds,* Academic Press, London.
[98] Stewart, F. M. and Levin, B. R. (1977). The population biology of bacterial plasmids: *a priori* conditions for the existence of conjugationally transmitted factors. *Genetics,* **87**, 209–228.
[99] Li, A. W., Krell, P. J. and Mahony, D. E. (1980). Plasmid detection in a bacteriocinogenic strain of *Clostridium perfringens. Can. J. Microbiol.,* **26**, 1018–1022.
[100] Chakrabarty, A. M. (1980). The biodegradation of PCB and chlorobenzoates in plasmids and transposons. In: Stuttard, C. and Rozee, K. R. (eds) *Environmental Effects and Maintenance Mechanisms,* Academic Press, London.
[101] Gabor, M. H. and Hotchkiss, R. D. (1979). Parameters governing bacterial regeneration and genetic recombination after fusion of *Bacillus subtilis* protoplasts. *J. Bacteriol.,* **137**, 1346–1353.
[102] Timmis, K. N. (1981). Gene manipulation *in vitro*. In: Glover, S. W. and Hopwood, D. A. (eds) *Genetics as a Tool in Microbiology, Society for General Microbiology Symposium 31,* Cambridge University Press, pp. 50–109.
[103] Twarog, R. and Blouse, L. E. (1968). Isolation and characterisation of transducing bacteriophage BP1 for *Bacterium anitratum* (*Achromobacter* sp). *J. Virol.,* **2**, 716–722.
[104] Juni, E. (1974). Simple genetic transformation assay for rapid diagnosis of *Moraxella osloensis. Applied Microbiology,* **27**, 16–24.
[105] Konicek, J. and Konickova-Radochova, M. (1975). Possibilities of the conjunction process in *Mycobacteria Folia. Microbiol.,* **20**, 382–388.
[106] Leisinger, T. (1983). Microbial degradation of recalcitrant compounds. In: Holdom, R. S., Sidwick, J. M. and Wheatley, A. D. (eds) *Environment Biotechnology: Future Prospects,* European Federation of Biotechnology, CEC, Brussels, pp. 119–125.
[107] Johnson, J. B. and Robinson, S. G. (1984). *Genetic Engineering and New Pollution Control Technologies,* Pollution Technology Review No. 106, Biotechnology Review No. 3, Noyes Publications, Park Ridge, New Jersey 131 pp.
[108] Powledge, T. M. (1983). Prospects for pollution control with microbes. *Biotechnology,* November, 734–755.
[109] Cook, A. M., Grossenbacher, H., Hogrefe, W. and Hutter, R. (1983). Biodegradation of xenobiotic industrial wastes: applied microbiology complementing chemical treatments. In: *Biotech 83 Proceedings of the International Conference on the Commercial Applications and Implications of Biotechnology Online Publications,* Northwood, London.
[110] Cook, J. (1933). Biotechnology in waste water treatment. *Water and Waste Treatment J.,* **26**, 24–29.
[111] Le Roux, N. W. and Mehta, K. B. (1980). Biological oxidation of odours. In:

Valentin, F. H. H. and North, A. A. (eds) *Odour Control—A Concise Guide*, Department of Industry, Warren Spring Laboratory, Stevenage, pp. 161–162.
[112] Ottengraf, S. P. P. and Van der Oever, A. H. C. (1983). Kinetics of organic compound removal from waste gases with a biological filter. *Biotech. Bioengineering*, **25**, 3089–3102.

8

Applications of molecular biology

D. R. Berry and **E. Senior**
Division of Applied Microbiology, Department of Bioscience and Biotechnology, University of Strathclyde, 204 George Street, Glasgow G1 1XW, Scotland

8.1 INTRODUCTION

Molecular biology is a relatively new branch of bioscience which has developed over the past 25 years. It has been stimulated by the advent of biochemical techniques, to handle and investigate macromolecules such as DNA, RNA and proteins, and of genetic techniques to manipulate the genotype of organisms, especially micro-organisms. Most of these investigations were initially only of interest to fundamental research until a combination of techniques was developed which permitted the *in vitro* manipulation of genes. This led to the development of the sophisticated technology of genetic engineering which is available at the present time [1]. Most of the work on genetic engineering has been carried out on the coliform bacterium *Escherichia coli* and to a lesser extent on the sporing bacterium *Bacillus subtilis* and the brewer's and baker's yeast *Saccharomyces cerevisiae*, and has been directed towards the formation of new medical products. However, the technology is not restricted to these organisms and the procedures for the genetic manipulation of a wide range of bacteria which are important in other areas of microbiology, such as environmental and food microbiology, have been described [2,3]. The purpose of this review is to introduce some of the basic procedures of genetic engineering and to indicate how they can be used to alter the performance of a micro-organism. Where possible, attempts are made to provide examples relevant to the field of waste treatment and to give some indication of the problems, as well as the prospects for the application of molecular genetics to this field. An attempt will also be made to identify areas in the field of waste treatment which appear to be amenable to exploitation using these techniques.

8.2 BASIC CONCEPTS OF GENETIC ENGINEERING

8.2.1 Introduction

The ability to manipulate the genetic make-up of a population of micro-organisms is not new. At its simplest it can involve the selection and breeding of a clone from a single organism which exhibits desirable properties. However, this restricts what can be achieved to the natural variability which occurs in that group of organisms. Greater variation can be obtained if new genetic information can be introduced from different groups of organisms which have different characteristics. The bacteria have several mechanisms by which this can be achieved. These mechanisms include conjugation, in which a whole or part of a chromosome is transferred, transduction, in which a phage acts as the vector for the transfer of a chromosomal segment, and transformation, in which a simple DNA molecule is transferred [4]. However, the amount of genetic information which can be transferred by these techniques in an unmodified manner is restricted to that which occurs naturally, usually in closely related organisms. The important advance which has arisen with the development of gene manipulation has been the ability to isolate DNA from any source and to introduce it into organisms for which procedures for gene manipulation have been developed. However, the successful introduction of a novel DNA into a bacterium or other organism requires that the following three steps must be successfully completed [5].

(1) insertion of the novel DNA into a special DNA molecule, the vector, which facilitates the transfer of the novel DNA into the new host;
(2) transfer of the modified vector into the host bacterium; and
(3) identification of the host bacterium which has taken up the modified vector and separation of this colony from other unmodified colonies.

8.2.2 Nature of cloning vectors

Gene manipulation can be carried out using natural plasmids, such as the pSC101, Col E1 and RSF 2124 plasmids of *E. coli.* However, many specialized plasmids have been developed for gene manipulation incorporating several features which facilitate their use. Plasmids are small circular DNA molecules which can replicate autonomously in the host cell. If they are to be used for gene manipulation they must also be capable of being transferred from cell to cell. Useful plasmids also contain genes for substrate utilization or for resistance to antibiotics or metals, which allow their presence in the host cell to be readily detected. These marker genes also permit bacteria containing the plasmid to be readily separated from other bacteria which do not contain the plasmid. Since the rate of transformation of large plasmids is lower than for small plasmids, then small plasmids are preferred for gene manipulation when transformation is to be used. A small plasmid also facilitates a more precise control of the insertion of the novel DNA segment and favours an increase in the number of plasmids in the whole cell [5]. A simplified diagram of perhaps the most widely used plasmid is shown in Fig. 8.1.

8.2.3 Insertion of novel DNA segments

Studies on phage have led to the identification of a large number of enzymes, restriction endonucleases, which cut DNA at specific sites in the DNA molecule. The site of the cut is determined by a sequence of 4–7 bases in the DNA, different restriction endonucleases recognizing different base sequences. In most cases the cut in the DNA molecule occurs at different points in the two strands of the DNA such

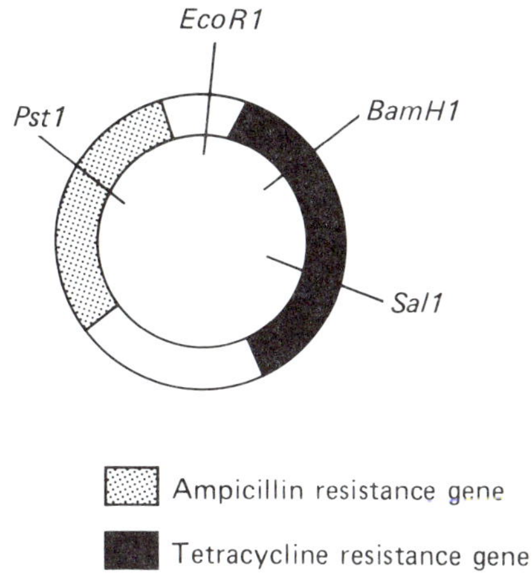

Fig. 8.1 — Diagram of a widely used plasmid, pBR 3222, showing the sites of action of four restriction enzymes: *Pst*1, *EcoR*1, *BamH*1, and *Sal*1.

that each of the two ends has a short tail of single-stranded DNA, which is referred to as a 'sticky end' because it has an affinity for the complementary tail produced at the other free end (Fig. 8.2). DNA molecules which have complementary 'sticky ends'

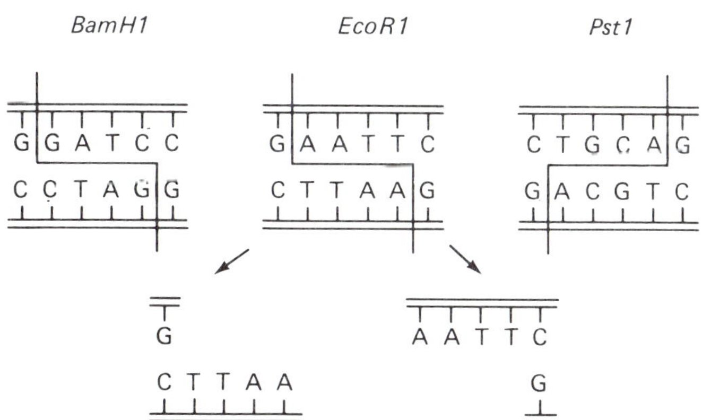

Fig. 8.2 — Mode of action of three restriction endonuclease enzymes showing how the DNA is cleaved by a staggered cut which leads to the cut DNA having 'sticky ends'. Each restriction endonuclease cuts at a specific site.

can be joined together again using a second enzyme, DNA ligase.

Using a combination of restriction endonuclease and DNA ligase it is possible to insert segments of foreign or novel DNA into plasmids. The DNA from one organism is extracted and cut into short lengths using one restriction endonuclease. The plasmid must then be cut and opened up using the same endonuclease. The selection of an appropriate endonuclease is dependent upon several factors, one of the most important being that the site for the endonuclease cut in the plasmid only occurs once, so that the plasmid is only opened up into a linear form and not broken into fragments, and the donor DNA is inserted into a single specific site. Plasmids have been developed which have a single site for several restriction endonucleases. The donor DNA fragment and the cut plasmid are then mixed and incubated together with a DNA ligase to produce new plasmids, some of which contain fragments of donor DNA. This plasmid preparation is then used to transfer a population of recipient bacteria. A population of plasmids which contains a large number of different DNA segments from a donor organism, and which is held in a host bacterium, is referred to as a gene bank. It is possible to calculate from the size of the donor genome and the average size of the DNA segments in the host DNA preparation how many transformed host cells need to be isolated to have a probability of finding all the genes of the donor strain in the gene bank [6]. The overall process is illustrated in Fig. 8.3.

Many vectors have been constructed for the well-studied organisms such as *E. coli, B. subtilis, S. cerevisiae* and *Streptomyces coelicolor*, which offer the facility not only of introducing new genes but also of controlling the level of expression using different promoters, e.g. *lac,* λ, *tryp* in *E. coli* [7], the time of expression, e.g. temperature-sensitive promoters or sporulation-specific promoters in *B. subtilis* [8], and finally if the protein is excreted or not, e.g. α-amylase promoter in *B. subtilis* [9,10]. There appears to be a high degree of universality of the 'signal' DNA sequences involved in the control of secretion of proteins since the same sequences operate in several bacteria and in yeast.

8.2.4 Transfer of plasmids

The most common procedure for introducing the plasmid into the host cell is transformation. In most Gram-negative bacterial species studied, a high rate of transformation is dependent upon the treatment of the bacteria with calcium chloride. However, even under optimum conditions, only a few per cent of the bacterial population are transformed. An alternative technique which has been successfully applied to bacilli, actinomycetes, yeasts and other organisms, is to produce protoplasts of the host cell and to transform these before allowing the cell wall to regenerate.

The rate of transformation is reduced when large segments of DNA are inserted into plasmids. However, techniques have been developed in which larger segments of DNA are packaged into the protein coat of the phage λ (transduction). Using these techniques plasmids containing up to 46 kb DNA can be transferred into *E. coli* at high frequencies by transduction. Because the genetic system of *E. coli* has been so extensively studied it is often desirable to prepare a gene bank, or to carry out plasmid manipulations in *E. coli*, even if the gene in question is eventually to be transferred to another host. This practice is widely carried out in yeast molecular genetics, and special vectors which operate both in *E. coli* and in *S. cerevisiae* have been developed. These are called shuttle vectors. This type of procedure may be very valuable for working with some of the more recalcitrant bacteria which occur in

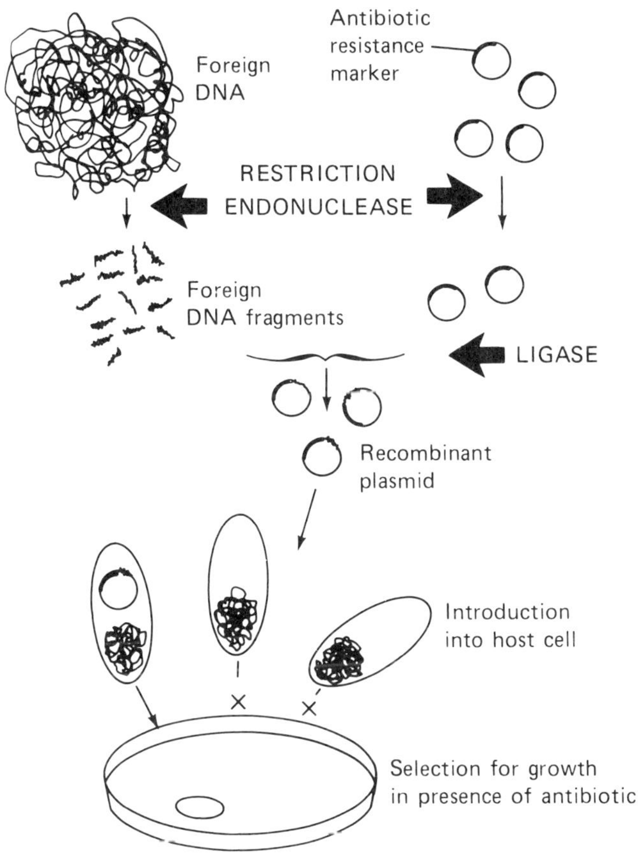

Fig. 8.3 — Strategy for cloning segments of foreign DNA into suitably marked plasmids and isolation of transformed bacteria containing the recombinant plasmid.

natural environments and which may be valuable in waste-treatment processes. Further information on the concepts and techniques of gene manipulation can be obtained from several texts [5,11–13].

8.2.5 Stability of genetically engineered organisms

One of the problems of developing highly specialized organisms for fermentation processes using genetic engineering or other techniques is that the organisms produced do not compete favourably with wild-type organisms or with contaminating organisms. This potentially represents a major problem in waste-treatment processes, since most of these operate in non-sterile conditions and may even require the presence of several organisms for the complete processing of the effluent. Instability and loss of genetically engineered organisms in a fermentation system can arise in at least three different ways:

(1) loss of the plasmid, resulting in a loss of the key properties;

(2) dilution of the organism from the system by plasmid-free organisms arising in the fermentation; and
(3) replacement of the organisms by contaminating organisms.

Natural plasmids are maintained in bacterial populations because they contain special genes which control the segregation of the plasmid into the two daughter cells produced at cell division. These are not always present in plasmids constructed for gene manipulation so plasmids can be lost by being segregated out at cell division. The presence of a plasmid imposes extra nutritional requirements on a bacterial host cell, which place it in a selectively disadvantageous position unless the plasmid offers some other advantage [14]. Furthermore, as the expression of a cloned gene increases, the greater is the physiological load it places on the host bacterium and the greater is the possibility of plasmid-free segments arising [15]. Loss of functional plasmids may also arise from changes in the structure of the plasmid by deletion or rearrangement of the plasmid DNA [16]. The loss of whole plasmids can be restricted by the use of selective markets such as antibiotic resistance or genes for auxotrophic markers; however, this would not prevent loss of key segments from a plasmid. One approach adopted to limit the loss of highly expressed genes is to control them using promoters which are only expressed under special conditions, so that the growth of the cell can be completed before the clone gene is expressed. The use of a temperature-sensitive expression system has been combined with the use of a two-stage continuous culture by Siegel and Ryu [17]. In this study, *E. coli* containing a plasmid which coded for *trpA* protein was grown at 25°C and at a dilution rate of $D = 0.358\ h^{-1}$. At this temperature the expression of the *trpA* gene was repressed by a represser-protein produced by a gene which was derived from the phage λ. However, this represser-protein was unstable at temperatures above 38°C, so when the *E. coli* was transferred to a second stage held at 41.7°C and at $D = 0.206\ h^{-1}$, large quantities of the *trpA* protein were produced. When the cells were grown at temperatures above 38°C, however, there was a rapid decrease in the number of colonies showing resistance to ampicillin, which indicated complete loss of the plasmid. The higher the temperature, and the greater the amount of *trpA* protein produced, the more rapid was the loss of plasmid. This use of genetically engineered organisms in two-stage fermentation processes may have wide application in waste-treatment processes. It could be applied as a continuous process as outlined above, or for producing organisms for use in immobilized fermentation systems. The problem of protecting genetically engineered strains from contaminating bacteria is similar to that encountered in most fermentations. It can be easily eliminated if the process can be operated as a sterile process, but this is normally too complex and expensive for waste treatment processes. Problems of contamination may be minimized by the use of a massive inoculum of the selective organism, or by using immobilized cell systems which retain the selected organisms in the fermenter at a high concentration. This approach has been used in fuel-alcohol fermentations [18]. It may be particularly invaluable in a process which is dependent upon mixed populations of organisms such as methane generation. Using this technique the relative abundance of different strains could be maintained at a more or less constant level irrespective of whether they had been subject to genetic manipulation or not.

8.3 GENETIC-ENGINEERING APPLICATIONS IN WASTE TREATMENT/EXPLOITATION

8.3.1 Introduction

As wastes generated by society continue to increase, both in volume and in complexity, the search for novel and efficient recycling processes gathers momentum and is motivated by the need both to conserve finite natural resources and to negate deleterious environmental impacts.

Since many sophisticated strategies, including physical, chemical and biological (and combinations of these), have been developed, it is perhaps not surprising that modern genetic-engineering techniques have increasingly been considered. The actual choice of strategy, however, depends on the distribution of the waste which may, for example, be contained at a specific point, such as a chemical plant or a food factory, or be dispersed over an area as a result of a pesticide application.

For the purposes of this discussion, microbiological intervention only will be considered with specific reference to selected targets for genetic-engineering application (Fig. 8.4). It must be recognized, however, that conventional approaches are likely to remain important for some time in recruiting micro-organisms [19] and, more particularly, interacting microbial associations [20], and as a consequence may sometimes obviate the need for genetic engineering.

Several different scenarios can be envisaged for the applications of genetic-manipulation techniques to the problems of waste treatment and exploitation.

8.3.1.1 Optimization of existing processes

Many fermentation processes are in operation to treat effluent and to exploit high-BOD by-products from the food and related industries. Most of these could be improved by manipulating the organism involved to obtain better yield, broader substrate specificity, increased tolerance to elevated temperatures, resistance to product inhibition, or other metabolic limitations. In most of these processes the producer-organism is well established. The improvement will be obtained by cloning new genes into a well-known and well-tested organism [21]. The use of genetic-engineering techniques to improve the yeast used in fuel-alcohol processes would be an example of this approach [22].

A second example is provided by work carried out on *Methylophilus methylotrophus*, which has been used for the production of microbial biomass from methanol. The carbon-conversion efficiency of this process was increased by 4–7 per cent by the introduction of the enzyme glutamate dehydrogenase from *E. coli* by using plasmid pSS 515, which has a broad host-range specificity as well as appropriate antibiotic-resistance markers [23].

8.3.1.2 Development of new processes

Many of the microbiological conversions which are known to occur could, if their performance could be improved, give rise to novel processes for the treatment of waste. The required improvement in performance may well be dependent upon the successful exploitation of gene-transfer technology. This approach would apply to such areas as:

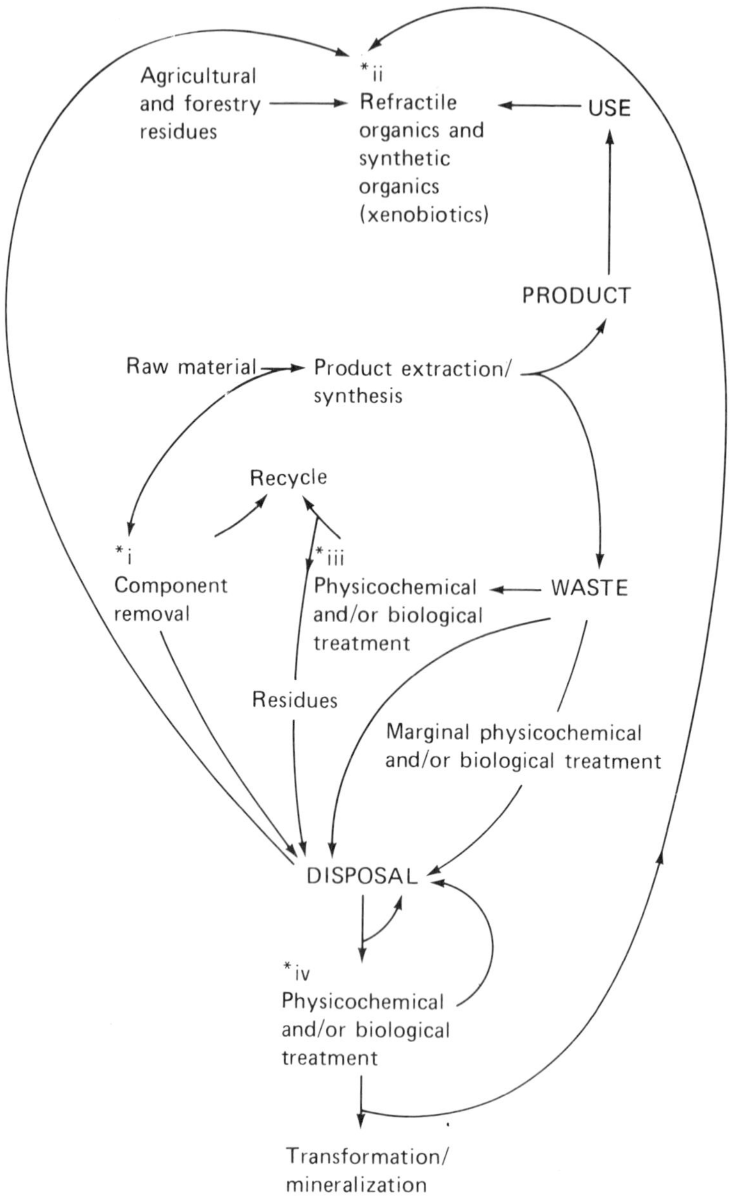

Fig. 8.4 — Generation and treatment/exploitation of wastes; i–iv denote target sites for exploitation by genetic-engineering intervention.

(a) lignin mobilization and utilization;
(b) detoxification of recalcitrant molecules; and
(c) assimilation and metabolism of toxic metals.

In some of these processes in which the required function is known to be associated with a single gene it is possible to transfer this function to an organism which is easy to handle and grow. However, other processes are dependent upon the functioning of complete metabolic pathways, or upon the integrity of complex cellular organelles. When this is the case the process must be carried out in the organism in question and the use of molecular genetics will be dependent upon the development of a suitable genetic system for the organism in question. The number of organisms which are amenable to genetic analysis has increased markedly in recent years and the development of broad host-range cloning vectors for Gram-negative bacteria opens up exciting prospects in this area [24]. A list of microbial functions which require a particular physiological or cellular environment has been compiled by Lehrbach and Timmis [25].

Table 8.1 — Bacterial properties whose expression requires particular physiological or metabolic cellular environments. From Lehbach and Timmis [25].

Property	Requirement for expression	Requirement Ppovided by
Sporulation	Differentiation pathway	Spore-forming bacilli
N_2 fixation in plant nodules	Plant root nodulation	*Rhizobium* sp.
Photosynthesis (chromatophores)	Photosynthetic apparatus, bacteria	Photosynthetic
Bacterial oxidation of sulphide minerals	Tolerance of low pH	*Thiobacillus ferro-oxidans*
Utilization of methane for growth	Complex membrane structure	Methylotrophs
Degradation of toxic aromatic compounds	Catabolic pathways, tolerance of compounds	*Pseudomonas* sp.
Methane production	Strict anaerobes with complex intermediary metabolism for the reduction of CO_2 to methane	Methanogens (Archaebacteria)
Ethanol production at high temperature	Growth at high temperature	Thermophilic bacteria
Production of acetone, butanol, isopropanol	Heterofermentative pathways for glucose	*Clostridium acetobutylicum*
Production of tumours in plants	Colonization and invasion of plant cells	*Agrobacterium tumefaciens*
Disease in fish	Invasion and growth in fish tissues	*Aeromonas* sp.

8.3.2 Agricultural and forestry residues

In the biosphere, catabolisms of natural polymers such as lignocelluloses, lignin, tannins and melanins, represent mineralization rate-limiting steps. Lignin, the second most abundant biopolymer on earth, mineralized by the carbon cycle [26], is composed of aromatic alcohols such as coniferyl, *p*-coumaryl and sinapyl, joined by intermonomer linkages (carbon–carbon and carbon-ether bonds) which are not directly hydrolysable [27]. In the presence of oxygen, catabolism proceeds comparatively slowly in environments such as soil [28,29], although the polymer itself does not serve as a carbon source. Under anoxic conditions, however, lignin is effectively biologically inert. Thus, gene manipulation to produce organisms capable of degrading the molecule under such conditions is a particular problem [30]. Additionally, consideration should be given to gene cloning for transformation of plant products such as cellulose to glucose, ethanol, butanol/acetone, and cellobiose; lignin to phenolics; and pectin to galacturonates and gluconates. Since a multiplicity of reactions is needed to convert heterogeneous natural materials to these metabolic intermediates and end products, genetic studies have already proved to be extremely valuable in identifying key elements in the catabolic pathways [31].

Although lignocellulosic materials have traditionally been pulped to remove lignin from the commercially important cellulose, this is an expensive process and represents a potential pollution threat. With recent developments in molecular biology, however, this potential may well be negated and, in addition, the economics of the process may be significantly improved [32].

8.3.3 Component removal

One possible area to obviate pollution potential, which, as yet, has received little attention, is the use of specific micro-organisms to effect component removal (Fig. 8.4) (i)) and, thus, prevent appearance of a waste. An example of this is the reduction in sulphur content of fuels [33], which in turn eliminates sulphur dioxide pollution of the air.

8.3.4 *In situ* waste treatment

Although microbiological methods are often preferred to chemical treatment on a cost basis [34], they are limited both by their narrow specificities [35] and their inability, in some instances, to reduce the concentrations of toxic chemicals to sufficiently low levels. Persistence of any chemical in the environment (Fig. 8.4(ii)), which has been attributed by Alexander [36] to the inability of micro-organisms to derive energy and cellular constitutents from the oxidative metabolism of these compounds, is in fact more likely if there are either no natural analogues or if natural analogues are rare [37]. The release of large quantities of synthetic compounds into the biosphere has, however, elicited a response from the indigenous microbial species in the form of the evolution of new degradative functions [34, 38] which may have included transfer of genetic material [39], since microbial populations and communities in nature appear to be capable of substantial movement of genes between both the same and different genera and species [40–42]. The evolution of an interacting microbial association may, in fact, be a much more important prerequisite to the evolution of a novel pathway than a series of evolutionary events occurring within one organism [42], and as a consequence development of microbial associations should precede genetic manipulation of a single strain [34].

Generally, the addition of xenobiotic molecules, which may be either directly toxic to biota or may be converted to toxic products [43, 44], results in a microbial population diversity which decreases as a result of species elimination, of the enrichment of particular successful populations [45], although selective toxicity can sometimes eliminate a dominant organism and lead to an increase in diversity.

In addition to the presence of appropriate species or microbial associations, degradation of a waste in any environment depends on the supply of appropriate nutrients [46]. For example, mineralization of crude oil in marine environments is limited by the supply of nitrogen and phosphorus, although oxygen supply is also critical [47]. Even within soil, this is a major consideration since the nutrient supply is discontinuous.

Karns *et al.* [37] identified three major problems in the soil ecosystem where the chemicals may be present in the vapour, adsorbed or aqueous/soluble phases [48]:

(1) the presence of innumerable carbon sources which might be utilized in preference to the xenobiotic molecules (or suppress induction of a degradative pathway);
(2) competition by the indigenous microflora for available minerals and growth factors [49]; and
(3) the inability of most natural microflora to degrade the introduced xenobiotics at appreciable rates to prevent accumulation.

In addition to the above, concentration of a specific molecule is critical since microbial degradation at low concentration may utilize a different degradative pathway than occurs with the same compound at high concentration [44]. Also, the *in situ* concentration may be too dilute to treat with a tailored culture but may still constitute a bio-hazard. One example of this is 2,3,7,8-tetrachlorodibenzo-*p*-dioxin (TCDD) at a concentration of 1 p.p.m. [37]. In general, for most organic chemicals, the concentration that is able to sustain microbial growth is found in the range 100–1000 mg/l [47].

Before selection of a species or association for adsorption or genetic manipulation [37,50–75] the ecological constraints must be carefully considered, since the species must proliferate under the particular environmental conditions [44,76] and, as a consequence, isolation must be made under ecologically relevant conditions [77]. For example, in nutritient-poor environments, oligotrophs [78] would be a better selection than eutrophic species. Similarly, starvation-susceptible strains, which would not survive once the chemical had been mineralized, would be of only limited value in environments receiving intermittent pollutants [76].

Selective advantage in a particular environment is linked with the growth of the introduced species on the substrate for which the genetic modification has been made. Thus, at low concentrations (p.p.b. or p.p.t.), it is essential that the mineralized xenobiotic is converted to microbial cells [79,80]. In the absence of this, genetically engineered strains may not function in nature because it is probably not feasible to introduce sufficient numbers of catabolically active cells to saturate the environment [76]. In this eventuality, however, the possibility exists that even if the host cell does not survive, the ‘foreign’ DNA or the altered DNA fragment will be passed to another organism in the environment which may be better adapted to growth within a particular ecological niche [81]. Finally, where the host does survive, it is likely that transfer or altered DNA will occur via, for example, transduction or conjugational-plasmid transfer [82]; thus, a fall in introduced species titre after contaminant mineralization [37] is not necessarily indicative of any serious ecological disturbance.

As a result of the development of adapted or genetically engineered strains, it is possible that chemical pesticides which could not normally be applied because of, for example, their toxicological effects, could then be used with application of the degrading species once the pest had been controlled [33]. Alternatively, chemicals could be specifically designed to minimize accumulation and potential environmental impact [47].

8.3.5 Contained waste treatment

For contained waste treatment (Fig. 9.4(iii)), the ecological constraints required for consideration are the same as those discussed above. In particular, attention must be paid to predation [44] of the micro-organisms inoculated and means should be found to minimize or overcome this stress, possibly by selection of grazing-resistent species, or by use of either floc-forming bacteria or species protected by sorption to surfaces [76]. Similarly, the pressures of competition between the introduced mutants and the indigenous organisms must be counteracted [68] which, according to Kobayashi [83], could be achieved by use of mutants prepared from organisms isolated from extreme environments analogous to the waste/wastewater. Finally, phage infections must be prevented, possibly by operation of treatment reactors under aseptic conditions [47].

Particular areas of opportunity for genetic intervention include:

(1) methanogenic fermentation to produce selected organic acids or other intermediates;
(2) rate enhancement;
(3) increased biochemical specificity;
(4) increased resistance to inhibitory or toxic response [84].
(5) versatile substrate uptake mechanisms;
(6) enhancement of enzyme production (thus increasing kinetic rates/process efficiency);
(7) simultaneous multiple substrate utilization (necessitating non-specific enzymes and/or multiple inducible enzymes with little or no catabolite repression); and
(8) methanogen resistance to air or dissolved oxygen [83].

However, before these applications could be fully effective, improved reactor technology is a major requirement [85].

Rittmann [86] specifically identified improvements in the biological treatment of municipal wastewaters::

(1) eliminate activated-sludge bulking;
(2) improve biofilm attachment;
(3) reduce oxygen limitations in aerobic processes;
(4) enhance phosphorus removal;
(5) biodegrade xenobiotic organics; and
(6) resist toxic upsets

And with wastewater sludges:

(1) eliminate anaerobic digester instability;
(2) enhance sludge dewaterability;

(3) make sludge composting occur more quickly; and
(4) eliminate heavy metals from sludge by genetic manipulation.

Commercial bacterial additives, which contain strains adapted and mutated for optimum efficiency under the conditions found in wastewater treatment systems, are, in fact, now available [87,88]. An important factor for consideration in all contained waste treatments, however, is species maintenance within the bioreactor, although, as discussed by Kobayashi [83], accidental release of genetically engineered species would not be a problem in environments where the organisms would find it difficult to survive. In situations where potential environmental impacts could possibly result, then inclusion of a repressed lethal gene would provide a safety factor. For example, in a situation in which the production of lysozyme is repressed by detergent, then the use of the organism in a sewage-treatment plant would not pose an environmental threat [33]. A second example of conditional lethality is the 'runaway plasmid' where the organism produces many copies of the plasmid and, hence, product, only when the cultural conditions are manipulated, resulting in a situation which is toxic to the cells. [33]. Complete environmental protection could, in fact, be effected by the use of immobilized enzymes, produced by gene cloning, although if the specific enzymes depended on cellular production and regeneration of co-factors such as NADH or NADPH their application might be less useful than intact cells [89].

8.3.5.1 Effluent from food processing

Most of the effluents from the food and beverage industry are rich in carbohydrates, proteins or other materials which provide a fertile substrate for microbial growth. These have been exploited for many years for the production of yeast and ethanol [90]. The use of molasses in a wide variety of fermentations is itself a sophisticated process for waste recycling. Since yeast, and to a lesser extent Zymomonas, have been subjected to extensive molecular biological studies and genetic investigation, it is worth discussing briefly some of the ways in which these organisms have been modified in an attempt to increase the efficiency of fermentations which utilize them.

One of the problems with brewer's and baker's yeast is that they are only capable of assimilating and fermenting a relatively limited number of carbohydrate substrates. In particular, most strains of yeast are not capable of growing on starch, and no brewer's or baker's yeast can utilize lactose. This is regrettable since many effluents from the food and dairy industry contain starch and lactose. Some traditional processes have endeavoured to circumvent this problem by utilizing two different yeasts. The simple process for the production of animal feed from starch waste used two yeasts: *Saccharomycopsis fibuligera* to generate amylase activity, and *Candida utilis* to produce fungal biomass [91]. Similarly, lactose-containing whey has been fermented to ethanol using either *Kluveromyces lactase* to provide β-galactosidase activity, or by using commercial preparations of β-galactosidase. The glucose and galactose generated were then fermented to ethanol by *Saccharomyces cerevisiae*. A considerable amount of work has been carried out to introduce amylolytic enzymes into brewer's and baker's yeast. Yeasts which have had amylase genes introduced from other organisms by genetic engineering are already available [92]. It is expected that genetically engineered yeast will be used in the brewing, distilling and food industries in the not too distant future. These same strains will be available for use in fuel-alcohol processes which are beginning to find application in certain areas of the world in utilization of low-grade cereals which are not acceptable for use in food products [93]. Similarly, strains of *Saccharomyces cerevisiae* are now available in which the ability to utilize lactose has been introduced by cloning in the β-galactosidase gene from *E. coli* [94]. Such strains may improve the economics of fermenting dairy effluents into ethanol or other industrial or food use.

The application of genetic-engineering techniques is not restricted to well-studied organisms such as yeast. The bacterium *Zymomonas mobilis* has been found to have several advantages over yeast as an organism for producing ethanol. In particular higher rates of ethanol production, higher yields and greater volumetric efficiencies have been obtained using *Z. mobilis*. However, it does suffer several limitations, especially in that it is only able to utilize a limited range of substrates [95]. In a relatively short time, however, genetic-engineering techniques have been developed which allow new physiological properties to be introduced into *Zymomonas*. Several plasmids have been transferred from *E. coli* into *Z. mobilis* and back from *Z. mobilis* to *E. coli* [96]. A larger number of plasmids which are native to *Zymomonas* have also been isolated. Although neither of these types of plasmids has proved ideal for producing stable transformers, a gluco-amylase activity from the fungus *Aspergillus niger* has been transferred to *Z. mobilis* using a combination of transformation and conjugation techniques.

The use of more conventional mutation and selection techniques has led to the development of improved strains which produce less hydrogen sulphide, less levan, an undesirable by-product of sucrose metabolism in *Z. mobilis*, improved flocculence properties and improved salt tolerance. This example clearly shows that once an organism has been selected as appropriate for a particular process, be it treatment of a waste or any other process, it is not necessarily difficult to develop genetic techniques to modify it and improve its process characteristics.

One property, however, which has been difficult to modify in both yeast and *Zymomonas* is the alcohol tolerance of the organism. In any process in which the product has to be removed by distillation, major savings arise if the concentration of the product can be increased. However, the final product concentration of ethanol fermentations, and also of the acetone/butanol fermentation, is limited by the toxicity of the product to the producer organism. Although it has proved difficult to obtain resistant mutants by direct mutation-selection techniques and to identify specific genes associated with alcohol toxicity, alcohol-resistant strains have been isolated. This was achieved using a fermentation technique which has been developed by Brown and Oliver [97] in which the yeast was grown at a steady state which gave a constant level of ethanol and a constant rate of release of carbon dioxide. The level of carbon dioxide was monitored and the rate of sugar-feed was controlled by the signal from the carbon dioxide detector such that an increase in carbon dioxide led to an increase in the sugar-feed rate. The technique is based on the assumption that growth is inhibited by ethanol and that if any mutant arises which is more ethanol-resistant, then growth rate will increase and carbon dioxide production will also increase. The increased dilution rate caused by the increased sugar-feed rate will then select for the new strain. This basic procedure may offer a generalized procedure for isolating strains with improved resistance to products or to other medium components, such as toxic metals in effluents. Once a gene for resistance can be identified it opens up the possibility of cloning the gene, identifying the gene product or enzyme involved, to lead to a greater understanding of the problem and also to an increasing level of expression of the key genes, possibly also leading to further improvements in the level of resistance [98].

Rapid advances have recently been made in the development of cloning systems in other bacteria and these may well find use in the treatment of wastes from the food and beverage industry. These include lactobacilli [99], which have the advantage of being widely accepted in the food industry, and *Pseudomonas* species [2,25,100], which may be used for the treatment of effluents containing lignocellulosic materials, or for the detoxification of the materials which have become contaminated with halo aromatic compounds. Using cloning techniques strains have been constructed which contain complete pathways for the degradation of chlorinated compounds such as 4-chlorobenzoate [25,75]. Progress has also been made in the development of cloning vectors for methanogens, so it is probable that strains of methanogens with improved process characteristics will become available in the future. If such strains lead to improved productivity in anaerobic digestion processes, they could become much more widespread in the treatment of wastes from the food and beverage industry.

8.3.5.2 Heavy metals

Micro-organisms may be used directly, in both *in situ* and contained waste-treatment systems, either to convert toxic forms into less toxic forms, or to accumulate the heavy metals [33,101]. The responsible genes, in many cases, are carried on transmissible bacterial plasmids [102]. In order that these capabilities might be fully exploited, however, it is essential that the basic biochemical and genetic bases of resistance to, and transformation of, heavy metals, are fully understood [103,104].

Alternatively, indirect control may be effected, either by the use of extracellular polymers [105] or immobilized bacterial cell walls [106], i.e. systems not containing viable microbial cells.

8.3.6 Final disposal to landfill

8.3.6.1 Catabolic processes

From refuse composition analysis [107–113] it is apparent that the semi-recalcitrant natural polymer content is increasing with time and is accompanied by an expanding array of xenobiotic molecules, the effective degradation of which is more likely under aerobic conditions and may involve, as discussed earlier, constitutive or inducible enzymes, co-metabolisms, plasmid transfer, mutations and other mechanisms of genetic transfer. In addition, it must be recognized that the changes in composition of refuse have resulted in C : N (organic fraction) ratios of >55 : 1, which may ultimately prove limiting to aerobic catabolism unless nitrogen supplementation is made, for example by addition of sewage sludge [114].

8.3.6.2 Refuse composting

With the search for novel and efficient recycling processes for solid wastes gathering momentum, it is perhaps not surprising that a traditional method such as composting has been re-examined. Development work in countries such as France, Italy, Japan, the Netherlands, the UK and the USA [109,115–118] has now resulted in the commercialization of refuse composting although, as discussed by Diaz *et al.* [114], the economics have not yet been proven in the USA. Composting of refuse is characterized by a period of intense microbial activity, in which labile molecules such as simple sugars are rapidly metabolized, followed by comparatively slow catabolism of natural polymers such as lignocelluloses, lignin, tannins and melanins. The latter reactions represent rate-limiting steps and, as such, possible targets for improvement by genetic manipulation.

8.3.6.3 Landfill leachate and treatment

An important requirement of all sites is protection of surface and groundwaters from landfill leachate. This may be effected either by provision of an impermeable barrier of natural or artificial material, or by microbiological [119–121] and physicochemical processes (attenuation) [122–124]. Landfill leachate is water which has percolated through emplaced waste, carrying with it soluble compounds and transportable organic and inorganic materials [125,126] together with micro-organisms such as bacteria and viruses [127–129]. It is generated as a consequence of a complex of first- and second-tier interacting factors [130]. Many chemicals, which may be classified as elements, radicals and organics (aliphatics, acyclics, terpenes and aromatics), have been detected in leachate from domestic refuse and co-disposal landfills [131], although the actual range is considerably extended when sites which have received major inputs of industrial wastes are also included [132].

The actual pollution potential of landfill leachate can be assessed by direct comparison with typical domestic sewage. Values reported by Garland and Mosher [126] suggested that concentrations of nitrogen, BOD, manganese, iron and chloride, were elevated by factors of 6, 50, 700, 500 and 13, respectively, in leachate. Alternatively, mass balance equations may be used to assess this potential [133].

Attenuation takes place through both vertical and lateral movement [114], and can occur in both the unsaturated [134] and saturated zones. In both instances, however, a critical factor is the rate of release of the initial flush of leachate, since high rates (or high concentrations) may exceed microbial enrichment rates and, as a consequence, only limited catabolism may result, particularly of xenobiotic molecules. Studies of saturated zone attentuation were made by Sutton and Barker [135], who showed that although molecules such as *n*-butyric acid, phenol, *p*-chlorophenol, dimethyl phthalate and chloride migrated through groundwater at essentially the same rate, they attenuated at different rates. Whether attenuation is in the unsaturated or saturated zones, it is possible that degradation of individual components may result in the formation of refractile compounds [122], low concentrations of which could migrate [136] long distances and ultimately threaten groundwater.

In order that the potential environmental impacts of both landfill leachate and generated products may be negated, then attention should perhaps be given to seeding unsaturated zones prior to the initiation of waste emplacement. Alternatively, collection [137,138] and treatment options must be considered.

Treatment strategies can include *in situ* exploitation of the refuse and the use of external facilities where the principles applied are the same as those for any industrial wastewater (Fig. 8.4(iv)). *In situ* treatment involves the use of the landfill as an anaerobic filter where the leachate is recycled back through the refuse mass [139–141]. The overall effect of this is to increase the moisture content of, and movement [142,143] through, the refuse mass which in turn promote microbial catabolic processes, particularly if provision is made for pH control and/or nutrient supplementation by sludge feeding [119,140] and/or microbial inoculation, and physicochemical mechanisms such as absorption, adsorption, ion exchange, volatilization, evaporation, dilution, filtration, chelation, complexation, precipitation, acid–base interactions, neutralization and oxidation–reduction interactions.

Soil application essentially utilizes the same principles as refuse mass recycle but may also include plant uptake [144].

8.3.6.4 Toxic and hazardous wastes and co-disposal

Where toxic and hazardous wastes are co-disposed with emplaced refuse, consideration must be given to pertinent factors such as waste type (solid, sludge, liquid), compatibility of reactive species [145], loading rate, evapotranspiration [146], leachability rate, refuse (type, quantity, density and age) [147], temperature and site water balance [148,149]. Although a maximum loading rate may be defined in relation to a known weight of refuse by which no inhibition of microbial catabolic processes, and thus no impairment of leachate quality, results, quantified rates, with few exceptions, are not yet available.

The treatment options are, however, essentially the same as for municipal refuse leachate, although consideration may well have to be given to the provision of specific inocula.

Reports by Kosson and Ahlert [141] and Venkataramani and Ahlert [150] showed that interacting microbial associations capable of catabolizing industrial landfill leachate could be enriched and isolated from soil and sewage sludge for use in land-based biological and closed culture treatments respectively. Use of genetically engineered or adapted single species in situations such as these would, however, be extremely difficult since resistance to other toxic chemicals would also have to be conferred. In addition, it is possible that where micro-organisms are able to survive in the presence of increased concentrations of heavy metals and other toxic chemicals, they may pick up plasmids carrying genes involved in detoxification, but the plasmids may also be carrying gene-coding for toxin production and other traits that are potentially harmful.

8.3.6.5 Landfill gas

Landfill gas may be regarded both as a liability and an energy-recovery opportunity [151,152]. Uncontrolled release of gas can result in problems such as odours [146,153], groundwater acidification [154] and reduced crop yields (including complete diebacks) [155]. Potential environmental impact problems, however, may be negated by either flaring [156] or soil sieving [146]. The use of low pore-size soils results in the trapping of reduced malodorants, which are then subsequently oxidized by aerobic microbial species prior to release. [153,157]. This represents a possible area for improvement by genetic manipulation, although, as discussed earlier, genetically engineered organisms often do not compete favourably with wild-type species.

REFERENCES

[1] Hood, L. E. (1984). Tools for genetic manipulation. In Omenn, G. S. and Hollaender, A. (eds) *Genetic Control of Environmental Pollutants*, Plenum Press, New York, 301.

[2] Omenn, G. S. and Hollaender, A. (1984). *Genetic Control of Environmental Pollutants*, Plenum Press, New York.

[3] Ball, C. (1984). *Genetics and Breeding of Industrial Micro-oganisms*, CRC Press.

[4] Avers, C. J. (1984). *Genetics*, Willard Grant Press, Boston.

[5] Old, R. W. and Primrose, S. B. (1985). *Principles of Gene Manipulation*, 3rd Edn, Blackwell Scientific, Oxford.

[6] Clarke, L. and Carbon, J. (1976). A colony bank containing synthetic Col E1 hybrid plasmids representative of the entire *E. coli* genome. *Cell,* **9**, 91.

[7] Klotz, L. C. (1983). Overproduction of proteins in recombinant organisms. *Ann. NY Acad. Sci.,* **413**, 1.

[8] Losick, R. (1982). Sporulation genes and their regulation. In: Dubnau, D. A. (ed.) *The Molecular Biology of the Bacilli,* Academic Press, New York, p. 179.

[9] Palva, M., Sarvas, M., Lehtovaara, D., Sibakov, M. and Kaariainen, L. (1982). Secretion of *Escherichia coli*, lactamase, from *Bacillus subtilis*, by the aid of amylase signal sequence. *Proc. Natl. Acad. Sci. USA* **79**, 5582.

[10] Palva, I., Pettersson, R. F., Kalkkinen, N., Lehtovaara, P., Sarvas, M., Soderlund, H., Takkinen, K. and Kaariainen, L. (1981). Nucleotide sequence of the promotor and NH_2 terminal signal peptide region of the α analase gene from *Bacillus amyloliqfuefaciens. Gene.,* **15**, 43–51.

[11] Glover, D. M. (1984). *Gene Cloning, The Mechanics of DNA Manipulation*, Chapman & Hall, London.

[12] Watson, J. D., Tooze, J. and Kurz, D. T. (1983). *Recombinant DNA, a Short Course,* Scientific American Books, New York.

[13] Maniatis, T., Fritsch, E. F. and Sambrook, J. (1982). *Molecular Cloning: a Laboratory Manual*, Cold Spring Harbor.

[14] Godwin, D. and Slater, J. H. (1979). Influence of growth environment on the stability of a drug resistance plasmid in *Escherichia coli* K.12. *J. Gen. Microbiol.,* **111**, 201.

[15] Imanaka, T. and Aiba, S. (1981). A perspective on the application of genetic engineering: stability of recombinant plasmid, *Am. NY Acad. Sci.,* **369**, 1.

[16] Nugent, M. E., Primrose, S. B. and Tacon, W. C. A. (1983). The stability of recombinant DNA. *Devel. Ind. Microbiol.,* **24**, 271.

[17] Siegel, R. and Ryu, D. D. Y. (1985). Kinetic study of instability of recombinant plasmid pPL c23trp A1 in *E. coli* using two stage continuous culture systems. *Biotechnol. Bioeng.,* **27**, 28.

[18] Marwaha, S. S. and Kennedy, J. F. (1984). Alcohol production from whey permeate by immobilised and free cells of *kluyveromyces marxianus* UCYC179. *Process Biochem.,* April, 79.

[19] Higgins, I. J., Best, D. J., MacKinnon, G. and Warner, P. J. (1984).

Recruitment of novel reactions: examples and strategies. In: Klug, M. J. and Reddy, C. A. (eds) *Current Perspectives in Microbiological Ecology*, ASM, Washington, p. 629.

[20] Senior, E. and Balba, M. T. M. Landfill biotechnology. In: Wise, D. L. (ed.) *Biotechnology Applied to Environmental Problems*, CRC Press, in press.

[21] Flannery, R. J. and Steinschneider, A. (1983). Fermentation economics in relation to genetic engineering. *Biotechnology,* **1**, 773.

[22] Stewart, G. G., Panchar, C. J. and Russell, I. (1983). Current developments in the genetic manipulation of brewing yeast strains—a review. *J. Inst. Brew.* **89**, 170.

[23] Windass, J. D., Worsley, M. J., Pioli, E. M., Pioli, D., Barth, R. T., Atherton, K. T., Dart, E. C., Byrom, D., Powell, K. and Senior, P. J. (1980). Improved conversion of methanol to single cell protein by *Methylophilus methylotrophus*. *Nature* **287**, 396.

[24] Tait, R. C., Timothy, J. C., Lundquist, R. C., Hagiya, M., Rodrigiez, R. L. and Kado, C. I. (1983). Construction and characterisation of a versatile broad host range DNA cloning system for gram-negative bacteria. *Biotechnology,* **1**, 269.

[25] Lehrbach, P. R. and Timmis, K. N. (1983). Genetic analysis and manipulation of catabolic pathways in *Pseudomonas*. In: Phelps, C. P. and Clarke, P. H. (eds) *Biotechnology*, Biochemical Society, London, p. 191.

[26] Harkin, J. M. (1967). Lignin: natural polymeric product of phenol oxidation. In: Battersby, A. R. and Taylor, A. I. (eds) *Oxidative Coupling of Phenols*, Marcel Dekker, p. 243.

[27] Zeikus, J. G. (1981). Lignin metabolism and the carbon cycle: polymer biosynthesis, biodegradation and environmental recalcitrance. *Adv. Microb. Ecol.,* **51**, 211.

[28] Hackett, W. F., Connors, W. J., Kirk, T. K. and Zeikus, J. G. (1977). Microbial decomposition of synthetic ^{14}C-labelled lignins in nature: lignin biodegradation in a variety of natural materials. *Appl. Environ. Microbiol.,* **33**, 43.

[29] Crawford, R. L. (1981). *Lignin Biodegradation and Transformation*, Wiley.

[30] Norrman, J. (1983). Anaerobic fermentation. In: Sidwick, J. M. (ed.) *Environmental Biotechnology: Future Prospects,* Vol. II, Commission of European Communities, FAST, p. 17.

[31] Brown, R. D., Jr and Gritzali, M. (1984). Microbial enzymes and lignocellulose utilization. In: Omenn, G. S. and Hollaender, A. (eds) *Genetic Control of Environmental Pollutants,* Plenum Press, New York, p. 239.

[32] Paterson, A., McCarthy, A. J. and Broda, P. (1984). The application of molecular biology to lignin degradation. In: Grainger, J. M. and Lynch, J. M. (eds) *Microbiological Methods for Environmental Biotechnology*, Academic Press, New York, p. 33.

[33] Levin, M. and Segal, M. (1984). Engineering organisms to survive: introduction. In: Omenn, G. S. and Hollaender, A. (eds) *Genetic Control of Environmental Pollutants,* Plenum Press, New York, p. 91.

[34] Johanides, V. (1983). Biodegradation of recalcitrant molecules. In: Sidwick,

J. M. (ed.) *Environmental Biotechnology: Future Prospects,* Vol. II, Commission of European Communities, FAST, p. 153.
[35] Leisinger, T. (1983). Microbial degradation of recalcitrant compounds. In: Sidwick, J. M. (ed.) *Environmental Biotechnology: Future Prospects,* Vol. II, Commission of European Communities, FAST, p. 119.
[36] Alexander, M. (1981). Biodegradation of chemicals of environmental concern. *Science* **211**, 132.
[37] Karns, J. S., Kilbane, J. J., Chatterjee, D. K. and Chakrabarty, A. M. (1984). Microbial biodegradation of 2,3,5-trichlorophenoxyacetic acid and chlorophenols. In: Omenn, G. S. and Hollaender, A. (eds) *Genetic Control of Environmental Pollutants,* Plenum Press, New York, p. 3.
[38] Chakrabarty, A. M. (1978). Molecular mechanisms in the biodegradation of environmental pollutants. *ASM News,* **44**, 687.
[39] Clarke, P. H. (1984). Evolution of new phenotypes. In: Klug, M. J. and Reddy, C. A. (eds) *Current Perspectives in Microbial Ecology*, ASM, Washington, p. 71.
[40] Weinberg, S. R. and Strotzky, G. (1972). Conjugation and genetic recombination of *Escherichia coli* in soil. *Soil Biol. Biochem.,* **4**, 171.
[41] Graham, J. B. and Istock, C. A. (1978). Genetic exchange in *Bacillus subtilis* in soil. *Mol. Gen.,* **166**, 287.
[42] Slater, J. H. (1984). Genetic interactions in microbial communities. In: Klug, M. J. and Reddy, C. A. (eds) *Current Perspectives in Microbial Ecology*, ASM, Washington, p. 87.
[43] Hedgement, G. D. (1972). The evolution of metabolic pathways in bacteria. In: Gunsalus, I. C. (ed.) *Degradation of Synthetic Organic Molecules in the Biosphere*, National Academy of Sciences, Washington, p. 56.
[44] Bourquin, A. W. (1984). Biodegradation in the estaurine–marine environments of the genetically altered microbe. In: Omenn, G. S. and Hollaender, A. (eds) *Genetic Control of Environmental Pollutants,* Plenum Press, New York, p. 97.
[45] Atlas, R. M. (1984). Use of microbial diversity measurements to assess environmental stress. In: Klug, M. J. and Reddy, C. A. (eds) *Current Perspectives in Microbial Ecology*, ASM, Washington, p. 540.
[46] Slater, J. H. and Somerville, H. J. (1979). Microbial aspects of waste treatment with particular attention to the degradation of organic compounds. In: Bull, A. T., Ellwood, D. C. and Ratledge, C. (eds) *Microbial Technology: Current State, Future Prospects,* SGM Symp. 29, p. 221.
[47] Salkinoja-Salonen, M. (1983). The behaviour of chloroorganic chemicals in the environment and their biological treatment. In: Sidwick, J. M. (ed.) *Environmental Biotechnology: Future Prospects,* Vol. II, Commission of the European Communities, FAST, p. 127.
[48] Middleton, A. C. (1984). Land disposal and spill site environments. In: Omenn, G. S. and Hollaender, A. (eds) *Genetic Control of Environmental Pollutants,* Plenum Press, New York, p. 137.
[49] Sayler, G. S., Kong, H.-L. and Shields, M. S. (1984). Plasmid-mediated biodegradative fate of monohalogenated biphenyls in facultatively anaerobic

sediments. In: Omenn, G. S. and Hollaender, A. (eds) *Genetic Control of Environmental Pollutants,* Plenum Press, New York, p. 117.
[50] Chakrabarty, A. M., Chou, G. and Gunsalus, I.C. (1973). Genetic regulation of octane dissimilation plasmid in *Pseudomonas. Proc. Natl. Acad. Sci. USA* **70**, 1137.
[51] Williams, P. A. and Murray, K. (1974). Metabolism of benzoate and the methyl-benzoates by *Pseudomonas putida (arvilla)* mt-2: evidence for the existence of a TOL plasmid. *J. Bact.,* **120**, 416.
[52] Worsey, M. J. and Williams, P. A. (1975). Metabolism of toluene and xylenes by *Pseudomonas putida (arvilla)* mt-2: evidence for a new function of the TOL plasmid. *J. Bact.,* **124**, 7.
[53] Friello, D. A., Mylroie, J. R. and Chakrabarty, A. M. (1976). Use of genetically engineered multi-plasmid micro-organisms for rapid degradation of fuel hydrocarbons. In: Sharpley, J. M. and Kaplan, A. M. (eds) *Proc. 3rd Int. Biodeg. Symp.,* Applied Science, London, p. 205.
[54] Senior, E., Bull, A. T. and Slater, J. H. (1976). Enzyme evolution in a microbial community growing on the herbicide Dalapon. *Nature,* **263**, 476.
[55] Chakrabarty, A. M., Friello, D. A. and Bopp, L. H. (1978). Transposition of plasmid DNA segments specifying hydrocarbon degradation and their expression in various micro-organisms, *Proc. Natl. Acad. Sci. USA,* **75**, 3109.
[56] Reineke, W. and Knackmuss, H. J. (1979). Construction of haloaromatic utilizing bacteria. *Nature* (London), **277**, 385.
[57] Bull, A. T. (1980). Biodegradation: some attitudes and strategies of micro-organisms and microbiologists. In: Ellwood, D. C., Hedger, J. N., Latham, M. J., Lynch, J. M., and Slater, J. H. (eds), Academic Press, New York, p. 107.
[58] Kellogg, S. T., Chatterjee, D. K. and Chakrabarty, A. M. (1981). Plasmid-assisted molecular breeding: new technique for enhanced biodegradation of persistent toxic chemicals. *Science* **214**, 1133.
[59] Kunz, D. A. and Chapman, P. J. (1981). Catabolism of pseudocumene and 3-ethyltoluene by *Pseudomonas putida (arvilla)* mt-2: evidence for new functions of the TOL (pWWO) plasmid. *J. Bact.,* **146**, 179.
[60] Vandenbergh, P. A., Olsen, R. H. and Colarnotolo, J. F. (1981). Isolation and genetic characterisation of bacteria that degrade chloroaromatic compounds. *Appl. Environ. Microbiol.,* **42**, 737.
[61] Chatterjee, D. K. and Chakrabarty, A. M. (1982). Genetic rearrangements in plasmids specifying total degradation of chlorinated benzoic acids. *Mol. Gen. Genet.,* **188**, 279.
[62] Chatterjee, D. K., Kilbane, J. J. and Chakrabarty, A. M. (1982). Biodegradation of 2,4,5-trichlorophenoxyacetic acid in soil by a pure culture of *Pseudomonas cepacia. Appl. Environ. Microbiol.,* **44**, 514.
[63] Furakawa, K. and Chakrabarty, A. M. (1982). Involvement of plasmids in the total degradation of chlorinate biphenyls. *Appl. Environ. Microbiol.,* **44**, 619.
[64] Jeenes, D. J. and Williams, P. A. (1982). Excision and integration of degradative pathway genes from TOL plasmid pWWO. *J. Bact.,* **150**, 188.

[65] Jeenes, D. J., Reineke, W., Knackmuss, H. J. and Williams, P. A. (1982). TOL plasmid pWWO in constructed halobenzoate-degrading *Pseudomonas* strains: enzyme regulation and DNA structure. *J. Bact.*, **150**, 180.
[66] Johnston, J. B. and Robinson, S. G. (1982). Opportunities for development of new detoxification processes through genetic engineering. In: Exner, J. H. (ed.) *Detoxification of Hazardous Waste*, Ann Arbor Science, p. 301.
[67] Kilbane, J. J., Chatterjee, D. K.. Karns, J. S., Kellog, S. T. and Chakrabarty, A. M. (1982). Biodegradation of 2,4,5-trichlorophenoxyacetic acid by a pure culture of *Pseudomonas cepacia*. *Appl. Environ. Microbiol.*, **44**, 72.
[68] Pierce, G. (1982). Development of genetically engineered micro-organisms to degrade hazardous organic compounds. In: Sweeny, T. C., Sykes, R. M. and Sproul. O. J. (eds) *Hazardous Waste Management for the 80s*, Ann Arbor Science, p. 431.
[69] Reineke, W., Jeenes, D. J., Williams, P. A. and Knackmuss, H. J. (1982). TOL plasmid pWWO in constructed halobenzoate-degrading *Pseudomonas* strains: prevention of meta pathway. *J. Bact.*, **150**, 195.
[70] Schwien, U. and Schmidt, E. (1982). Improved degradation of monochlorophenols by a constructed strain. *Appl. Environ. Microbiol.*, **44**, 33.
[71] Chakrabarty, A. M., Karns, J. S., Kilbane, J. J. and Chatterjee, D. K. (1983). Selective evolution of genes for enhanced degradation of persistent, toxic chemicals. In: Arber, W., Peacock, W. J., Illmensee, K. and Starlinger, P. (eds) *Genetic Manipulation: Impact on Man and Society,* ICSU Press.
[72] Kilbane, J. J., Chatterjee, D. K. and Chakrabarty, A. M. (1983). Detoxification of 2,4,5-trichlorophenoxyacetic acid from contaminated soil by *Pseudomonas cepacia*. *Appl. Environ. Microbiol.*, **45**, 1697.
[73] Beringer, J. E. and Hirsch, P. R., (1984). The role of plasmids in microbial ecology. In: Klug, M. J. and Reddy, C. A. (eds) *Current Perspectives in Microbial Ecology*, ASM, Washington, p. 63.
[74] Eaton, R. W. and Timms, K. N. (1984). Genetics of xenobiotic degradation. In: Klug, M. J. and Reddy, C. A. (eds) *Current Perspectives in Microbial Ecology*, ASM, Washington, p. 694.
[75] Weightman, A. J., Don, R. H., Lehrbach, P. R. and Timmis, K. N. (1984). The identification and cloning of genes encoding haloaromatic catabolic enzymes and the construction of hybrid pathways for substrate mineralization. In: Omenn, G. S. and Hollaender, A. (eds) *Genetic Control of Environmental Pollutants,* Plenum Press, New York, p. 47.
[76] Alexander, M. (1984). Ecological constraints on genetic engineering. In: Omenn, G. S. and Hollaender, A. (eds) *Genetic Control of Environmental Pollutants,* Plenum Press, New York, p. 151.
[77] Alexander, B. and Harper, E. (1984). Pollution control in practice. In: Lack, T. J. (ed.) *Environmental Protection: Standards, Compliance and Costs,* Ellis Horwood, p. 198.
[78] Poindexter, J. S. (1981). Oligotrophy: fast and famine existence. *Adv. Microb. Ecol.*, **5**, 63.
[79] Larson, R. J. (1980). Role of biodegradation kinetics in predicting environmental fate. In: Maki, A. W., Dickson, K. L. and Cairns, J. (eds) *Biotransformation and Fate of Chemicals in the Aquatic Environment,* ASM,

Washington, p. 67.
[80] Subba-Rao, R. V., Rubin, H. E. and Alexander, M. (1982). Kinetics and extent of mineralization of organic compounds at trace levels in freshwater and sewage. *Appl. Environ. Microbiol.*, **43**, 1139.
[81] Curtiss, R., III (1976). Genetic manipulation of micro-organisms: potential benefits and biohazards. *Ann. Rev. Microbiol.*, **30**, 307.
[82] Freter, R. (1984). Factors affecting conjugal plasmid transfer in natural bacterial communities. In: Klug, M. J. and Reddy, C. A. (eds) *Current Perspectives in Microbial Ecology*, ASM, Washington, p. 105.
[83] Kobayashi, H. A. (1984). Application of genetic engineering to industrial waste/wastewater treatment. In: Omenn, G. S. and Hollaender, A. (eds) *Genetic Control of Environmental Pollutants,* Plenum Press, New York, p. 195.
[84] Patterson, J. W. (1984). Perspective on opportunities for genetic engineering application in industrial pollution control. In: Omenn, G. S. and Hollaender, A. (eds) *Genetic Control of Environmental Pollutants,* Plenum Press, New York, p. 187.
[85] Cooney, C. L. (1983). Bioreactors: design and operation. *Science* **219**, 728.
[86] Rittmann, B. E. (1984). Needs and strategies for genetic control: municipal wastes. In: Omenn, G. S. and Hollaender, A. (eds) *Genetic Control of Environmental Pollutants,* Plenum Press, New York, p. 215.
[87] Jähnig, C. (1980). Neue Leistungsfähige Mikroorganismen Optimieren Biologische Kläranlagen. *Chemie-Technick,* **9**, 497.
[88] Wheatley, A. D. (1983). Opportunities for the recovery of materials from effluents. In: Sidwick, J. M. (ed.) *Environmental Biotechnology: Future Prospects*, Vol. II, Commission of European Communities, FAST, p. 16.
[89] Cheetham, P. S. J. and Bucke, C. (1984). Immobilisation of microbial cells and their use in waste water treatment. In: Grainger, J. M. and Lynch, J. M. (eds) *Microbiological Methods for Environmental Biotechnology*, Academic Press, New York, p. 219.
[90] Reed, G. and Peppler, J. J. (1973). *Yeast Technology*, AVI Publishing Co., Westport, Connecticut, USA.
[91] Gray, P. and Berry, D. R. (1980). The production of feedstuff biomass from liquid organic wastes by fermentation. In: Bewick, M. W. M. (ed.) *Handbook of Organic Waste Conversion*, Van Nostrand Reinhold, New York, p. 339.
[92] Innis, M. A., Holland, M. J., McCabe, P. C., Cole, E., Wittman, V. P., Tal, R., Watt, K. W. K., Gelfand, D. H., Holland, J. P. and Meade, J. H. (1985). Expression: glycosylatin and secretion of *Aspergillus* glycoamylase by *S. cerevisiae. Science* **228**, 21.
[93] Lyons, T. P. (1981). In: *Gasohol, a Step to Energy Independence*, Alltech Technical Publications, Lexington, Kentucky.
[94] Dickson, R. C. (1980). Expression of a foreign eukaryotic gene in *Saccharomyces cerevisiae*: galactosidase from *Kluyveromyces lactis. Gene,* **10**, 347.
[95] Skotnicki, M. L., Warr, R. G., Goodman, A. E., Lee, K. J. and Rogers, P. L. (1983). High productivity alcohol fermentations using *Zymomonas mobilis.* In: Phelps, C. F. and Clarke, P. H. (eds) *Biotechnology,* Biochemical Society,

London, p. 53.
[96] Skotnicki, M. L., Lee, K. J., Tribe, D. E. and Rogers, P. L. (1982). Genetic engineering of micro-organisms for chemicals. Hollaender, A. (ed.), Plenum Press, New York, p. 271.
[97] Brown, S. W. and Oliver, S. G. (1982). Isolation of ethanol tolerant mutants of yeast by continuous selection. *Eur. J. Appl. Microbiol Biotechnol.*, **16**, 119.
[98] Fogel, S. and Welch, J. W. (1982). Tandem gene amplification mediates copper resistance in yeast. *Proc. Natl. Acad. Sci. USA*, **79**, 5342.
[99] Gasson, M. J. (1983). Genetic transfer systems in lactic acid bacteria. *Antonie van Leeuwenhoek*, **49**, 275–282.
[100] Knackmuss, H. (1983). Xenobiotic degradation in industrial sewage, haloaromatics as target substrates. In: Phelps, C. P. and Clarke, P. H. (eds) *Biotechnology*, Biochemical Society, London, p. 173.
[101] Silver, S. and Misra, T. K. (1984). Bacterial transformations of and resistances to heavy metals. In: Omenn, G. S. and Hollaender, A. (eds) *Genetic Control of Environmental Pollutants*, Plenum Press, New York, p. 23.
[102] Summers, A. O. (1984). Genetic adaptations involving heavy metals. In: Klug, M. J. and Reddy, C. A. (eds) *Current Perspectives in Microbial Ecology*, ASM, Washington, p. 94.
[103] Smith, D. H. (1967). R-factors mediate resistance to mercury, nickel and cobalt. *Science* **156**, 1114.
[104] Novik, R. P. and Roth, C. (1968). Plasmid linked resistance to inorganic salts in *Staphylococcus aureus*. *J. Bact.*, **95**, 1335.
[105] Lester, J. N., Sterritt, R. M., Rudd, T. and Brown, M. J. (1984). Assessment of the role of bacterial extracellular polymers in controlling metal removal in biological waste water treatment. In: Grainger, J. M. and Lynch, J. M. (eds) *Microbiological Methods for Environmental Biotechnology*, Academic Press, New York, p. 197.
[106] Beveridge, T. J. (1984). Mechanisms of the binding of metallic ions to bacterial walls and the possible impact on microbial ecology. In: Klug, M. J. and Reddy, C. A. (eds) *Current Perspectives in Microbial Ecology*, ASM, Washington, p. 601.
[107] Thomé-Kozmiensky, K. J. (1977). Ubersicht uber die moglichkeiten und alternativen des material recycling. *Abfallwirtschaft an der Technischen Universitat Berlin*, **1**, 5.
[108] Humphrey, A. E. (1978). Utilisation of solid wastes by thermal processes. *J. Appl. Chem. Biotechnol.*, **28**, 289.
[109] Albonetti, S. G. and Massari, G. (1979). Microbiological aspects of a municipal waste composting system. *European J. Appl. Microbiol. Biotechnol.*, **7**, 91.
[110] Raveh, A. and Avnimelch, Y. (1979). Leaching of pollutants from sanitary landfill models. *J. Water Pollut. Control Fed.*, **51**, 2705.
[111] Marchant, A. J. (1981). Practical aspects of landfill management of landfill gas—a local authority view. In: *Landfill Gas Symposium*, Harwell, Paper 7.
[112] Hanashima, M., Yamasaki, K., Matsufuji, Y., Tanaka, M. and Ikeguchi, T. (1983). Technological progress of internal reclamation in Japan. In: *Reclamation 83 Papers*, Industrial Seminars Ltd, p. 327.

[113] Parker, A. (1983). Behaviour of wastes in landfill-methane generation. In: Holmes, J. R. (ed.) *Practical Waste Management*, Wiley, Ch. 8.
[114] Diaz, L. F., Savage, G. M. and Golueke, C. G. (1982). *Resource Recovery from Municipal Solid Wastes, Volume II Final Processing,* CRC Press.
[115] Albonetti, S. G. and Massari, G. (1979). Microbiological aspects of a municipal waste composting system. *European J. Appl. Microbiol. Biotechnol.,* **7**, 91.
[116] Kubota, H., Matsuda, S. and Sasaki, M. (1984). Composting has promising future in Japan. *BioCycle,* **25**, 28.
[117] White, P. T. (1983). The fascinating world of trash. *National Geographic,* **163**, 424.
[118] Diaz, L. F. and Golueke, C. G. (1984). Co-composting refuse and sludge. *BioCycle,* **25**, 21.
[119] Mather, J. D. (1977). Attenuation and control of landfill leachates. *J. Inst. Solid Wastes Management,* **67**, 362.
[120] Williams, G. M. (1982). Studies of leachate attenuation in intergranular aquifers. In: *Landfill Leachate Symposium*, Harwell, Paper 7.
[121] Gerhardt, R. A. (1984). Landfill leachate migration and attenuation in the unsaturated zone in layered and nonlayered coarse-grained soils. *Ground Wat. Monit. Rev.*, Spring, 56.
[122] Tester, D. J. and Harker, R. J. (1982). Groundwater pollution investigations in the Great Ouse basin. II Solid waste disposal. *Water Pollut. Control,* **81**, 308.
[123] Bagchi, A. (1983). Design of natural attenuation landfills. *J. Envir. Eng.,* **109**, 892.
[124] Campbell, D. J. V., Parker, A., Rees, J. F. and Ross, C. A. M. (1983). Attenuation of potential pollutants in landfill leachate by Lower Greensand. *Waste Management Res.,* **1**, 31.
[125] Ho, S., Boyle, W. C. and Ham, R. K. (1974). Chemical treatment of leachates from sanitary landfills. *J. Water Pollut. Control Fed.,* **46**, 1776.
[126] Garland, G. A. and Mosher, D. C. (1975). Leachate effects from improper land disposal. *Waste Age,* **6**, 42.
[127] Jackson, A. G. and Streng, D. R. (1976). Gas and leachate generation in various solid waste environments. In: Genetelli, E. J. and Cirello, J. (eds) *Gas and Leachate from Landfill: Formation, Collection and Treatment*, EPA-600/9-76-004, p. 83.
[128] Harris, R. C. (1983). Landfill leachate generation. A water authority viewpoint. *Wastes Management,* **73**, 606.
[129] Strauch, D., Münz, H. and Hammel, E. (1984). Hygienisch–bakteriologische einflüsse auf sickerwasser und unterstromgrundwasser von mülldeponien durch einbau von klärschlamm. *GWF-Wasser/Abwasser,* **125**, 427.
[130] Senior, E. (1987). Design, control and exploitation of the landfill bioreactor. In: Forster, C. F. and Wase, D. A. J. (eds) *Environmental Biotechnology*, Ellis Horwood, in Press.
[131] Senior, E. and Balba, M. T. M. (1984). The use of single stage and multi-stage fermenters to study the metabolism of xenobiotic and naturally-occurring molecules by interacting microbial associations. In: Grainger, J. M. and

Lynch, J. M. (eds) *Microbiological Methods for Environmental Biotechnology*, Academic Press, New York, p. 275.
[132] Reinard, M., Goodman, N. L. and Barker, J. F. (1984). Occurrence and distribution of organic chemicals in two landfill leachate plumes. *Environ. Sci. Technol.*, **18**, 953.
[133] Naylor, J. A., Rowland, C. D., Young, C. P. and Barber, C. (1978). The investigation of landfill sites. *Water Research Centre Technical Report*, 91.
[134] Robinson, H. D. and Lucas, J. L. (1985). Leachate attenuation in the unsaturated zone beneath landfills; instrumentation and monitoring of a site in Southern England. *Water Sci. Technol.*, **17**, 477.
[135] Sutton, P. A. and Barker, J. F. (1985). Migration and attenuation of selected organics in a sandy aquifer—a natural gradient environment. *Ground Water*, **23**, 10.
[136] Sudicky, E. A., Cherry, J. A. and Frind, E. O. (1983). Migration of contaminants in groundwater at a landfill: a case study. 4. A natural-gradient dispersion test. *J. Hydrol.*, **63**, 81.
[137] Wong, J. (1977). The design of a system for collecting leachate from a lined landfill site. *Water Resour. Res.*, **134**, 404.
[138] McDougall, W. J., Fusco, R. A. and O'Brien, R. P. (1980). Containment and treatment of the Love Canal landfill leachate. *J. Water Pollut. Control Fed.*, **52**, 2914.
[139] Holmes, R. (1980). The water balance method of estimating leachate production from landfill sites. *Solid Wastes*, Jan., 20.
[140] Tittlebaum, M. E. (1982). Organic carbon content stabilisation through landfill leachate recirculation. *J. Water Pollut. Control Fed.*, **54**, 428.
[141] Kosson, D. S. and Ahlert, R. C. (1984). *In situ* and on-site biodegradation of industrial landfill leachate. *Envrion. Progress*, **3**, 176.
[142] Pohland, F. G. and Kang, S. J. (1975). Sanitary landfill stabilisation with leachate recycle and residual treatment. *A.I.Ch.E. Symp. Ser.*, **145**, 308.
[143] Barber, C., (1983). Treatability and treatment of leachate from domestic wastes in landfills. *Reclaimation 83 Papers*, Industrial Seminars Ltd, p. 362.
[144] Scott, M. P. (1982). Options for the treatment of municipal and chemical waste leachate. *Publ. Hlth., Engr.*, **10**, 119.
[145] Pearce, P. (1983). Landfilling: a long-term option for hazardous waste disposal? *UNEP Industry and Environmental Special Issue*, 57.
[146] Young, P. J. and Parker, A. (1983). The identification and possible environmental impact of trace gases and vapours in landfill gas. *Waste Management Res.*, **1**, 213.
[147] Blakey, N. C. (1984). Behaviour of arsenical wastes co-disposal with domestic solid wastes. *J. Water Pollut. Control Fed.*, **56**, 69.
[148] Marriott, J. (1981). Some practical aspects of control of leachate from landfill sites. *Solid Wastes*, **71**, 513.
[149] Campbell, D. J. V. (1983). Understanding water balance in landfill sites. *Wastes Management*, **73**, 594.
[150] Venkataramani, E. S. and Ahlert, R. C. (1985). Acclimated mixed microbial responses to organic species in industrial landfill leachate. *J. Hazard. Mater.*,

10, 1.

[151] Lucas, J. L. and White, G. C. (1983). Design and instrumentation of a semi-permeable attentuation blanket beneath a domestic waste landfill. In *Reclamation 83 Papers*, Industrial Seminars Ltd, p. 299.

[152] Bogardus, E. R. (1984). Should you recover landfill gas?, *BioCycle,* **25**, 48.

[153] Baker, J. M., Peters, C. J., Perry, R. and Knight, C. P. V. (1984). Odour problems associated with solid waste disposal. *Publ. Hlth. Eng.,* **12**, 115.

[154] Farquhar, G. J. and Rovers, F. A. (1973). Gas production during refuse decomposition. *Water, Air and Soil Pollut.,* **2**, 483.

[155] Parry, G. D. R. (1981). After use of landfill sites. In: *Landfill Gas Symposium,* Harwell, Paper 8.

[156] Knop, R. (1984). Use of landfill gas as an automotive fuel. In: Ferrero, G. L., Ferranti, M. P. and Naveau, H. (eds) *Proc. Int. Symp., Anaerobic Digestion and Carbohydrate Hydrolysis of Waste*, Luxembourg, Elsevier, p. 405.

[157] Bohn, H. L. (1975). Soil and compost filters of malodorant gases. *J. Air Pollut. Control Assoc.,* **25**, 953.

9

Bioleaching

G. Ferraiolo and M. Del Borghi
University of Genova, Italy

9.1 INTRODUCTION

Bacterial leaching, or bioleaching, adds a biological dimension to general processes which have been in use for many years. Conventional leaching has been used for a wide range of industrial processes ranging from hydrometallurgy to the manufacture of cane sugar. As applied in the chemical and process industries, it is a liquid/solids extraction process in which the solid phase is either soluble, or becomes soluble through physicochemical mechanisms, in a suitable liquid solvent from which it is later removed for further processing. With bioleaching, solubilization occurs by the action of micro-organisms. The process kinetics and the extraction techniques vary according to the microbial population and state of the mineral material, as will be described later.

Bioleaching has become an advancd multi-disciplinary process involving, *inter alia*, chemistry, microbiology, and chemical and process engineering. It is a biotechnological innovation with a growing number of environmental reasons for its application. This chapter describes the biological principles involved in the main applications, the techniques used in practice, and finally assesses the relative economics of the process.

9.2 HISTORICAL PERSPECTIVE

The first bioleaching application was almost two centuries ago. In the eighteenth century copper was extracted from its ore in Rio Tinto, Spain, almost certainly by the hydrosolubilization of the metal. This was probably achieved under the influence of bacteria, but the mechanisms were completely unknown at the time. The high efficiency of the process was attributed to an 'undetectable' and 'mysterious' quality attaching either to the pyrites ore itself, or to the local climate. Indeed, although suitable ore was present in large quantities along the south-west coast of the United

States and the technique was known there, it was not applied until 1952 because it was believed that it would not be effective in the non-Spanish climate [1]. In reality the remarkable success of the Spanish process was due to growth of a particular microbial population which flourished in the local ambient conditions [2].

As long ago as 1906 De Grazia and Camiola demonstrated the solubilization of leucite minerals through the influence of bacterial action [8]. However, the biokinetics of such processes have only been studied much more recently. Several different kinetic models were put forward [3–7] for the catalytic process of metal solubilization. A major area of application has been the bio-oxidation of sulphide ores for metal extraction such as iron [9–14], copper and arsenic [15–19], antimony [17,31,43], cadmium [35,36], lead [36], silver and gold [37], and chromium [38].

About twenty years ago the possibility of exploiting uranium minerals through bioleaching was first studied with reasonably successful results, particularly in Canada [39–43]. More recently, laboratory-scale work has been undertaken to optimize uranium bioleaching [44]. The main areas of study have been the influence of pH and metal concentration on the rate of removal of the metal in continuous processes. Optimum microbial species were also identified which gave a significant degree of extraction of uranium *in situ* from ores containing of the order 0.05–0.15 per cent U_3O_8. However, preliminary conclusions suggest that the efficiency of *in situ* and 'heap' bioleaching does not seem to be predictable enough for industrial-scale operation, at least not for the particular sedimentary deposits examined.

Better results have been achieved in studies using batch laboratory reactors [45]. Preliminary laboratory–scale work has been followed by pilot-scale investigations using sample sizes of about 20 t [46]. The results obtained are shown in Fig. 9.1. Very high metal recovery efficiencies are observed, the level being largely dependent on the particle size of the ore.

9.3 GENERAL BIOLOGICAL PRINCIPLES

In general terms the microbial mechanisms in bio-leaching are very similar to those occurring in conventional heterogeneous catalysis, upon which many chemical processes are based. Thus, the biological effect, aimed at increasing reaction rates catalytically, is fundamentally controlled by the transport phenomena that conventional chemical and process engineering deal with. Among these phenomena the supply and process transfer of energy play a critical role.

The bacteria involved in the extraction of metallic compounds from mineral sources are called chemolithotrophic micro-organisms (Fig. 9.2). They can obtain all the NADH and ATP energy necessary for growth from the oxidation of inorganic substances such as ammonia, nitrate, hydrogen, sulphur compounds or iron. They have evolved the special ability to couple energy-yielding inorganic oxidations (electron producing) to essentially the same electron transport and energy conservation systems which are found in heterotrophs (i.e. ATP synthesis by oxidative phosphorylation). Virtually all chemolithotrophs are also autotrophs, i.e. they are able to synthesize all their organic components from carbon dioxide as the sole source of carbon. Thus they grow in wholly inorganic aqueous environments, providing there is an oxidizable substrate together with carbon dioxide and the essential mineral nutrients required by all bacteria.

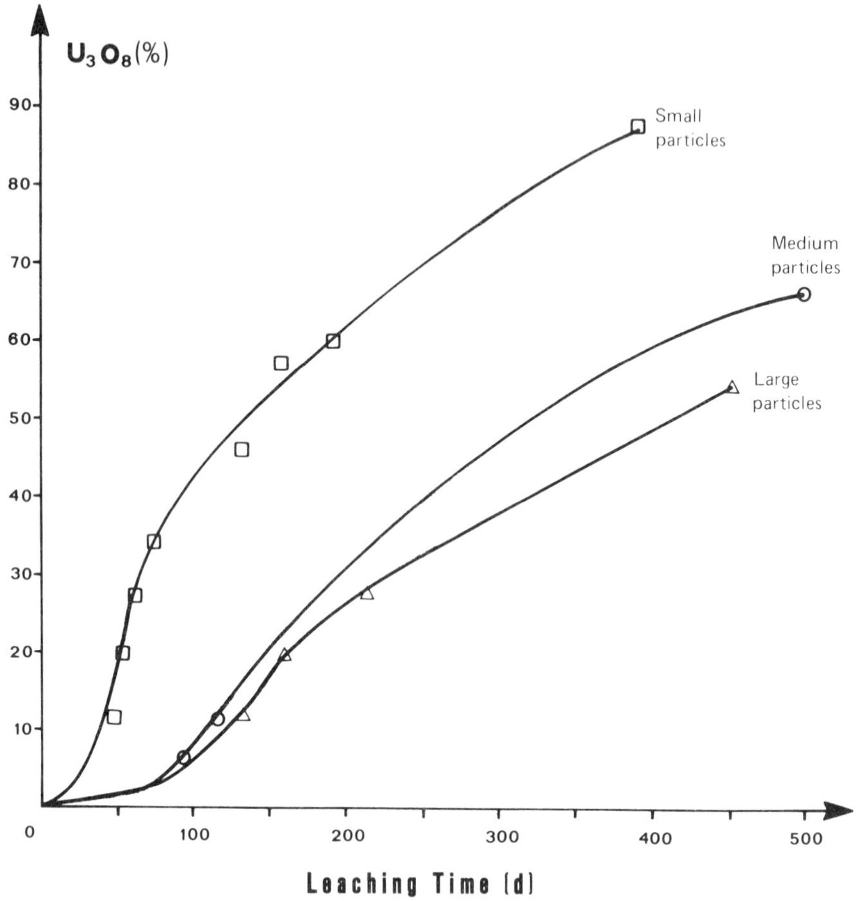

Fig. 9.1 — Leaching times using ores of decreasing particle size [45].

Chemolithotrophs can assimilate certain organic nutrients, though usually at the expense of inorganic energy metabolism; in nature they show a 'mixotrophic' metabolism in which cell carbon comes both from CO_2 and organic compounds. In bioleaching it is usually preferable not to allow organic materials into the growth environment, so that inorganic oxidations are maximized. Chemolithotrophs have been very successful in solving the problems of handling substrates of relatively low molecular energy yield and poor reducing capacity. Biochemically they approach the bioenergetic efficiencies of heterotrophs. While many chemolithotrophs grow very slowly, some species have developed an extremely rapid turnover of their energy substrates so that relatively rapid growth becomes possible. Fortunately for bioleaching processes, *Thiobacillus ferro-oxidans* is one such species and can grow on ferrous iron (electron donor) with a doubling time of 5–6 h; it oxidizes 30 times its own weight of iron per hour during growth. Each mole of CO_2 fixed by this organism uses 18.8 mol of Fe^{2+} with as high as 80% efficiency. *Thiobacillus ferro-oxidans* can

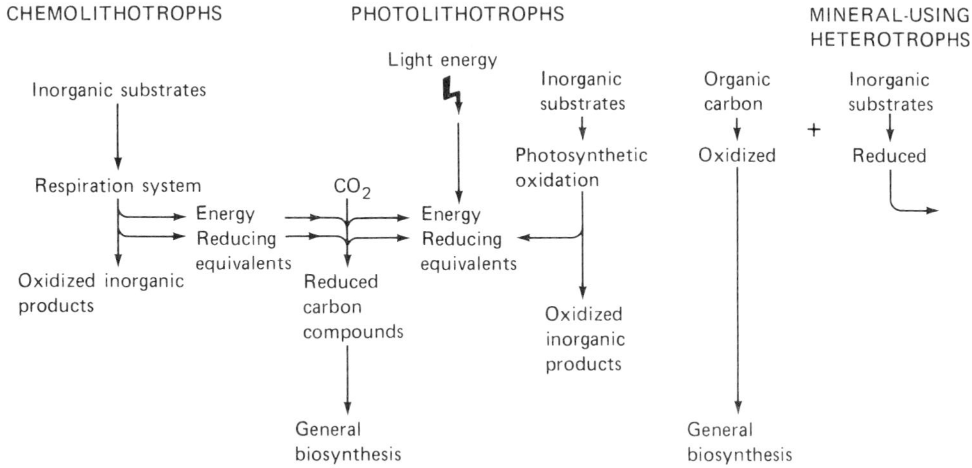

Fig. 9.2 — Principal pathways for mineral transformation in micro-organisms [70].

harness energy for growth from the oxidization of both iron and sulphur compounds, hence its particular usefulness in leaching of pyrites (FeS_2) and chalcopyrites ($CuFeS_2$) [71].

Other bacteria of the *Thiobacillus* genus can leach mineral sulphides by mechanisms shown generally in Fig. 9.3.

The main reactions occurring in the process are summarized below. The sulphuric acid required by *Th. ferro-oxidans* is derived from the activity of sulphur-oxidizing bacteria or from *Th. ferro-oxidans* itself attacking FeS_2:

$$2FeS_2 + 7O_2 + 2H_2O \rightarrow 2FeSO_4 + 2H_2SO_4 \quad (1)$$

$$4FeSO_4 + 2H_2SO_4 + O_2 \rightarrow 2Fe_2(SO_4)_3 + 2H_20 \quad (2)$$

Both oxidations (1) and (2) are activated by oxygen contained in leaching waters. Once the oxidation from Fe^{2+} to Fe^{3+} is achieved by obtaining ferric sulphate ($Fe_2(SO_4)_3$), further oxidation of the pyrites mineral can be rapidly obtained through the catalytic action of thiobacteria:

$$7Fe_2(SO_4)_3 + FeS_2 + 8H_2O \rightarrow 15FeSO_4 + 8H_2SO_4 \quad (3)$$

At the same time the hydrolysis of $Fe_2(SO_4)_3$ leads to the precipitation either of $Fe(OH)_3$ or $HFe_3(SO_4)_2(OH)_6$, according to the following equations:

$$Fe_2(SO_4)_3 + 6H_2O \rightarrow 2Fe(OH)_3 + 3H_2SO_4 \quad (4)$$

$$3Fe_2(SO_4)_3 + 12H_2O \rightarrow 2HFe_3(SO_4)_2(OH)_6 + 5H_2SO_4 \quad (5)$$

both of which allow the removal of iron from the leaching solution. In addition to the

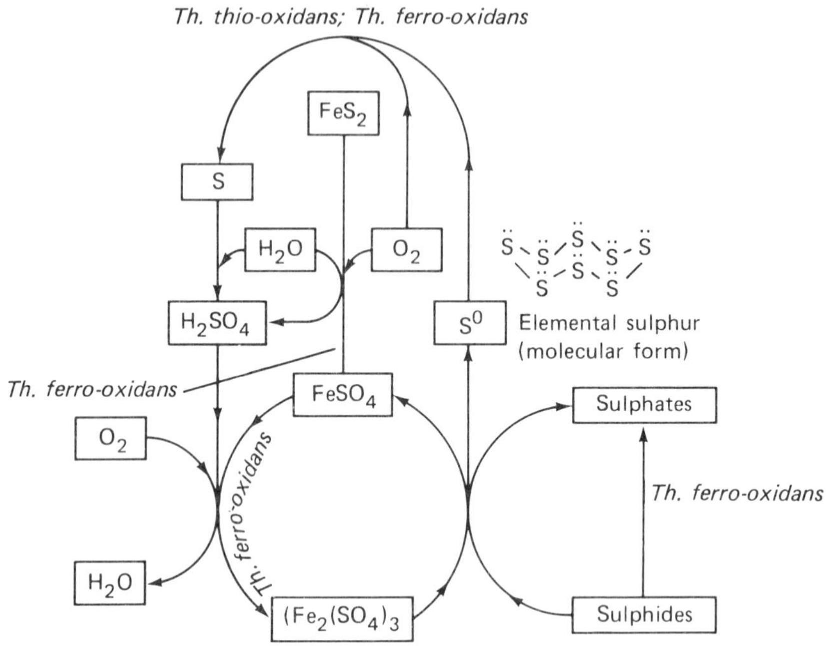

Fig. 9.3 — Oxidation of mineral sulphides by thiobacteria [75].

stepwise production of $Fe_2(SO_4)_3$ through Eqns (1) and (2), a direct bio-oxidation of sulphide is probably also occurring:

$$2FeS_2 + 7.5O_2 + H_2O \text{ bacteria} \rightarrow Fe_2(SO_4)_3 + H_2SO_4 \qquad (6)$$

Many iron oxidizers can obtain their energy from oxidation of sulphides in minerals such as the natural sulphides of Cu, Pb, Ni, Zn, Co. Oxygen is always the electron acceptor, sulphur or Fe^{2+} the electron donor.

The main microbial species active in the sulphur cycle are:

S-oxidizers ($H_2S \rightarrow SO_4^{2-}$): Non-photosynthetic bacteria, such as *Beggiatoa*, *Thiobacillus*, *Thiomicrospira* and *Sulpholobus*.
Photosynthetic bacteria, such as *Chromatium*, *Thiocystis*, *Thiospirillum* and *Chlorobium*.
Sulphate reducers ($SO_4^{2-} \rightarrow H_2S$): *Desulphovibrio*, *Desulphuromonas* and *Desulphomaculum*.

9.4 APPLICATIONS OF BIOLEACHING

9.4.1 Mining and metallurgical processes

Section 9.2 has already described the early applications to the recovery of twelve or more metals from their sulphide ores, and also uranium from U_3O_8-bearing rock. It is worth mentioning also that heterotrophic micro-organisms have been used for similar applications aimed at conserving resources, for example, the bioleaching of leucite to recover K_2O and Al_2O_3 (the latter from a non-conventional source [53]). The leucite appears to dissolve mainly by indirect chemical attack in the presence of heterotrophs. The rate of dissolution then slows down with the formation of inhibiting coatings on the surfaces of the mineral particles. The effectiveness of the process is due to the action of moulds. *Thiobacillus* sp. cannot leach pyrites in the presence of leucite.

9.4.2 Environmental protection

Bioleaching has taken on new perspectives recently, mainly due to ecological pressures. It so happens that the processes directed towards the separation of copper from arsenic [17] can also be used to treat toxic materials and to solve other environmental problems.

Environmental problems are not only found where large quantities of waste products accumulate from mining and metallurgical activities. Many other types of waste prove to be environmentally hazardous due to their content of toxic materials and/or the new 'state' of the waste after processing. A typical example is the large quantity of coal fly ash that has to be disposed of in countries such as Italy where energy production is increasingly dependent on coal-fired power stations [47]. This form of waste material is produced in extremely large quantities and it contains large quantities of valuable though toxic and hazardous metals. The very low concentration of toxic substances makes recovery by traditional physicochemical methods unprofitable. Bioleaching could offer an effective and economical alternative. Indeed, work in Germany has demonstrated the feasibility of removing quite high quantities of valuable metals from fly ash and various metallurgical wastes [48–50]. The results are summarized in Table 9.1 [50]. This shows that copper, chromium, zinc and vanadium can be extracted almost completely. Yields have been obtained that are very similar to those obtained by chemical leaching using sulphuric acid. The advantage of bioleaching seems to be selectivity of metal solubilization allowing selective extraction of each metal from the leach suspension.

Bioleaching of leucite for K_2O and Al_2O_3 recovery has been examined by several workers. Rossi has pointed out both the attractions and limitations of this process [51–53] and believes it might represent a non-polluting technology compared to the conventional Bayer method for the industrial extraction of alumina.

Further details of the ecological implications of bioleaching are given in the proceedings of recent symposia [54,55].

9.4.3 Energy and resource conservation

Coal utilization represents a real alternative to oil as an energy source even for those countries not having indigenous coal. However, there is a trend in the EC towards reducing emissions of sulphur dioxide to the atmosphere. Thus, the use of coal for power generation may require expensive flue-gas desulphurization techniques to be introduced, unless very low sulphur content coal is available. A critical situation is met in Sardinia, where the local coal contains as much as 7 per cent of sulphur. Desulphurization of fossil coal is becoming a realistic technical option. Unfortunately, the conventional physicochemical methods are not financially attractive yet.

Table 9.1 — Economic analysis of microbial leaching in basin and heap bioleaching [93].

Metal	Production (lb/d)	Cultivation and concentration cost (cent/lb)	Leaching costs (cent/lb)	Extraction costs (cent/lb)	Total costs (cent/lb	Heap bioleaching (cent/lb)	Metal prices (cent/lb)
Cu	60 000	1.1	1.6	13	15.7	20–40	60
Co	2 300	5.5	8.1	13	26.6	—	300
Ni	26 800	2.7	3.9	13	19.6	—	150

Sulphide concentrate: 11.5% Cu; 0.4% Co; 5.14% Ni
Amount treated: 550 000 lb
Ratio solid : liquid: 1 : 5
pH: 2.3
Temperature: 35°C
Time: 4 d
Yield: 95%
Capital investment: US$2 750 000.

The cost of desulphurized coal is approximately double that of the original fuel [56,57].

A feasible alternative could be the application of appropriate bacterial leaching processes. Academic studies were made some time ago [58] and these have been investigated recently [59–61].

In practice microbiological desulphurization of coal by oxidation of inorganic sulphur can be achieved by the same process technology as is used for the oxidation of sulphide ores [62–64]. However, competitiveness with conventional physicochemical processes remains to be demonstrated. Better results may be achieved by bioleaching using acidophilic micro-organisms instead of the strains normally used for sulphide ore bioleaching [65]. Unfortunately, results achieved so far do not yet allow extrapolation to an industrial scale.

The only commercial-scale data on the bacterial removal of pyrites from coal are given by Capes *et al.* [63], who have shown that the addition of suitable bacteria to weathered coal resulted in a reduction in sulphur content from 6.1 to 2.7 per cent.

The organisms include heterotrophic derivations from *Thiobacillus ferro-oxidans* cultures which grow on either organic or reduced sulphur, but not on Fe^{2+}. They are known to produce autotoxic organic metabolic by-products which build up to concentrations inhibiting iron and sulphur oxidation. The co-presence of acid-tolerant heterotrophs is said to be an indirect aid to sulphur oxidation (coal desulphirization). This is probably due to the ability of these bacteria to remove the autotoxic organic by-products [73,74].

The removal of sulphur from coal by microbial metabolic activity is influenced by a number of factors: principally, the type of inoculum, the initial pH, supplementary nutrients and the extent to which the coal has been pulverized. Of the possible supplemental nutrients, $(NH_4)_2SO_4$ has been shown to increase the oxidation of pyrites within coal, the effect increasing with decreasing coal particle size [72].

9.5 TECHNOLOGY

Bioleaching is often heavily influenced by the quantities and characteristics of the minerals or residues to be leached. Commonly the minerals to be bioleached occur as bulk aggregate materials containing only low concentrations of the desired metals. Thus, conventional biochemical reactors such as the 'Pachuca' CSTR (continuous stirred tank reactor), percolation columns and biological rotating surfaces have been examined on bench and pilot scales. Before describing each of these reactors in turn, it is worth noting that the industrial application of bioleaching is largely dependent upon the availability of reliable kinetic models, which are very important for normal process development and design work. Modelling depends upon a knowledge of the biokinetics, the microbial mechanisms occurring in the various stages making up the extraction process, the roles of surface diffusion and inhibition phenomena, and the influence of specific physicochemical variables on the viability of the leaching micro-organisms. Thus, the principal objective, process optimization, is made difficult because knowledge in these areas is very incomplete. References [66,67] show the derivation of three equations which have been successfully tested out in practice.

The full model has been successfully applied [66] to coal desulphurization. Process engineers may find the process equations and their derivation useful in other bioleaching contexts.

The proposed model takes into account not only the reactions in the liquid phase, but also the bacterial growth on the particle surface. The liquid phase dilution rate is defined as:

$$D = \frac{F}{V_l}$$

where F is the volumetric rate and V_l is the volume of liquid in the reactor. The solid dilution rate is defined as:

$$D_s = \frac{A}{A_t}$$

where A is the flow of solid surface area into the reactor and A_t is the total amount of the solid surface area in the reactor.

According to the above assumptions, a bacterial mass balance can be written as follows:

$$FX_b + AX_s = U_sX_sA_t + U_bX_bV \tag{7}$$

In Eqn. (7) F is the volumetric flow rate (ml/h), X_b is the bacterial concentration in solution (μg protein/cm^3), A is the surface area flow (m^2/h), X_s is the concentration of bacteria on the solid surface (μg protein/m^2), U_s is the specific growth rate on the solid (h^{-1}), A_t is the total amount of solid surface in the reactor (m^2), U_b is the specific growth rate in the liquid (h^{-1}), and V is the liquid volume (ml). The feed is assumed to be sterile.

Dividing Eqn. (7) by V and A_t the following equation can be derived:

$$\frac{DX_b}{A_t} + \frac{D_sX_s}{V} = \frac{U_sX_s}{V} + \frac{U_sX_s}{V} + \frac{U_bX_b}{A_t} \tag{8}$$

where $D = F/V$ and $D_s = A/A_t$.

Solving Eqn (8) for D yields:

$$D = \frac{U_sX_sA_t + U_bX_bV}{X_bV + X_sA_t} \tag{9}$$

The specific growth rate in solution U_b for the growth of *Thiobacillus ferro-oxidans* on ferrous iron is known to follow Monod kinetics:

$$U_b = \frac{U_m[Fe^{2+}]}{K_m + [Fe^{2+}]} \tag{10}$$

where U_m is the maximum specific growth rate in solution (h^{-1}) and K_m is a constant (M).

Substituting Eqn. (10) into Eqn. (9) yields:

$$D = \frac{U_sX_sA_t}{X_bV + X_sA_t} + \frac{U_m[Fe^{2+}]}{[X_bV + X_sA_t][K_m + Fe^{2+}]} \tag{11}$$

The bacterial mass balance model is completed with the description of the transfer of bacteria between the liquid phase and the solid phase.

The rate of adsorption has been modelled by second-order irreversible kinetics:

$$-\frac{d[X_b]}{dt} = K[X_b][S] \tag{12}$$

where $S = A_t/V$ and K is a constant.

Expressed in terms of a new variable, Z, the number of bacteria per unit volume leaving solution to attach to the solid surface, is given by:

$$[X_b] = [X_b]_0 - [Z] \tag{13}$$

$$S = [S]_0 - a[Z] \tag{14}$$

where $[X_b]_0$ and $[S]_0$ are the initial concentrations of bacteria and solid surface area in the solution respectively, and a is the effective area occupied per bacterium.

Substitution of Eqns. (13) and (14) into Eqn. (12) and rearrangement yields:

$$\frac{d[Z]}{dt} = K\left[[X_b]_0 - [Z]\right]\left[[S]_0 - a[Z]\right] \tag{15}$$

Integration of Eqn. (15) yields:

$$K_t = \frac{1}{[S]_0 - a[X_b]_0}\ln\left[\frac{[X_b]_0([S_0]_0 - a[Z])}{[S]_0([X_b]_0 - [Z])}\right] \tag{16}$$

Eqn. (16) allows calculation of the concentration of bacteria on the particle surface as a function of time through measurement of bacterial concentration in solution. The kinetic constant K and the area occupied per bacterium (a) must be experimentally determined for a particular type of solid.

Eqns. (11) and (15) provide a description of bacterial growth and bacterial transport between the phases. The bacterial leaching rate is related to bacterial growth through the relation:

$$L = \frac{U_s X_s S}{Y} \tag{11}$$

where Y is a yield coefficient.

Eqns. (11), (16) and (17) provide the description of the bacterial leaching process.

9.5.1 *In situ* bioleaching

In situ bioleaching can be used effectively to remove either metals from low-grade ores, or to extract them from almost exhausted mines [75–77]. An example is given in Fig. 9.4. It shows the extraction of copper from the Dergtyarskii mine in the USSR. The leaching solution is injected into the walls and roof of an underground chamber [75]. The copper-bearing leachate is recovered using a pump located in a deep shaft. The copper is then separated and the microbial solution is regenerated.

9.5.2 Heap bioleaching

Commercially, millions of tonnes of rock containing high sulphide and low metal concentrations are transferred from mines to dumping areas. These are generally located in valleys to assure heap stability and to facilitate leachate recovery [78–91]. An example of this type of system is given in Fig. 9.5 [78]. The heaps are sprayed with acidified water. This also introduces the air needed for chemical oxidation and biological reactions. Micro-organisms need not be added because they occur naturally and develop rapidly inside the heaps when conditions are suitable. The leaching solution percolates through the heap and collects in basins or tanks at the base of the heap. The cycle can last continuously for several years before metal exhaustion occurs.

Heap bioleaching is a crude operation because of the quantities of ore involved

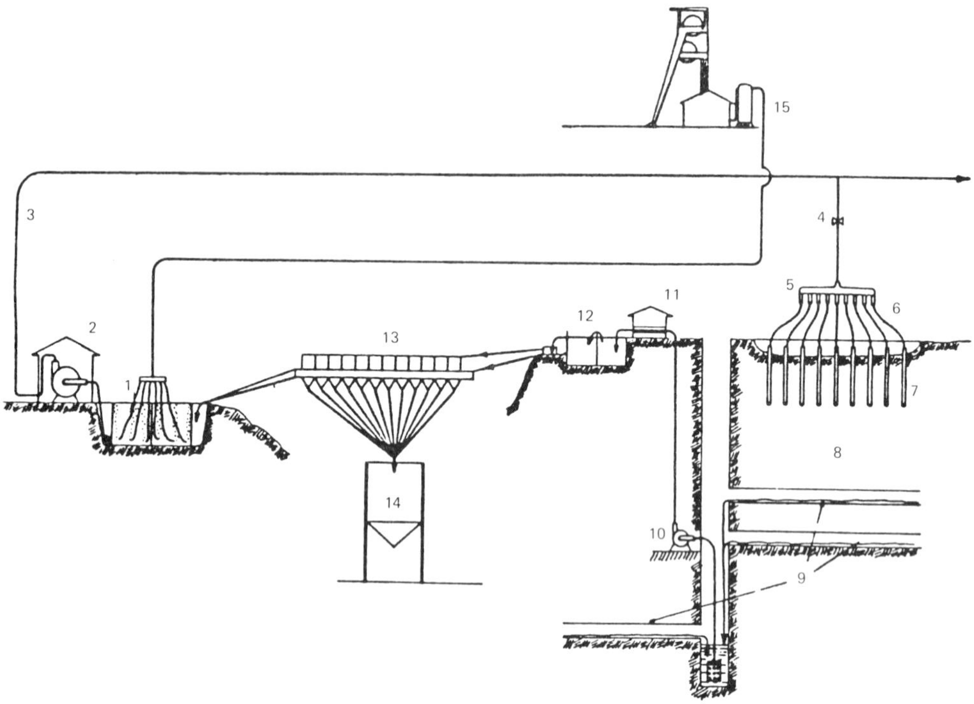

Fig. 9.4 — Bioleaching in Dergtyarskii (USSR) mine. Diagram of the experimental plant [75]. 1, bacterial regeneration basin; 2, pumping station to the shaft; 3, solution pipeline; 4, sectioning valve; 5, distribution; 6, polyethylene pipes; 7, emission shaft; 8, mineral; 9, mines levels; 10, solution extraction pump; 11, control station; 12, clarification basin; 13, precipitation tanks; 14, drying of the copper cement; 15, air pumping station.

and the methods used for constructing the heaps. Indeed, compaction during transport of ore, the heap configuration and the lack of control over particle size can create problems such as inadequate aeration and low leaching rates. Nowadays heaps are constructed with more care than in the past. The rocks are often crushed to permit better leachate percolation. Also, to prevent ground pollution, heaps are usually built in impermeable ground.

However, from the biological viewpoint the process is still uncontrolled and relies entirely on natural activity.

9.5.3 Bioleaching in conventional reactors

The whole leaching process can be controlled and accelerated by employing slurry reactors of the type used for traditional leaching. There are two main types of slurry reactor. The Pachuca, or air-stirred, reactor consists of columns or vessels into which air is targeted. The air bubbles rise in the inner column causing aeration, circulation and suspension of the mineral particles. The continuous stirred tank reactor (CSTR) is a conventional fermentation vessel. It is agitated mechanically and temperature, pH and ore concentration are controlled.

Both systems are usually followed by a sedimentation stage in which the enriched solution is separated for subsequent metal recovery. Whilst the use of reactors can

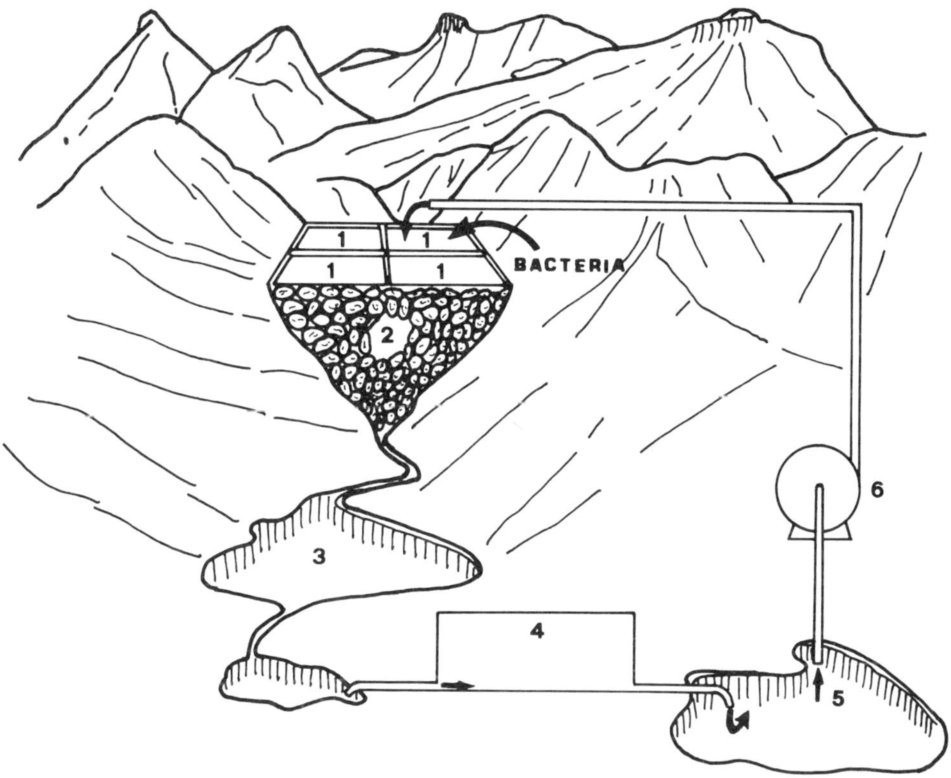

Fig. 9.5 — Heap or dump bioleaching scheme [78]. 1, basins; 2, heap or dump; 3, clarification basins; 4, reaction tanks; 5, regeneration basins; 6, pumping station.

result in improved process control and increased efficiency, the technique has not so far been applied on full scale.

A comparison of the performance of various types of laboratory reactor has been made by Atkins and Pooley [92] with iron pyrites from an open-cast mine at Tharsis, Rio Tinto, Spain, and using *Thiobacillus ferro-oxidans*. Comparative results are shown in Fig. 9.6. The Pachuca reactor and the percolating columns were more efficient than the stirred tank reactor. Percolating systems in particular offered a low-cost technique for treatment of low-grade high-volume ores.

9.6 ECONOMICS

In the absence of full-scale operational experience it is impossible to assess economics with certainty. Thus economic data are, at best, imprecise and incomplete. Nevertheless after bioleaching was adopted at the Dergtyarskii mine, the operating costs for copper extraction showed an 80 per cent decrease [75]. There is a large difference in attitude between the costs of processes designed solely for commercial

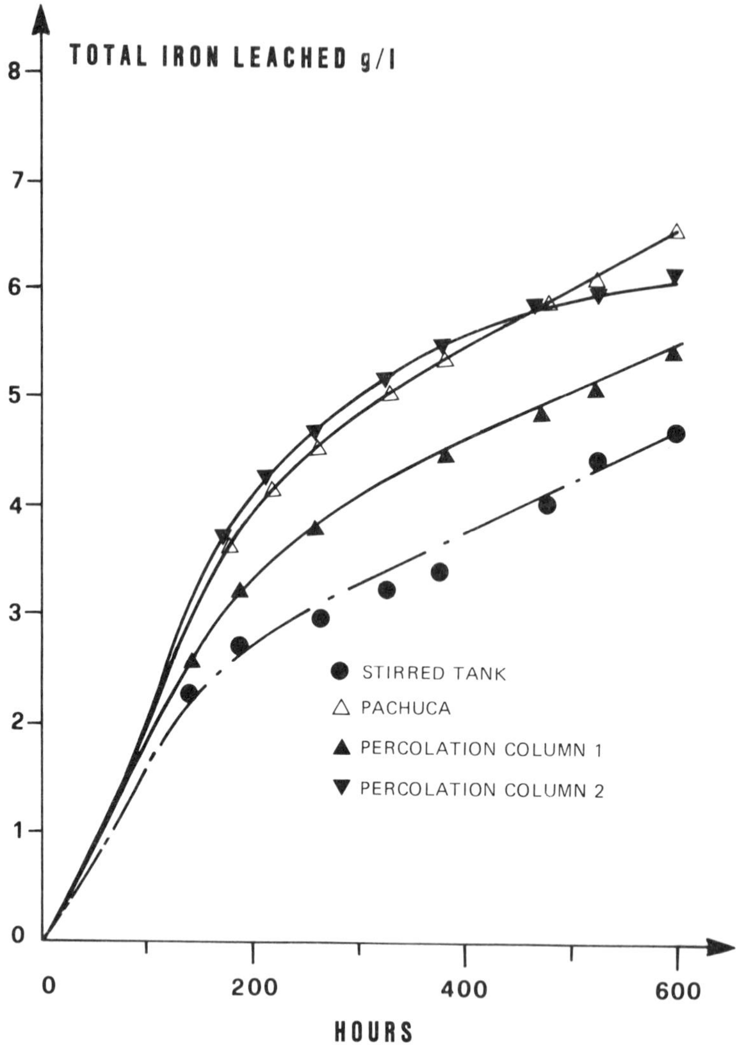

Fig. 9.6 — A comparison of bacterial leaching techniques using stirred tank reactor, Pachuca reactor and two types of percolation columns [92].

purposes and those principally directed towards solving a difficult environmental problem. From the environmental viewpoint cost might be unimportant when set against environmental benefit. Furthermore, bioleaching has no adverse side effects in the environment providing groundwater pollution is avoided. It requires neither high temperature nor high pressure and hence involves relatively low capital and operating costs.

Torma *et al.* [93] have undertaken a comparison of the costs of traditional leaching carried out in heap and bioleaching carried out in basins, in each case for the

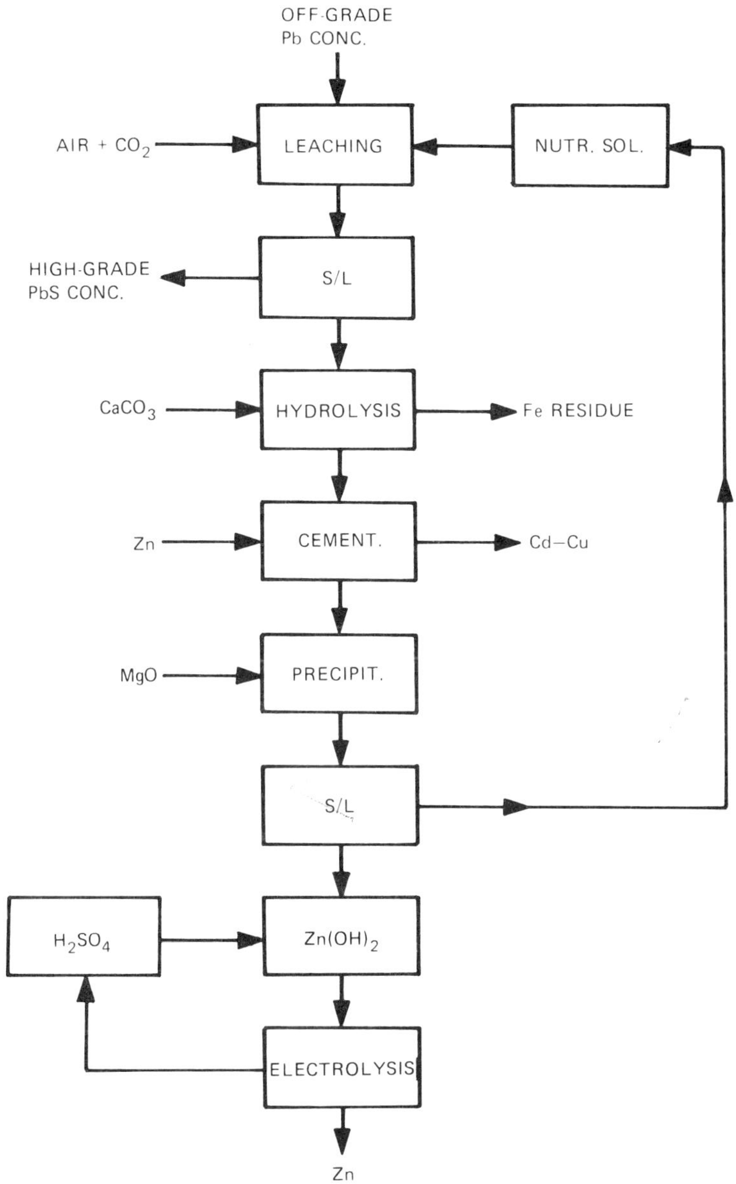

Fig. 9.7 — Schematic representation of a microbiological leaching process of an off-grade lead sulphide concentrate [94].

extraction of copper, nickel and cobalt from a concentrate containing pentlandite [94]. The results are summarized in Table 9.1.

Economic analyses have also been presented by McElroy and Bruynesteyn [95] for the continuous bioleaching of chalcopyrites concentrates. A similar assessment

Table 9.2 — Cost analysis for the treatment of 100 000 kg/d PbS concentrate [94].

Metal	Metal content	Yearly metal production (kg/a)	Market value ($/a)	Leaching expenses ($/a)	Cost of mining ($/a)	Profit ($/a)
Zn	7.7%	2 700 000	2 050 000	1 420 000	306 000	324 000
Cu	2.4%	830 000	1 350 000	940 000	120 000	290 000
Cd	0.02%	7 000	60 000	40 000	4 000	16 000

$7 300 000 being the investment [94], the yearly return of revenue of about 6.3×10^5 appears to be acceptable.

has been undertaken by Torma for the selective microbial extraction of cadmium, copper and zinc from a low-grade lead concentrate (Fig. 9.7). A cost analysis carried out on a 100 t/d lead concentrate bioleaching process is summarized in Table 9.2.

ACKNOWLEDGEMENT

The authors wish to acknowledge the assistance obtained from the Institute due ISAR (Savona, Italy) for providing them with technical and economic data and other information, as well as with facilities that helped considerably in the realization of this chapter.

REFERENCES

[1] van Arsdale, G. D. (1953). *Hydrometallurgy of Base Metals*, McGraw Hill, New York.
[2] Rossi, C. (1974). La liscivizione microbica dei minerali: progressi e prospettive. *Bollettino della Associazione Mineraria Subalpina*, Anno XI, numero 1–2 Ediz. SpE, Torino.
[3] Sato, M. (1060). Oxidation of sulphides Orebodies II. Oxidation mechanism of sulphide minerals at 25°C, *Econ. Geol.*, **55**, 1202–1231.
[4] Majima, H. and Peters, E. (1968). Electrochemistry of sulphide dissolution in hydrometallurgical solutions. *VIII International Mineral Processing Congress*, Paper E–1, Leningrad.
[5] Peters, E. and Majima, H. (1969). *The Physical Chemistry of Leaching Sulphide Minerals.* Annual Meeting ALME, New York.
[6] Majima, H. and Peters, E. *Electrochemical Mechanisms for the Decomposition of Metal sulphides.* Research Report Uni. of Brit. Columbia, School of Mineral Eng.
[7] Torma, A. E. and Legault, G. (1973). Role de la surface des mainerais sulfuses lors de leur biodegradation par *Thiobacillus ferro-xidans. Amm. Microbial (Inst. Pasteur)*, **124A**, 111–121.
[8] De Grazia, S. and Camiola, G. (1906). Sull'intervento dei microorganismi nella utiliazione della profana leucitica del suolo da parte delle piante superiori. *Le Stazioni Spermentali Agrarie Italiane, Modena*, **39**, 829–840.
[9] Silverman, M. P., Rogoff, M. H. and Wender, I. (1961). Bacterial oxidation of pyritic materials in coal. *Applied Microbiology*, **9**, 491–496.
[10] Bryner, L. C. and Jameson, A. K. (1958). Micro-organisms in leaching sulfide minerals. *Appl. Microbiol.*, **6**, 281–287.
[11] Silverman, M. P. (1967). Mechanism of bacterial pyrite oxidation. *J. Bact.*, **94**, 1046–1051.
[12] Rossi, G. (1971). La lisciviazione microbica dei mine rali. I. L'azione dei microorganismi reperiti in acque acide di miniere Italiane sulla pirite. *Resoconti AMS*, **76**, 5–23.
[13] Le Roux, N. W., North, A. A. and Wilson, J. C. (1973). Bacterial oxidation of pyrite. Paper 45, *Tenth International Mineral Processing Congress*, London.
[14] Takakuwa, S. (1975). *Plant and Cell Physiol.*, **16**, 1027.

[15] Agafanova, G. S., Klassen, V. I. and Mat'Yanof, Yu. A. (1970). Un metodo di intensificazione della lisciviazione microbica del rame, *Zvetnie Metalli*, **43**, 89–91.
[16] Wyckoff, R. W. G. (1970). Deux espèces de chalcopyrites mises en évidence par les bactéries. *Bull. Soc. fr. Minèral. Cristallogr.*, **93**, 120–122.
[17] Pol'Chin, S. I., Caravaico, G. I., Tausgniaiscaia, Z. A. and Panin, V. V. (1970). La lisciviazione microbica selettiva dell'arsenico e del rame da concentrati di solfuro ed ossido di stagno; il meccanismo della lisciviazione. *Proceedings IXth International Mineral Processing Congress*, Praga, pp. 374–353.
[18] Rossi, G. (1971). La lisciviazione microbica dei minerali. II. L'azione dei microrganismi reperti in acque acide di miniere Italiane sulla calcopririte. *Resoconti della Associazione Mineraria Sarda*, **76**, 25–52.
[19] Pol'Chin, S. I., Abramov, E. V., Panin, V. V., Kim, D. X. and Lavrinenko, A. A. (1972). L'estrazione selettiva del rame e dell'arsenico da soluzioni microbiche e loro rigenerazione. *Zvietnaia Metallurghiia*, **15**, 27–31.
[20] Rudolfs, W. and Helbronner, A. (1922). Oxidation of zinc sulfide by microorganisms. *Soil Science*, **14**, 459–464.
[21] Zimmerley, S. R., Wilson, D. G. and Prater, J. D. (1958). Cyclic leaching process employing iron oxidizing bacteria, US Patent No. 2.829.964.
[22] Malouf, E. E. and Prater, J. D. (1961). Role of bacteria in alteration of sulfide minerals. *J. Metals*, **13**, 353–356.
[23] Marklewitz, B., Hasche, D. and Schwartz, W. (1961). Untersuchungen über das Verhalten von Thiobacterien gegenüber Schwermetallen. *Z. Allg. Mikrobiol.*, **1**, 179–191.
[24] Razzel, W. E. and Trussel, P. C. (1963). Microbiological leaching of metallic sulfides. *Appl. Microbiol.*, **11**, 105–110.
[25] Trussel, P. C., Duncan, D. W. and Walden, C. C. (1964). Biological mining. *Canad. Min. Journ.*, **57**, 46–49.
[26] Duncan, D. W., Walden, C. C. and Trussel, P. C. (1966). Biological leaching of mill products. *Trans. Can. Inst. of Min. and Met.*, **69**, 329–333.
[27] Torma, A. E., Walden, C. C. and Branion, R. M. R. (1970). Microbiological leaching of a zinc sulfide concentrate. *Biotechn. and Bioeng.*, **12**, 501–517.
[28] Torma, A. E., Walden, C. C., Duncan, D. W. and Branion, R. M. R. (1972). The effect of carbon dioxide and particle surface area on the microbiological leaching of a zinc sulfide concentrate. *Biotechnol. Bioeng.*, **14**, 777–786.
[29] Sutton, J. A. and Corrick, J. D. (1961). Bacteria in mining and metallurgy: leaching selected ores and minerals; experiments with *Thiobacillus thiooxidans*. *BuMines Rept. of Inv.* 5839, 16 pp.
[30] De Cuyper, J. A. (1964) Bacterial leaching of low grade copper and cobalt ores. *Unit Processes in Hydrometallurgy, New York–London*, **24**, 126–142.
[31] Rossi, G. (1971) La lisciviazione microbica dei minerali. III. L'azione dei microorganismi repertiti in acque acide di miniere Italiane sulla stibina. *Resoconti dell'Associazione Mineraria Sarda*, **76**, 1–15.
[32] Torma, A. E. (1971). Microbiological oxidation of synthetic cobalt, nickel and zinc sulfides by *Thiobacillus ferroxidans*. *Rev. Can. Biol.*, **30**, 209–216.
[33] Torma, A. E. (1972). Biohydrometallurgy of cobalt and nickel. *TMS Paper selection*, **A72-7**, AIME, New York.

[34] Bryner, L. C., Beck, J. V., Davis, D. B. and Wilson, D. G. (1954). Microorganism in leaching sulfide minerals. *Industrial and Engineering Chemistry*, **46**, 2587–2592.

[35] Brissette, C., Champagne, J. and Jutras, J. R. (1971). Bacterial leaching of cadmium sulfide. *Can. Min. and Met. Bull.*, **67**, 85–88.

[36] Torma, A. E., Ouellet, R. and Gabra, G. G. (1974). Presented at *Ann. Conf. Chem. Inst. Can.*, Regina, Saskatchewan, June 2–5.

[37] McElroy, R. O. and Duncan, D. W. (1974). Copper extraction by rapid bacteriological process. US Patent 3,856,913 (Dec. 24).

[38] Ehrlich, H. L. (1983). Leaching of chromite ore and sulfide matte with dilute sulfuric acid generated by *Thiobacillus thiooxidans* from sulfur. In: *Recent Progress in Bioidrometturgy*, G. Rossi and A. E. Torma (eds.), Associazione Mineraria Sarda.

[39] Harrison, V. F., Gow, W. A. and Hughson, M. R. (1966). Factors influencing the application of bacterial leaching to a Canadian uranium ore. *Journal of Metals*, **59**, 1189–1194.

[40] Fisher, J. R. (1966). Bacterial leaching of Elliot Lake uranium ore. *Can. Min. and Met. Bull.*, **59**, 588–592.

[41] Duncan, D. W. and Bruynestein, A. (1972). Enhancing bacterial activity in a uranium mine. *Can. Min. and Met. Bull.*, 32–36.

[42] Tuovinen, O. H. and kelly, D. P. (1973). Toxicity and tolerance of uranium in *Thiobacillus ferrooxidans. Journal of Gen. Micr.* **75**, XXI.

[43] Tomizuka, N. and Takahara, Y. (1972). In: Tenu, G. (ed.) *Proc. IV. Intern. Ferment. Symp. (Kyoto), Ferment. Technol. Today*, Society Fermentation Technology, Osaka, Japan, pp. 513–520.

[44] Tomizuka, N., Yagisawa, M., Someya, J. and Takahara, Y. (1976). *Agr. Biol. Chem.*, **40**, 1019.

[45] Brierley, C. L. and Brierley, J. A. (1973). *Can. J. Microbiol.*, **19**, 183.

[46] W. Floeter, Sadowski, R. and Schoening, G. (1983). *A Quantitative Evaluation of the Biological Oxidation During the Leaching of Uranium Ore*, Uranerzbergbau-GmbH, 5300 Boon 1, 367 Koelnstrasse, FRG.

[47] Ferraiolo, G., del Borghi, M. and Solisio, C. (1982). Product recovery from solid wastes, sludges and residues. The prospect in Italy. *Workshop Meeting 'Environmental Biotechnology*, Versailles.

[48] Ebner, H. G. (1977). In: Schwartz, W. (ed.) *Conference Bacterial Leaching 1977*, GBF Monograph Series, No. 4, Verlag Chemie, Veinheim, New York.

[49] Ebner, H. G. (1978). *Metal Recovery and Environmetal Protection by Bacterial Leaching of Inorganic Waste Materials*, University of Dortmund, FRG.

[50] Bosecker, K. (1983). *Microbial Recycling of Industrial Waste Products*, Federal Institute for Geosciences and Natural Resources, Stilleweg 2, 3000 Hannover 51, FRG.

[51] Rossi, G. (1971). *Resoconti Ass. Miner. Sarda*, (Iglesias), **76**, 5.

[52] Rossi, G. (1969). *Resoconti Ass. Miner. Sarda*, (Iglesias), **74**, 5.

[53] Rossi, G. (1978). *Metallurgical Applications of Bacterial Leaching and related Microbiological Phenomena*, Academia Press.

[54] Murr, E., Torma, A. E. and Brierley, J. A. (1978). *Metallurgical Applications of Bacterial Leaching and related Microbiological Phenomena*, Academia Press.

[55] Rossi, G. and Torma, A. E. (1983). *Recent Progress in BioHydrometallurgy*, AMS, Iglesias, Italy.

[56] Ferraiolo, G. *et al.* (1980). *Desulphurization Techniques*, EFCE Publication Series No. 13, Society of Chemical Industry, London.

[57] Peloso, A. (1984). *Preliminary informal results of a working panel on desulphurization techniques*, established by CSIA/ATI, member of the International Union of Air Pollution Prevention Associations.

[58] Par, S. W. and Powell, A. R. (1919). A study of the forms in which sulfur occurs in coal, *Illinois Engineering Experiment Station Bull.*, No. 11.

[59] Carpenter, L. V. and Herndon, L. K. (1933). Acid drainage from bituminous coal mines. *West Va. Univ. Eng. Exp. Sta. Research Bull.*, **10**.

[60] Temple, K. L. and Delchamps, E. W. (1953). Autotrophic bacteria and the formation of acid in bituminous coal mines. *Applied Microbiology*, **1**, 255–258.

[61] Brierley, C. L. (1978). *CRC Crit. Rev. Microbiol*, **5**, 207.

[62] Capes, C. E., McIlhinney, A. E., Sirianni, A. F. and Puddington, I. E. (1973). Bacterial oxidation in upgrading pyritic coals, *Can. Min. and Met. Bull.*, **66**, 89–91.

[63] Capes, C. E., Lhinney, A. E. McJ., Sirianni, A. S. and Puddington, I. E. *Can. Min. and Met. Bull.*, 88–91.

[64] Apel, W. A., Dugan, B. R., Filippi, J. A. and Reys, N. S. (1976). *Applied Environ. Microbiol.*, **32**, 159.

[65] Dugan, R. and Apel, W. A. (1978). *Microbiological Desulfurization of Coal*, Ohio State University, Columbus.

[66] Myerson, A. S. and Kline, P. C. Continuous bacterial coal desulfurization employing *Thiobacillus ferroxidans. Biotechnol. Bioeng.*, **26**, 92–99.

[67] Chang, Y. C. and Myerson, A. S. Growth model of the continuous bacterial leaching of iron pirite by *Thobacilus ferroxidans. Biotechnol. Bioeng.*, **24**, 889.

[68] Netter, H. (1959). *Theoretische Biochemie.* Berlin.

[69] West, E. S. and Tood, W. R. *Textbook of Biochemistry*, New York.

[70] Silverman, M. P. and Erlich, H. L. (1964). Microbial formation and degradation of minerals. *Advances in Applied Microbiology*, **6**, 153–206.

[71] Temple, K. L. and Colmer, A. R. (1951). The autotrophic oxidation of iron by a new bacterium: *Thiobacillus ferroxidans. J. Bact.*, **62**, 605–611.

[72] Cork, D. J. and Cusanovich, M. A. (1978). *Sulfate Decomposition: A Microbial Process*, University of Arizona, Tucson.

[73] Tuttle, J. H. and Dugan, P. R. (1976) *Can. J. Microbiol*, **22**, 719.

[74] Tuttle, J. H., Dugan, P. R. and Apel, W. A. (1977). *Appl. and Environ. Microbiol.*, **33**, 459–469.

[75] Stepanov, B. A., Ivanov, V. I., Golomzik, A. I. and Nagurniak, F. I. (1965). La lisciviazione microbica dei minerali sulfuri. *Fiziko-Techniceschie Problemi Razrabotchi Poleznich Iscopaemich*, 118–121.

[76] Takamura, Y., Kurihara, K., Oniki, H. and Watanabe, A. (1972). *Recent Research Activities and Application of Bacterial Leaching in Japan*, Print. No. TIVa2, Joint Meeting MMIJ-AIME, Tokio.

[77] Fletcher, J. B. (1971). *In-place leaching at Miami Mine, Miami, Arizona. AIME Trans.*, **250**, 310–314.

[78] Beck, J. V. (1967). The role of bacteria in copper mining operations. *Biotechnol. Bioeng.*, **9**, 487–497.

[79] Jennings, P. H., Tarassoff, P. and Ford, R. E. (1972). *Heap Leaching Tests on Gaspe Copper Oxide Ore*, AIME 101st Annual Meeting, San Francisco.

[80] Power, K. L. (1964). Copper dump leaching at Axasarco's Silver Bell Unit, Arizona. *Unit Processes in Hydrometallurgy*, 806–823.

[81] Malouf, E. E. (1968). Dump leaching. In: Pfleider, P. (ed.) *Surface Mining*, AIME, New York, pp. 762–770.

[82] Andersen, J. E., Herwig, G. L. and Moffiti, R. B. (1966). Heap leaching at Rum Jungle. *Australian Mining*, 15 April, 35–39.

[83] Woodcock, J. T. (1967). Copper waste dump leaching. *Proc. Aust. Inst. Min. Met.*, No. 224, 47–66.

[84] Andersen, J. E. and Allman, M. B. (1968). Some operational aspects of heap leaching at RUM Jungle. *Proc. Aust. Inst. Min. Met.*, No. 225, 27–31.

[85] Harris, J. A. (1969). Development of theoretical approach to the heap leaching of copper sulphide ores. *Proc. Aust. Inst. Min. Met.*, No. 230, 81–92.

[86] Allman, M. B. (1969). An experiment in heap leaching. *Mining Congress Journal*, 28–31.

[87] Johnson, P. H. and Bhappu, R. B. (1970) *Heap Leaching Studies on Oxide and Sulphide Copper Ores*, AIME Preprint, No. 70-B-70, Denver.

[88] Jacobson, R. H., McKee Chester, R., Ronald, J. R., Brierley, J. A. and Bhuappu, R. B. (1972). *Optimization of Dump and Heap Leaching — Theoretical and Practical Studies*, Preprint No. T IVa3, Joint Meeting MMJ-AIME, Tokyo.

[89] Malouf, E. E. (1972). *Copper Leaching Practices*, Preprint No. 72-AS-84, AIME, San Francisco.

[90] Hannan, W. S., Jr. (1972). *Leach Dump Operation at Bisbee*, Preprint No. 72-AS-20, AIME, San Francisco.

[91] Cooper, F. D. (1968). *Copper Hydrometallurgy. A Review and Outlook,* USBM Information Circular 8394, 18 pp.

[92] Atkins, A. S. and Pooley, F. D. (1983). *Comparison of Bacterial Reactors Employed In The Oxidation of Sulphide Concentrates*, Department of Mining Engineering, North Staffordshire Polytechnic, Stoke on Trent; Department of Mineral Exploitation, University College Cardiff.

[93] Torma, A. E., Bolduc, J. P. and Oliver, C. A. (1973). *Recent Progress in Biohydrometallurgy of Metal Sulfides*, Paper No. 15, Leaching Session, 12th Annual Conference of Metallurgists, CIMM, Quebec.

[94] Torma, A. E. *Complex Lead Sulfide Concentrate Leaching by Micro-organisms*, New Mexico Institute of Mining and Technology Socorro, New Mexico.

[95] McElroy, R. O. and Bruynesteyn, A. (1978). *Continuous Biological Leaching of Chalcopyrite Concentrates: Demonstration and Economic Analysis*, BC Research, Vancouver.

[96] Istituto due ISAR, Savona, Italy. Private communication.

10

Lignin and cellulose biodegradation

F. Alfani and **M. Cantarella**
University of Napoli, Italy

10.1 INTRODUCTION

10.1.1 Availability in natural and industrial environments

Lignin and cellulose, which constitute the structural components of vascular land plants, are the most important renewable sources of organic carbon on earth. Bassham [1] valued the carbon incorporated into the lignocellulose of arboraceous plants at half of the global amount annually fixed by photosynthesis. According to Ghose [2] this is equivalent to 1.8×10^{12} tons of biological substances. Cellulose and lignin are also present in quantity in industrial and municipal effluents and residues. The development of a process for their biodegradation could offer a solution to a major problem of waste disposal and environmental impairment caused by both man and industry. In fact, municipal wastes could be converted by biological composting into fertilizers and humus, so achieving several important benefits. Agricultural utilization would reduce the consumption of inorganic fertilizers, not only because of their direct nutrient contribution, but also because they would improve the capacity of soil to retain chemicals; the pollution of rivers and the sea caused by emission of inorganic fertilizers would be reduced; the quality of soil would be improved by the addition of organic materials; and the emission of polluting and toxic gases generated during municipal waste incineration would be avoided. Composting is more fully described in Ch. 13.

Large quantities of lignocellulose residues must also be handled in food factories and plants for primary agricultural production. These materials could be treated biologically. They are dispersed in water and are relatively rich in cellulose and lignin, which could be converted into chemicals, fuel and proteins, thus recovering, at least partially, the costs of waste treatment and disposal. The recovery of cellulose from waste paper, mainly newsprint, and its conversion to fermentable sugar, is another potentially attractive process. Lignin, lignin-degradation products and chlorinated lignins must be recovered from pulp and paper-mill effluents in order to reduce both colour and toxicity. This is presently done with difficulty, and then only partially, by expensive processes such as physicochemical treatment, ultrafiltration and activated-carbon adsorption. The successful biological treatment of these wastewaters would solve waste-disposal problems and allow the recovery of process waters which could then be recycled within a closed-circuit paper-mill [3].

Lignin and related aromatics are relatively inert biologically and, especially in anaerobic environments, can cause severe pollution by the accumulation of toxic and recalcitrant organic materials. Biomass in the form of agricultural and forest wastes is most readily available in large quantities. Conversion of a fraction of this material into fuel, chemicals, gas and feed protein would make a significant contribution to the overall problems of resource recycle and conversion [4]. The conversion of cellulose and lignin is difficult and costly whether by biological or chemical processes. The production of gaseous and liquid feedstocks by direct thermal methods (e.g. pyrolysis) is technically feasible but, since the moisture content of biomass is generally high, pyrolytic and chemical treatment seem to be less attractive than biological processes. A large capital investment is required for a plant converting lignin to phenolic compounds in a two-stage process consisting of hydro-cracking followed by hydrodealkylation [5]. Whether the overall process would be cost-effective is not yet clear.

10.1.2 Biological considerations

Lignin is a heterogeneous organic polymer which is interspersed with hemicellulose surrounding cellulose microfibrils. The lignin sheath must be disrupted before the polysaccharides are accessible to enzyme attack and therefore its decomposition is, rightly, considered the key to the recycling of most of the earth's carbon. Cellulose is a linear homopolymer of anhydroglucose units. It is difficult to hydrolyse owing to its crystalline structure and its close association with a variety of other chemical species in the biomass. In fact, cellulose does not occur in a pure form in agricultural wastes from whatever source. Pectin, lignin, hemicelluloses, proteins, minerals and other polysaccharides, such as starch, are commonly present.

The degradation of lignin is limited by the presence in the molecule of biologically stable carbon–carbon and ether linkages which protect the organic material from the degradative enzymes of micro-organisms. On the other hand, cellulose can be enzymatically converted to fermentable sugars, but mechanical and solvent pretreatment [6] is needed to increase the accessibility of cellulose to hydrolysis, presumably because this breaks the lignin seal and disrupts the crystalline structure of the cellulose.

Biochemical processes for the conversion of lignocellulose materials are based on studies of lignin and cellulose degradation in various natural environments. The body of experimental evidence suggests that the lignin degradation system is oxidative, non-specific and extracellular. Lignin, like other high molecular weight and insoluble polymers, cannot enter the microbial cell by diffusion or active transport, therefore biodegradation must involve extracellular catalysts. However, according to Hall [7], the first step in lignin decay might be non-enzymatic and could be caused by 'activated oxygen'. The recent discovery [8] of an extracellular enzyme produced by lignin cultures of *Phanerochaete chrysosporium* brings into question the activated-oxygen concept. Nevertheless, the presence of oxygen seems to be essential. No significant mineralization of lignin under anaerobic conditions has been observed [9], with the exception of natural and synthetic lignin incubated anaerobically with anoxic sediments of aquatic ecosystems [10]. Several micro-organisms, fungi imperfecti, soil bacteria and basidiomycetes can degrade lignin and related aromatic compounds, but their activity depends on the lignin substrate. Despite detailed research into the enzymology of lignin biodegration, existing knowledge in this area is still poor. Studies have suffered from a lack of specific, sensitive and rapid assays for lignin-degrading activity.

Much less obscure is the enzymology of cellulose degradation. Bacteria and fungi degrade cellulose and synthesize new microbial cells and metabolic products such as carbon dioxide and methane, but very few of these offer cellulase systems capable of *in vitro* conversion of cellulose into useful products, such as soluble sugars. Cellulase enzymes consist of a multiplicity of different components which can be classified into three major types: endoglucanases, exoglucanases and cellobiase. The mode of action and the kinetics of cellulase enzymes has been studied mostly using fungal cellulases isolated from *Trichoderma* and *Aspergillus* species and bacterial cellulases from *Clostridium* species. Bacterial and fungal systems work at different pH optima and exhibit different extracellular endo- and exo-activity ratios.

10.1.3 Process considerations

Full-scale plants for the bioconversion of lignocellulose materials are not yet in existence. However, experience from laboratory-scale units indicates that a much fuller understanding of lignin biodegradation is essential for establishing a reliable technology. An efficient delignification step would enable production of lignin-derived chemicals, thereby contributing to reduced treatment costs and better return on investment. The amount of cellulose accessible to hydrolysis would also be increased and the amount of inert material carried through the process reduced. As a consequence the capital cost would be less because a smaller plant capacity can be used for a given waste throughput [11].

Interdisciplinary research should be devoted to increasing the reactivity of cellulose so that complete conversion with minimal pretreatment is attained. Developments are required to alter the economics of biomass conversion [12]. Further research is also needed to find strains of micro-organisms which produce high-activity cellulases.

10.2 CELLULOSE AND LIGNIN CHARACTERIZATION

The technology of cellulose and lignin bioconversion is often underestimated in relation to the difficulties of converting laboratory findings into commercial-scale process designs which can be operated economically. A major reason for this is an inadequate understanding of the unique chemistry of cellulose, lignin and their many natural combined forms. This section highlights the most important chemical information on structure of these raw materials.

10.2.1 Chemical structures

Cellulose from grass, softwood and hardwood does not differ in composition, although its crystalline structure does vary according to its origin. Repeating units of β-D-glucose, linked together by 1,4′-β-glycosidic bonds, form a long linear polymeric chain. The glucose units do not occupy an identical position in the polysaccharide skeleton since they are alternately rotated through 180° as required by the β-linkage formation (Fig. 10.1). The length of the cellulose polymer varies in the raw materials

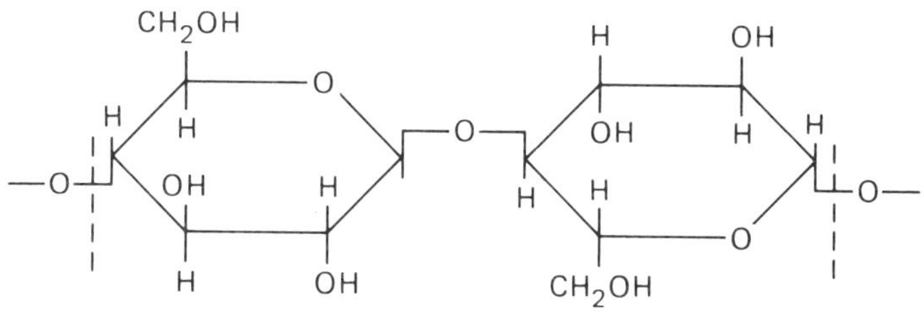

Fig. 10.1 — Structural formula of cellulose.

and is measured by the degree of polymerization (DP). The highest value, 15 000, has been observed for cotton. In wood, values range from 7000 to 10 000. In agricultural wastes they are much lower, generally less than 1000. Consequently, the molecular weight of natural cellulose can reach values up to 2 000 000 but is generally within the range 300 000–500 000.

This linear glucose polymer, without side chains, achieves a highly-ordered crystalline structure by a close association of the sterically compatible molecules assisted by the formation of intra- as well as intermolecular hydrogen bonds. These very numerous hydrogen bonds hold the chains together and are not broken by water. Thus cellulose is totally insoluble in water, despite the presence of three hydroxyl groups on each anhydroglucose unit.

As recently stated by Tsao [13], the crystalline structure of cellulose is still a subject of controversy. However, two general categories of crystalline model have been suggested. According to the fibrilized-fringe, unicellular extended-chain model, the cellulose chains can be schematically represented [12] as straight lines in parallel, with the non-reducing ends located in one region and the amorphous portion in the opposite region. In between there is a crystalline region. In this model, probably the most popular, some regions of disorder are also dispersed along the chain length [13]. The alternative hypothesis of a folding-chain model for cellulose structure was initially suggested by Chang [14] to explain the enhanced hydrolysis of cellulose observed after solvent pretreatment. In solvent-pretreated cellulose, the number of folds per molecule increases and the fold length drops from DP = 160 for natural, untreated cellulose to DP = 30. Since the solvent does not cause an appreciable reduction in DP of the original whole molecule, the decrease in fold length is consistent with the increase in fold numbers. In parallel, it may be observed experimentally that there is an enhancement of the rate of cellulose hydrolysis during solvent pretreatment. It is thought that the solvent increases the number of weak links close to the folds, which in turn increases the chain schism [4]. Further details of cellulose structure may be found in the literature [14–17].

Lignin structure is much more difficult to describe, mainly because during the isolation of this polymer from woody tissues secondary reactions generally occur. These alter the chemical and physical properties of the lignin [3]. The major changes are in bond cleavages, the extent of lignin condensation, and the content of certain functional groups. Changes also occur during various isolation techniques, as summarized by Amer and Drew [18].

Lignin, a highly branched polymer, differs somewhat in chemical composition from various biomass sources. Hydroxycinnamyl alcohols are always the precursors of the lignin. The three primary precursors are coniferyl alcohol (3-methoxy-4-hydroxycinnamyl alcohol) principally in softwood, and coniferyl alcohol, sinapyl alcohol (3,5-dimethoxy-4-hydroxycinnamyl alcohol) and coumaryl alcohol (4-hydroxycinnamyl alcohol) in hardwoods and grasses (Fig. 10.2). Hardwood lignin and

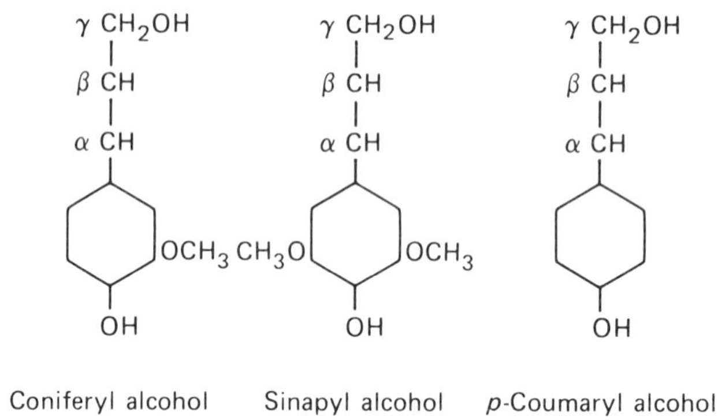

Fig. 10.2 — Lignin precursors.

softwood lignin are also called guaiacylsyringyl lignin and guaiacyl lignin, respectively.

The resulting polymer contains phenylpropane units derived from alcohol monomers with a diverse range of stable carbon–carbon bonds and aryl ether linkages [19]. In grass lignins significant quantities of esterified phenylpropanoid acids complete the chemical structure [20]. The presence of covalent carbon–carbon bonds characterizes the lignin as a recalcitrant polymer which is difficult to degrade. Hall [7] has reported one of the most detailed structural models for softwood lignin published to date; other workers [21,22] have reported a schematic structure for softwood conifer (spruce) lignin. The aromatic and phenolic character, as well as the three-dimensional polymeric network of this complicated large molecule, are apparent in both structures. Although the methoxyl substitution and the degree of carbon–carbon linkage between phenyl groups differ somewhat in hardwood lignin, the important features of lignin molecules remain the same [22]. However, hardwood lignin has a lower degree of cross-linking, as suggested by the easier dissolution of guaiacylsyringyl lignins. Minor differences in the relative proportion of the three alcohol precursors have been observed depending on the plant tissues and the location of the lignin within the plant cell wall [3].

The molecular weight of lignin varies considerably. In soluble lignin preparations the molecular weight ranges from below a thousand to over a million; hardwood lignin has a lower apparent molecular weight [23]. Also, the estimated molecular weight of lignin varies with biomass source and production process.

10.2.2 Formation

The biosynthetic pathway of *in vivo* lignification is not yet completely understood. The mechanism seems to be controlled by the supply of lignin precursors, the transport of lignin monomers into the cell wall and the polymerization of cinnamyl alcohols [3]. Generally, the synthesis of lignin starts from phenylalanine, and in grasses from both phenylalanine and tyrosine. These amino acids are synthesized from the carbohydrates formed during the photosynthetic assimilation of atmospheric carbon dioxide through the shikimic acid pathway.

A clear, theoretical explanation of the enzyme system of lignification and the regulation of lignin biosynthesis in plant cells has been given by Higuchi *et al.* [24]. Phenylalanine ammonialyase (PAL) and tyrosine ammonialyase (TAL) catalyse the removal of ammonia from L-phenylalanine and L-tyrosine to form *trans*-cinnamic acid and *p*-coumaric acid, respectively. Specific hydroxylases (HL) promote the successive hydroxylation of cinnamic acid to *p*-coumaric acid and successively to caffeic acid. This latter is converted to ferulic acid by the action of *O*-methyltransferases (OMT), which is then hydroxylated to 5-hydroxyferulic acid, an intermediate methylated in a further step to sinapic acid. Finally, acids are enzymatically reduced to the corresponding alcohols (Fig. 10.3). According to the above scheme, the higher

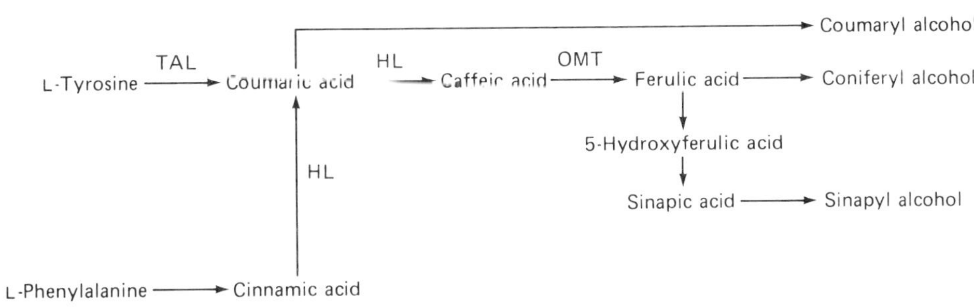

Fig. 10.3 — Lignin pathway.

percentage of coumaryl-derived lignin in grasses is determined by the absence of tyrosine in plants, while the difference between hardwood lignin (guaiacylsynringyl lignin) and softwood lignin (guaiacyl lignin) is related to the absence of active *O*-methyltransferases in gymnosperms towards 5-hydroxyferulic acid conversion to sinapic acid, a fundamental step in the cycle of sinapyl alcohol formation. Once the cinnamyl alcohols are formed, an oxidative polymerization occurs, catalysed by peroxidase or laccase. The hydroxyl groups of alcohols are oxidized, thus producing radical species in mesomeric forms which then randomly couple in a non-enzymatic fashion with the formation of oligomeric intermediates, rich in phenolic hydroxyls, and finally of lignin macromolecules.

Unlike lignin, the biosynthesis of native cellulose is less complex. Precursors of cellulose molecules are nucleoside 5′-diphosphate glucose, mainly GDP-glucose and UDP-glucose depending on biomass source. Cellulose synthetase catalyses the addition of NDP-glucose to the growing cellulose chain, thus increasing the unit numbers (DP) of the linear polymer:

$$\text{NDP-Glucose} + (\text{–}C_6H_5O_5\text{–})_n \rightarrow \text{NDP} + (\text{–}C_6H_{10}O_5\text{–})_{n+1} + H_2O$$

10.2.3 Morphological distribution in plant cell walls

Lignin and cellulose are intimately associated with hemicellulose, proteins and other low-percentage components in the cell walls. Lignin has a structural function since it imparts rigidity to the cell walls and protects plant tissue from microbial invasion [9]. On the other hand, cellulose plays the role of fibre-reinforcing material in the amorphous matrix of hemicellulose and lignin [23], similar to carbon fibres in synthetic composite polymers.

Different techniques, including selective dissolution of the cell wall and ultraviolet microscopy, have been used to establish the association between lignin and carbohydrates within the cell wall at the ultra-microscopic level. Fergus *et al.* [25,26] have made a major contribution to the understanding of the distribution of lignin in wood. Lignin occurs in the middle lamella at a higher concentration than in the fibre wall. However, since the middle lamella represents roughly 10 per cent of the total cell volume the largest portion of the lignin content (80 per cent) is found in the fibre wall. This lignin plays a number of regulatory roles essential to the life of plants [3], such as energy storage, bonding action between cells, impeding the penetration of destructive enzymes and waterproofing. Thus, lignin improves the mechanical, physicochemical and biochemical resistance of plants to stress.

It has been suggested [23] that in the cell wall cellulose is organized in elementary fibrils, the width of which varies between approximately 100 Å and 300 Å depending on the degree of microfibril aggregation and the amount of amorphous material around the crystalline core. Their length is a function of the degree of cellulose polymerization and of chain overlap. Values greater than 5 μm are normal. In the secondary wall, which is formed during the growth and maturation of the cell and comprises of 70–90 per cent cellulose, the microfibrils are differently oriented in three layers. In the transition lamella, which is the outermost layer of the fibre and surrounded by the heavily lignified middle lamella, they form two groups of overlapping opposed spirals. In the middle layer, the main secondary wall, they occur in a helical arrangement. The structure of the inner layer is not yet fully understood [27]. Finally, up to three layers of elementary cellulose fibrils occur in the thin primary walls (300 Å).

10.3 LIGNOCELLULOSE RESIDUE AVAILABILITY

Although solar energy accumulated in plants as lignocellulose materials makes up only 0.1 per cent of total irradiated energy, large quantities of organic matter are produced every year by photosynthesis. A significant fraction of the biomass accumulates on the ground as agricultural and forest wastes. Bassham [1] estimated dry biomass productivity at 155.2 Gt per year, which is in good agreement with the value of 164 Gt per year recently reported by others [28]. Since the percentage of biomass coming from cultivated land is 5.9 per cent of the total and for every pound of crop harvested one pound of solid waste is produced (such as cobs, stalks, husks, leaves and roots) and assuming that an average of 50 per cent of the crop residue is harvested in order to avoid deterioration of the soil condition, then the amount of raw material may be estimated as being equivalent to 2.4 Gt/a. McHale [29] has estimated that 75 per cent of biomass generated on grassland is residue and therefore another 11.3 Gt/a are available. Moreover, roughly 35 per cent of forest biomass is left over after harvesting and primary wood production. This is potentially available as a further source of biomass equivalent to 22.6 Gt/a. Other environmental considerations are important. Care has to be exercised to maintain the organic content and productivity of cropland so that there is little need to convert marginal areas into intensively cultivated plantations, a process which would reduce the diversity of natural vegetation and threaten wildlife and other natural biota. Furthermore, even the mildest processing, such as bioconversion, needs water and subsequent wastewater disposal. Increased levels of CO_2 in the atmosphere, for example from burning of fossil fuels, is reported to increase the oxidative turnover of residues and exposed humus [30], which could make the controlled recycle of residues important for long-term soil fertility.

In addition to the sources of biomass already referred to, animal feedlot and industrial wastes contain much cellulose and lignin. In a recent survey [31] 546 biogas plants were found in operation at the beginning of 1983 in the European Community member states and Switzerland, representing a total digester working volume of 269 000 m^3: 95 000 m^3 on farms and 174 000 m^3 in industry. The cellulose (but not lignin) is reduced along with other organic materials and the biogas produced represents a yearly output of 33 000 t of oil-equivalent worth 7 million European Currency Units (ECU). These wastes, if untreated, would have a negative value since they are highly polluting. The reduction in BOD_5 and COD which is achieved during treatment is of course the main motivation for investing in biogas systems.

Other categories of cellulosic wastes and crops, such as crop residues, municipal solid wastes, sewage sludges, algae and aquatic plants, are suitable substrates for biomethanation, and the potential contribution to the energy requirements of the European Community has been evaluated as being equivalent to 31.5 Mt of oil-equivalent: this represents only 3 per cent of the 1985 European energy consumption but is still worth 7 thousand million ECU [32,33]. Anaerobic digestion is only suitable for recycling cellulose and hemicellulose since lignin has been shown to be resistant to anaerobic biodegradation [9,34,35]. Lignin can, however, be degraded in an oxidative atmosphere and waste treatment using aerobic ligninolytic systems has recently attracted much research effort [36].

Wastewaters from wood and pulp factories represent a major source of lignin. Lignin derivatives, which amount to between 3 and 13 per cent of pulp produced, are released in the effluent. This might be utilized as a substrate and converted to chemicals, some of which cannot be obtained from petroleum. However, the process is not economically feasible unless the lignocellulose wastes have a substantial negative value in a given locality.

10.4 BIOCONVERSION

10.4.1 Degradation in nature

Although many fungi and bacteria are known to degrade cellulose and lignin in nature, and despite the importance of this process, the mechanisms of the processes are not yet fully understood. Doubts still exist whether the cellulase system is the only enzyme complex responsible in all organisms or if other systems are also of significance; whether in different microbes the cellulase is composed of the same enzymes or whether the different number of cellulolytic components depends mainly on the producing organisms or may even vary in the same cellulase system. As a consequence of the higher complexity of the molecule, the roles played by different populations in lignin biodegradation have not yet been fully identified.

Following a recent historical perspective presented by Kirk [37], the most important steps towards gaining a better understanding of lignin biodegradation have been taken. Prior to 1936 it was shown that lignin in wood is decomposed by white-rot fungi; further research performed between 1936 and 1951 confirmed that higher fungi degrade lignin in nature; whilst between 1951 and 1969 evidence was presented that bacteria degrade lignin, and the first decay models were proposed. Only recently have decomposition rates of lignin and model compounds in soils and other environments been measured. In the last few years, radioisotope methods have been successfully applied to define the biochemical aspects of lignin biodegradation starting from the early studies of Crawford [38] and Kirk *et al.* [39].

Both bacteria and fungi apparently cause various modifications to the natural lignin molecule, even though only a few completely decompose lignin to CO_2 and H_2O. In general, lignolytic systems in nature must occur as a mixed flora of different micro-organisms since white-rot fungi (basidiomycetes and a few ascomycetes) were found to be the only single organisms capable of decaying wood in nature. Brown-rot fungi (basidiomycetes), soft-rot fungi (ascomycetes) and bacteria play different roles in lignin biodegradation but they cannot efficiently convert the polymer to CO_2 in axenic culture, although some evidence to the contrary has been reported in the literature. Although the mechanism of degradation may also vary depending on the lignin source, it is recognized that white-rot fungi attack the unaltered lignin polymer and cleave carbon–carbon and aryl ether bonds, causing the formation of intermediate molecular weight polymers and the release of low molecular weight fragments. Brown-rot fungi achieve demethylation and limited oxidation but do not cleave aromatic rings efficiently. Soft-rot fungi can degrade lignin under moist conditions but do not perform a substantial degradation to CO_2. Finally, bacteria actively degrade mono- and dilignols with molecular weights up to 350. The bacterial degradation of the lignin macromolecule is difficult to assess. Only a few strains, such as *Streptomyces* and *Nocardia* spp., show a capacity for attacking lignin and lignin derivatives.

The reader is referred to published reviews [40–43] for further studies on lignin-degrading micro-organisms and the mechanisms of microbial degradation. Lastly, the point whether natural lignin is degraded in anaerobic environments deserves comment. Studies carried out before 1984 suggest that natural and synthetic lignin is not degraded anaerobically in anoxic soils and sediments [44,45]. An explanation for the biodegradative recalcitrance of lignin in anaerobic environments has also been given [46]. On the other hand, studies into the anaerobic degradation of lignin-derived monomeric aromatic compounds [47–50] and low molecular weight modified lignin and lignin-related dimers with aryl ether bond, suggest the hypothesis that oxygen is neither required for the cleavage of intermonomeric linkages nor needed for the breakdown of these polymeric molecules. Recently, radiolabelled synthetic lignin and lignocellulose derived from marine and freshwater grasses and hardwood were degraded anaerobically to CO_2 and CH_4 with anoxic sediments collected from a salt-marsh, a freshwater marsh and a mangrove swamp [10]. The rate of biodegradation is slow, but the finding seems to confirm that, although lignocelluloses are recalcitrant to anaerobic biodegradation, lignin is biodegradable in the absence of oxygen.

The biodegradation of cellulose occurs through the action of a great number of bacteria and fungi. The first important anaerobic bacterium *Bacteriodes succinoges,* was isolated from rumen by Hungate [51]. A few other bacteria, such as *Cellulomonas* spp., *Clostridium thermocellum* and *Streptomyces flavogriseus,* are capable of producing highly active cellulases. More fungi than bacteria can utilize cellulose as a substrate and produce metabolic products, such as CO_2 and CH_4. A quite exhaustive listing of cellulolytic micro-organisms has been reported [27]. However, only a few micro-organisms secrete cellulase complexes, so-called 'true' or 'complete' cellulases, which can degrade all forms of cellulose [52]. Moreover, only a few fungi produce cellulase enzyme systems capable of extensively degrading insoluble cellulose to soluble sugars *in vitro.* The fungus *Trichoderma reesei,* formerly called *T. viride,* is mostly employed in laboratory studies dealing with the enzymatic hydrolysis of cellulose, since it secretes a complete cellulase capable of converting different forms of cellulose to glucose. Several mutants with more than three times the activity of the natural type and less subject to catabolite repression have been produced in fermenters [53]. Bacteria mainly occur in the rumen fluid but have also been isolated from soils. Rumen bacteria are mostly anaerobic, although micro-aerophilic and some aerobic flora also occur.

The oxidative nature of cellulose degradation has been investigated, and the works of Eriksson and co-workers [54], Wood and McCrae [55] and Reese and Mandels [56] indicate that the mechanism is not necessarily oxidative. In fact, the rate of cellulose degradation is slightly lower under anaerobic than under aerobic conditions and the presence of a CO_2 atmosphere has no effect on the hydrolysis rate.

Questions which are still under debate in cellulose biodegradation are the existence of many components in a cellulase system and the microbial utilization of the insoluble macromolecular cellulose. Gong *et al.* [57] have explained the origin of the different types of cellulases produced by the same species of fungus as a 'fact of life'. Since for a micro-organism which possesses limited genetic pools it is wasteful to transcribe and translate many enzymes for the same function, they postulate that multiple enzymes arise from partial proteolysis of the same enzyme. Mandels and coworkers [58] explained enzyme multiplicity as the consequence of a large number of circumstances, such as different nutrition of the cells, genetic non-homogeneity and synthetic pathways. Several explanations have been put forward to describe cellulose degradation in nature. It has been proposed that cellulases may not be required since H_2O_2/Fe systems randomly attack cellulose [59,60] and, therefore, micro-organisms having glucose oxidase could degrade cellulose. However, cellulose hydrolysis to sugars generally involves micro-organisms capable of synthesizing and secreting enzymes with specific affinity for the hydrolysis of -1,4-glucosidic bonds of the polymer chain. Cellulase production can be triggered by the contact of the cell surface with the insoluble cellulose, or by the continuous release of constituent cellulase by micro-organisms, or by the ability of a cell to synthesize cellulase under starvation conditions. On the basis of results obtained studying growth and cellulase biosynthesis of *Trichoderma reesei,* Gong *et al.* [57] reached the conclusion that the occurrence of constituent cellulases seems the more likely explanation. *Trichoderma viride* and other cellulolytic micro-organisms are also able to synthesize trace amounts of cellulases which are independent of carbon sources present in the media.

The estimated dimensions of cellulolytic enzymes range from 25 to 80 Å in diameter for spheres, 40 Å for cellulase from *T. viride* [61], and from 15×80 Å to 40×250 Å for ellipsoids [62]. Therefore, the enzymes can enter easily by diffusion in the gross capillaries of cellulose which vary between 2000 and 100 000 Å. A satisfactory level of knowledge of the mode of action of cellulase systems now exists and will be discussed in the following section. Three major components are present in cellulases, independently of the micro-organisms, and have been defined as endoglucanases, exoglucanases and cellobia, respectively.

10.4.2 Enzymology of lignin and cellulose degradation

Lignin is interspersed with hemicellulose and forms protective seals of cellulose microfibrils which prevent access of degradative enzymes to the cellulose and hemicellulose in woody plant tissues in nature. Different fungi, bacteria and microflora in the soil have developed systems able to modify and efficiently degrade this heterogeneous aromatic polymer, since no long-term accumulation of lignocellulose residues takes place in nature. Among the micro-organisms involved in lignin biodegradation, fungi seem to play the dominant role and have been most studied, in particular the white-rot basidiomycete *Phanerochaete chrysosporium* and formerly its imperfect stage *Sporotrichum pulverulentum.* Currently there is much research effort being devoted to the biochemistry of lignin degradation. The identification of individual reactions of the lignin degradation process is essential for defining the biochemical mechanism. In turn, the biochemical information is necessary for optimum design of industrial bioprocesses. To meet this end, different experimental approaches have been developed. They consist of studies on fungal degradation of extractive lignin at the macromolecular level, on the biodegradation of lignin model compounds, on the structural identification of the low molecular weight compounds and, most recently, on the isolation, purification and characterization of lignolytic enzymes.

It may be assumed that a very complicated biodegradation takes place, with many enzymes working together. Also, the possibility of an interaction between the degradation of lignin and that of carbohydrates with a mutual effect of the enzymes involved cannot be excluded.

Lignin has no hydrolysable repeating units as occur in polysaccharides, proteins and nucleic acids and, since it is unlikely that lignin is first decomposed to monomers and then the monomers disintegrated, many complex reactions must occur during its fungal degradation. The polymer is non-stereoregular and, therefore, biodegradation is probably heavily oxidative and non-specific. Reaction patterns include: (a) cleavage of the C–C bonds in the side chains; (b) the reductive cleavage of –O–4 bonds; (c) 3–O– and 5–O–demethylation and 4–O–methylation, which could occur either at the macromolecular level or on lignin fragments; (d) oxidative cleavage of aromatic rings; and (e) other oxidative, reducing and hydroxylation reactions [19,63].

For a long time phenol-oxidizing enzymes (laccase with O_2^-, peroxidase with H_2O_2, tyrosinase) and mono- and dioxygenases produced by wood-rotting fungi have been related to lignin degradation and extensively studied, since they were suspected to be key enzymes [40,64]. Among these, laccase (EC 1.10.3.2), abundantly secreted from *Polyporus versicolor*, has been purified and characterized, but, in spite of all the studies, its role is still not clear. Its action is to abstract hydrogen from phenolic hydroxyl groups to form phenoxy radicals, which are then converted into quinones. However, in lignin 80 per cent of the phenolic groups are etherified and therefore laccase is not capable of oxidizing many of them. Other activities for this enzyme have been reviewed [65,66]. Polymerization activity has been related to the occurrence of ether-linkage formation and to the promotion of carbon–carbon linkages, whereas depolymerization activity has been postulated on the basis of observing demethylation of lignin and model compounds, the elimination of the side chains of model compounds and the liberation of aliphatic aldehydes. The sum of these actions represents the contribution of laccase in lignin biodegradation. However, laccase alone is not capable of depolymerizing or fragmenting lignin extensively unless, in nature, it is coupled with the action of other enzymes capable of splitting ether linkages. Laccase and peroxidase may also function in concert with different sugar-oxidizing enzymes [66] which are present in white-rot fungi and are able to reduce quinones or quinoid compounds produced by the action of laccase. It has been proposed that cellobiose-quinone oxidoreductase [67] and glucose oxidase [68] are linked to the degradation of cellulose and lignin. It has also been suggested that phenol-oxidizing enzymes play some kind of regulatory role in the production of both lignin- and polysaccharide-degrading enzymes by oxidation of lignin and lignin-related phenols when *S. pulverulentum* is growing on wood [69].

On the other hand, the nature and structure of lignin, which is optically inactive, heterogeneous and random, suggest that other non-specific catalysts might be involved in its degradation. Until the first discovery of a lignin-degrading enzyme [8] which is extracellular, oxidative and requires hydrogen peroxide for activity, it was known that oxidative extracellular agents, non-specific towards the substrate, were involved in lignin biodegradation. The nature of these agents was a matter for debate since, in spite of all the research on lignolytic micro-organisms and fungi, no lignolytic-specific enzymes were isolated. The possibility that lignin degradation might be non-enzymatic was researched, especially after Hall's hypothesis was formulated [7]. Hall suggested that non-enzyme-bound activated oxygen-derived species (hydrogen peroxide, H_2O_2; superoxide, O_2^-; hydroxyl radical and singlet oxygen, $^1O_2$) enzymatically generated might be responsible for the attack and fragmentation of lignin in the initial stages of its degradation by micro-organisms. Other workers [70–72] reported that lignolytic activity, side-chain cleavage and demethylation of model compounds were associated with the production of H_2O_2 during the initial biodegradation of lignin by lignolytic cultures of *P. chrysosporium*. Current thinking suggests that the involvement of O_2^- in lignolytic cultures of *P. chrysosporium* is doubtful, that $^1O_2$ has no role, whilst the role of $^{\bullet}OH$ is still equivocal [20,35].

The purification of an H_2O_2-requiring an enzyme [8] capable of catalysing some key reactions of lignin degradation has weakened the hypothesis that catalysis is due to non-enzyme-bound activated-oxygen species derived from H_2O_2. This extracellular enzyme has been purified and recently separated into two H_2O_2-requiring enzymes [73]. The first one, an apparent H_2O_2-requiring oxygenase, contains one molecule of haem as iron protoporphyrin IX, which possibly interacts with both H_2O_2 and molecular oxygen [74]. The second enzyme, also a haem protein, is an Mn^{2+}-dependent lactate-activated peroxidase [73]. It has been reported that the purified homogeneous enzyme oxygenase is able to catalyse diarylpropane and β-aryl ether and diol α, β cleavage as well as olefin hydroxylation [74] in several lignin model compounds. The large number of reactions catalysed by this homogeneous haem protein suggests that a non-specific enzyme is responsible for the biodegradation of lignin polymer. Studies on metalloporphyrins have shown that these haem enzyme models mimic an important function of the lignin-degrading enzymes [75], thus suggesting that the prosthetic group might be responsible for the non-specific attack. Recently, the discovery of three extracellular enzymes of *P. chrysosporium* has been reported [76]. Dimethylase, esterase and oxidase activities were assessed and all three enzymes were found to be H_2O_2-dependent and activated by Mn^{2+} ions.

The chemical structure of cellulose is relatively simple compared to lignin and the identification of the enzymes involved in its biodegradation has been less difficult. As discussed in a previous section, cellulose is a linear homopolymer of anhydroglucose units linked by -1,4-glucosidic bonds, and individual molecules are linked together with intra- as well as intermolecular hydrogen bonds to form elementary fibrils. During the formation of the latter, ordered areas alternate with amorphous regions. All significant chemical and enzymatic reactions take place in these regions and the difficulties encountered during hydrolysis are due to the crystallized nature of cellulose rather than to any chemical bonds. Moreover, as pointed out in other sections, cellulose does not occur in pure form in nature but is always associated with a variety of other polymers such as hemicellulose, lignin, pectin, starch and proteins. The combined action of more enzymes, probably from different micro-organisms, allows degradation in nature and in biotechnological processes such as composting (Ch. 13).

As far as the breakdown of cellulose substances is concerned it is well known that numerous micro-organisms, such as *Trichoderma viride*, *T. koningii*, *Coniphora cerebella*, *Sporotrichum pulverulentum*, *Polyporus adustus*, *Fusarium solani*, *Aspergillus awamori* and *Aspergillus wentii* among fungi, and *Clostridium tyhermocellum*, *Thermomospora* spp. and *Cellulomonas* spp. among bacteria, produce in the extracellular fluid of growth a multi-component enzyme system called cellulase. In this hydrolytic system three major components—endoglucanases, exoglucanases and cellobiase—have been identified, and isoenzymes are nearly always present. Moreover, depending on source and growth conditions, the proportions and the multiplicity of the different components vary. For example, at least four different endoglucanases [77–79], two cellobiohydrolases [80,81], each one consisting of a number of isoenzymes, and three cellobiases [82] have been isolated and identified from commercial preparations of *T. reesei*. Each of these enzymes has unique substrate specificity and biochemical properties. The action of all these components allows the conversion of the highly ordered cellulose polymer into its monomeric units.

Most of the work done on the biochemistry of cellulolysis has concerned cellulase produced by *Trichoderma* spp. [83–85]. The different components of the cellulase complex have been isolated, purified to homogeneity and the mode of action intensively studied [55,57,85]. These enzymes act both individually and collectively to hydrolyse cellulose and cellodextrins.

Different hypotheses have been formulated to explain the participation of all the components to the hydrolysis of cellulose, but the exact mechanism is still a matter for debate. In 1950, Reese *et al.* [86] first proposed a two-step process in which an enzyme activity, named C_1, was shown to be able to modify cellulose, so causing disruption of the hydrogen bonds. Then the modified cellulose was hydrolysed randomly by endoglucanases, C_x.

Since then many studies that have been undertaken using purified components have produced evidence which contradicts this first hypothesis. In fact, it was found that a highly purified C_1 component, when acting alone, is unable to initiate attack on highly ordered cellulose. On the other hand its attack on amorphous cellulose is limited, whereas it can hydrolyse oligosaccharides to remove cellobiose [54,83,84,87]. Later the C_x component showed significant activity only on amorphous cellulose. It was also established that C_1 acted synergistically with C_x when solubilizing highly ordered cellulose [55]. All these findings led to the current concept of how these enzymes synergistically interact to degrade crystalline cellulose through a primary attack by the endoglucanases, C_x, followed by the release of either cellobiose or glucose from the non-reducing ends of exposed chains. At present the mechanism for enzymatic cellulose degradation that is most commonly proposed is the following [4,12]: (i) endoglucanases, C_x, randomly attack the internal -1,4-linkages; (ii) exoglucanases which are present in two major components (a) cellobiohydrolase, also named C_1, 1,4-D-glucan cellobiohydrolase (EC 3.2.1.91), cleaves off cellobiose units from the non-reducing ends of glucan and (b) exoglucohydrolase, (1,4)-glucan glucohydrolase removes glucose units from the non-reducing ends of the chain; (iii) glucosidase, (EC 3.2.1.21) acts on soluble products hydrolysing cellobiose, and perhaps other cellodextrins as well, to yield glucose. Finally, reaction products, mainly cellobiose and glucose, have been reported to inhibit the components of the cellulase complex [80,84].

10.5 POTENTIAL CHEMICALS FROM LIGNIN AND CELLULOSE

The range of products that could be obtained via the bioconversion of lignin and cellulose is wide and industrially attractive in view of their potential utilization as chemicals, fuel and fodder. However, it must be kept in mind that cellulose and lignin often occur at low concentrations and together with other chemical species; as a result their bioconversion to useful products may not be economically feasible. In fact, the activity of specific enzymes could be limited or destroyed by the presence of inhibitors and the recovery of products from the effluent stream could be difficult and costly. Also, in many situations, both in residues and wastes, the non-biological fractionation of components can fairly easily be performed and a variety of almost pure compounds can be obtained. Generally, in the case of dilute sources, it is convenient to convert lignin and cellulose to fuels, whenever possible, using suitable micro-organisms, or to achieve a partial degradation to intermediates which can be oxidized further to reduce the BOD_5 and COD of the stream. In the case of concentrated sources, the components can be used conveniently as feedstocks for making chemicals; the scale of chemical production and the added value of chemical products and by-products is attractive. However, chemicals produced from biomass must compete with those made from oil. Since high-price/low-volume chemicals will not benefit too much from an increase in oil prices and the construction of large plants for the production of low-price/high-volume chemicals is limited by biomass availability in the surrounding area, the best opportunity may lie with those in the middle of the price range [88].

Glucose and phenolic products can most readily be made from cellulose and lignin, respectively. Glucose plays a central role in all processes for cellulose utilization since it is the major product of hydrolysis reaction and many micro-organisms can grow on glucose which could serve as a substrate for the production of fuel, alcohol and single-cell proteins. On the other hand, phenolic intermediates from lignin can be utilized either for the production of lignochemicals, which have a structure that cannot be obtained from petroleum [3], or for their conversion to polymers and plastics. The fermentation of glucose to ethanol is one of the oldest bioconversion processes used by man. The utilization of ethanol for replacing lead as an octane-enhancer in petrol has recently received considerable attention. At the present time, the cost of ethanol produced by fermentation of cellulose biomass is higher than that of chemically produced ethanol. However, estimates suggest that this technology will become more competitive with ethanol production, for example from grain and sugar crops [89]. Moreover, the development of these technologies will help to solve the problem of unemployment since from 5 to 12 times more labour is required to produce the same quantity of fuel from biomass than from oil [30]. Ethanol can also be converted to ethylene and butadiene, which are chemicals widely used in the production of polymers and synthetic rubber. Finally, several other uses, such as solvents, beverages and for biological energy are possible for ethanol, even though it appears less suitable than when ethanol is produced starting from wastes.

Other routes for glucose conversion have been studied and offer the possibility of obtaining a range of organic chemicals. In France, AFME (Agence Française pour la Maitrise de l'Energie) has, since 1983, been undertaking a large project on the production of alternative fuels from biomass and the process is based on the fermentation of sugars to ABE (acetone, butanol and ethanol) through the bioaction of *Clostridium acetobutylicum*. Lactic acid can also be obtained by direct fermentation of glucose. In this fermentation the mass balance is more favourable than in the production of ethanol, since the formation of gaseous compounds, such as carbon dioxide, does not occur. The lactic acid can be dehydrated in one step to acetaldehyde and acrylic acid, a chemical which already has a thousand million pounds per year market [88]. Glucose can be directly converted to acetic acid with a good mass balance using *Clostridium thermoaceticum*. If the raw material is available at low cost, this technology would be competitive with conventional technologies. Several other chemicals derived from glucose and carbohydrates possesss chemical and physical properties to replace petroleum derivatives, and perhaps in the near future the chemistry of sugars will be re-examined.

A possibility, which has been widely considered, is the production of single-cell proteins (SCP) as fodder for animals. At the present time there are essentially two processes for the production of SCP from lignocellulose materials. First, SCP is obtained by the direct growth of micro-organisms on pretreated lignocellulose materials; second, SCP is produced by the growth of micro-organisms in a sugar solution obtained by the enzymatic hydrolysis of pretreated lignocellulose materials. The recent developments and the problems of this bioconversion have been reviewed by Tanaka and Matsuno [90]. Several problems still remain to be solved in order to make SCP production successful and economically attractive.

In general, studies for industrial applications of lignin and lignin derivatives are at a research level and a cost–benefit analysis of most of the proposed biological processes cannot be undertaken. A major area of interest in the research into lignin bioconversion processes is the part conversion of waste lignocellulose materials, such as found in the paper and pulp-making industries. The microbial decolorization of Kraft bleach-plant effluents is also being researched. Isolated lignin products and lignosulphonates from these processes can be used as dispersants, emulsion stabilizers, lignin-based plywood, chipboard adhesives and asphalt binders. The utilization of large volumes of lingosulphonates can be expected in the area of enhanced oil recovery if oil-field displacement tests continue to produce promising results. Aromatic polymers and low molecular weight chemicals, such as vanillin, cresylic acids, phenol and benzene can be derived from lignin instead of from oil. However, the small market volume and the relatively low product volume seem to be limiting factors in commercial development of bioprocesses for such speciality chemicals [3].

In conclusion, the production of chemicals, fuels and single-cell proteins from lignocellulose residues and wastes cannot yet compete economically with that of feedstocks derived from oil. However, the tonnage and general availability of lignocellulose in certain parts of the world remains attractive enough for research to continue. If significant advances can be made in conversion rate, recovery of intermediate products, and reactor designs to accommodate mixed species or mixed multi-step enzymes, the economics could be transformed.

REFERENCES

[1] Bassham, J. A. (1975). In: Wilke, C. R. (ed.) *Cellulose as a Chemical and Energy Resource,* Wiley, New York.
[2] Ghose, T. K. (1977). *Adv. Biochem. Eng. Biotechnol.,* **6**, 39.
[3] Janshekar, H. and Fiechter, A. (1983). *Adv. Biochem. Eng. Biotechnol.,* **27**, 120.
[4] Bisaria, V. S. and Ghose, T. K. (1981). *Enzyme Microb. Technol.,* **3**, 90.
[5] Sarkanen, K. V. (1980). In: Varmavoun, A. (ed.) *Proc. IUPAC 27th Int. Congr. Pure and Applied Chemistry,* Pergamon Press, Oxford.
[6] Ladisch, M. R. (1979) *Process Biochem.,* **14**, 21.
[7] Hall, P. L. (1980), *Enz. Microbiol. Technol.,* **2**, 170.
[8] Tien, M. and Kirk, T. K. (1983). *Science,* **221**, 661.
[9] Zeikus, J. G. (1980). In: Kirk, T. K., Higuchi, T. and Chang, H.-M. (eds) *Lignin Biodegradation: Microbiology, Chemistry, and Potential Applications,* Vol. I, CRC Press, Boca Raton, p. 103.

[10] Benner, R., Maccubbin, A. E. and Hodson, R. E. (1984). *Appl. Environ. Microbiol.*, **47**, 998.
[11] Rosenberg, S. L. and Wilke, C. R. (1980). In: Kirk, T. K., Higuchi, T. and Chang, H.-m. (eds) *Lignin Biodegradation: Microbiology, Chemistry, and Potential Applications,* Vol. II, CRC Press, Boca Raton, p. 199.
[12] Ladisch, M. R., Lin, K. W., Voloch, M. and Tsao, G. T. (1983). *Enzyme Microb. Technol.*, **5**, 82.
[13] Tsao, G. (1984). In: Ferrero, G. L., Ferranti, M. P. and Naveau, H. (eds) *Anaerobic Digestion and Carbohydrate Hydrolysis of Waste,* Elsevier, London, p. 83.
[14] Chang, M. (1971). *J. Polym. Sci.*, **36**, 343 (1971).
[15] Stamm, A. J. (1984). *Wood and Cellulose Science,* Ronald Press, New York.
[16] Blackwell, J., Kolpak, F. J. and Gardner, H. K. (1977). In: Arthur, J. C., Jr (ed.) *Cellulose Chemistry and Technology,* 49, American Chemical Society, Washington, DC.
[17] Chang, M. and Tsao, G. T. (1981). *Cellul. Chem. Technol.*, **15**, 383.
[18] Amer, G. I. and Drew, S. W. (1980). *Ann. Rep. Ferment. Process,* **4**, 67.
[19] Higuchi, T. (1982). *Experientia,* **38**, 159.
[20] Crawford, R. L. and Crawford, D. L. (1984) *Enzyme Microb. Technol.*, **6**, 434.
[21] Goldstein, I. S. (1976). *Bioeng. Symp.*, **6**, 298.
[22] Higuchi, T. (1980). In: Kirk, T. K., Higuchi, T. and Chang, H.-m. (eds) *Lignin Biodegradation: Microbiology, Chemistry and Potential Applications,* Vol. I, CRC Press, Boca Raton, p. 1.
[23] Goldstein, I. S. (ed.) (1981). In: *Organic Chemicals from Biomass,* CRC Press, Boca Raton, p. 9.
[24] Higuchi, T., Shimada, M., Nakatsubo, F. and Tanahashi, M. (1977). *Wood Sci. Technol.*, **11**, 155.
[25] Fergus, B. J. and Goring, D. A. I. (1970). *Holzforschung,* **24**, 113.
[26] Fergus, B. J., Proctor, A. R., Scott, J. A. N. and Goring, D. A. I. (1969). *Wood Sci. Technol.*, **3**, 117.
[27] Dunlop, C. E. and Chiang, L. (1980). In: Shuler, M. L. (ed.) *Utilization and Recycling of Agricultural Wastes and Residues,* C.R.C. Press, Boca Raton, p. 19.
[28] Tanaka, M. and Matsuno, R. (1985). *Enzyme Microb. Technol.*, **7**, 197.
[29] McHale, J. (1970). *Ecological Context,* George Brazillier, New York.
[30] Energy Research Advisory Board (1983). *Solar Energy,* **30**, 1.
[31] Demuynck, M., Nyns, E. J. and Palz, W. (eds) (1984). *Biogas Plants in Europe,* D. Reidel, Dordrecht.
[32] Palz, W. and Chartier, P. (eds) (1980). *Energy from Biomass in Europe,* Applied Science, London.
[33] Hall, D. O. (1983). In: Strub, A., Chartier, P. and Schlesser, G. (eds) *Energy from Biomass,* Applied Science, London, p. 43.
[34] Melchior, J. L., Naveau, H. P. and Nyns, E. J. (1981). *Second International Symposium on Anaerobic Digestion,* Travemunde.
[35] Kirk, T. K. (1984). In: Gibson, D. T. (ed.) *Microbial Degradation of Organic Compounds,* Microbiology Series, Vol. 13, Ch. 14, Marcel Dekker New York.

[36] Eriksson, K. E. and Kirk, T. K. (1984). In: Robinson, C. W. (ed.) *Comprehensive Biotechnology,* Vol. 3, Pergamon Press, Toronto.
[37] Kirk, T. K. (1983). In: Higuchi, T., Chang, H.-m. and Kirk, T. K. (eds) *Recent Advances in Lignin Biodegradation,* Uni Publishers, Kyoto.
[38] Crawford, R. L., Robinson, L. E. and Cheh, A. (1979). In: Kirk, T. K., Higuchi, T. and Chang, H.-m. (eds) *Lignin Biodegradation: Microbiology, Chemistry and Applications,* CRC Press, West Palm Beach, p. 61.
[39] Kirk, T. K., Connors, W. J., Bleam, R. D., Hackett, W. F. and Zeikus, J. G. (1975). *Proc. Natl. Acad. Sci. USA,* **72**, 2515.
[40] Kirk, T. K. (1971). *Annu. Rev. Phytopathol.,* **9**, 182.
[41] Ander, P. and Eriksson, K. E. (1978). *Prog. Ind. Microbiol.,* **14**, 1.
[42] Higuchi, T. (1971). *Adv. Enzymol.,* **34**, 207.
[43] Crawford, D. L. and Crawford, R. L. (1980). *Enzyme Microb. Technol.,* **2**, 11.
[44] Hackett, W. F., Connors, W. J., Kirk, T. K. and Zeikus, J. G. (1977). *Appl. Environ. Microbiol.,* **33**, 43.
[45] Odier, E. and Monties, B. (1982). *Appl. Environ. Microbiol.,* **46**, 661.
[46] Zeikus, J. G., Wellstein, A. L. and Kirk, T. K. (1982). *FEMS Microbiol. Lett.,* **15**, 193.
[47] Healy, J. B., Jr and Young, L. Y. (1979). *Appl. Environ. Microbiol.,* **38**, 84.
[48] Healy, J. B., Jr, Young, L. Y. and Reinhard, M. (1980). *Appl. Environ. Microbiol.,* **39**, 436.
[49] Taylor, B. F. (1983). *Appl. Environ. Microbiol.,* **46**, 1286.
[50] Colberg, P. J. and Young, L. Y. (1982). *Can. J. Microbiol.,* **28**, 886.
[51] Hungate, R. E. (1949). *J. Bacteriol.,* **53**, 631.
[52] Wood, T. M., Hoffmann, R. M. and Brown, J. A. (1984). In: Ferrero, G. L., Ferranti, M. P. and Naveau, H. (eds) *Anaerobic Digestion and Carbohydrate Hydrolysis of Waste,* Elsevier, London, p. 125.
[53] Ruy, D. D. Y. and Mandels, M. (1980). *Enzyme Microb. Technol.,* **2**, 91.
[54] Eriksson, K. E., Pettersson, B. and Westermark, U. (1974). *FEBS Lett.,* **49**, 282.
[55] Wood, T. M. and McCrae, S. I. (1979). In: Brown, R. D. Jr and Jurasek, L. (eds) *Adv. Chem. Ser.,* Am. Chem. Soc., Washington, DC, **181**, 181.
[56] Reese, E. T. and Mandels, M. (1980). *Biotechnol. Bioeng.,* **22**, 323.
[57] Gong, G., Ladisch, M. R. and Tsao, G. T. (1979). In: Brown, R. D. Jr and Jurasek, L. (eds) *Adv. Chem. Ser.,* Am. Chem. Soc., Washington, DC, **181**, 261.
[58] Mandels, M., Miller, G. L. and Slater, R. W. Jr (1961). *Arch. Biochem. Biophys.,* **93**, 115.
[59] Koenings, J. W. (1972). *Mater. Org.,* **7**, 133.
[60] Halliwell, G. (1965). *Biochem. J.,* **95**, 35.
[61] Stone, J. E., Scallon, A. M., Donefer, E. and Ahlgren, E. (1969). *Adv. Chem. Ser.,* **95**, 219.
[62] Cowling, E. G. and Brown, W. (1969). *Adv. Chem. Ser.,* **95**, 152.
[63] Chen, C. H. and Chang, H.-m. (1935). In: *Biosynthesis and Biodegradation of Wood Components,* Academic Press, New York, p. 535.
[64] Higuchi, T. (1981). *Wood Research,* **67**, 47.

[65] Ishihara, T. (1980). In: Kirk, T. K., Higuchi, T. and Chang, H.-M. (eds) *Lignin Biodegradation: Microbiology, Chemistry and Potential Applications,* Vol. I, CRC Press, Boca Raton, p. 17.
[66] Ishibara, T. and Nishida, A. (1983). In: Higuchi, T., Chang, H.-M. and Kirk, T. K. (eds) *Recent Advances in Lignin Biodegradation Research,* Uni Publishers, Kyoto, p. 134.
[67] Wastermark, U. and Eriksson, K.-E. (1974). *Acta Chem. Scand.,* **B28**, 204; *Acta Chem. Scand.,* **B28**, 209.
[68] Green, T. R. (1977). *Nature,* **268**, 78.
[69] Ander, P. and Eriksson, K.-E. (1976). *Arch. Microbiol.,* **109**, 1.
[70] Forney, L. J., Reddy, C. A., Tien, M. and Aust, S. D. (1982). *J. Biol. Chem.,* **257,** 11455.
[71] Kutsuki, H. and Gold, M. H. (1982). *Biophys. Res. Comm.,* **109**, 320.
[72] Bes, B., Ranjeva, R. and Boudet, A. M. (1983). *Biochimie,* **65**, 283.
[73] Kuwahara, M., Glenn, J. K., Morgan, M. A. and Gold, M. H. (1984). *FEBS Lett.,* **169**, 247.
[74] Gold, M. H., Kuwahara, M., Chiu, A. A. and Glenn, J. K. (1984). *Arch. Biochem. Biophys.,* **234**, 353.
[75] Shimada, M., Habe, T., Umezawa, T., Higuchi, T. and Okamoto, T. (1984). *Biochem. Biophys. Res. Comm.,* **122**, 1247.
[76] Huynh, V.-B. and Crawford, R. L. (1985). *FEMS Microbiology Letters,* **28**, 119.
[77] Shoemaker, S. P. and Brown, R. D. (1978) *Biochim. Biophys. Acta,* **253**, 133.
[78] Shoemaker, S. P. and Brown, R. D. (1978) *Biochim. Biophys. Acta,* **523**, 147.
[79] Berghem, E. R., Pettersson, L. G. and Axio-Fredriksson, U.-B. (1976) *Eur. J. Biochem.,* **61**, 621.
[80] Berghem, E. R. and Pettersson, L. G. (1973). *Eur. J. Biochem.,* **37**, 21.
[81] Fagerstam, L. G. and Pettersson, L. G. (1979). *FEBS Lett.,* **98**, 363.
[82] Gong, C. S., Ladisch, M. R. and Tsao, G. T. (1977). *Biotechnol. Bioeng.* **19**, 959.
[83] Selby, K. and Maitland, C. C. (1967). *Biochem. J.,* **104**, 716.
[84] Halliwell, G. and Griffin, M. (1973). *Biochem. J.,* **135**, 587.
[85] Wood, T. M. (1975). *Biotechnol. Bioeng. Symp.,* **5**, 111.
[86] Reese, E. T., Sin, R. G. H. and Levinson, H. S. (1950). *J. Bacteriol.,* **53**, 485.
[87] Wood, T. M. and McCrae, S. I. (1972). *Biochem. J.,* **128**, 1183.
[88] Sheppard, W. J. and Lipinsky, E. S. (1982). In: Strub, A., Chartier, P. and Schlesser, G. (eds) *Energy from Biomass,* Applied Science Publishers, London, p. 63.
[89] Emert, G. H. and Katzen, R. (1980). *Chemtech.* **10**, 610.
[90] Tanaka, M. and Matsuno, R. (1985). *Enzyme Microb. Technol.,* **7**, 197.

11

Methane from solid wastes

J. M. Grainger
Department of Microbiology, University of Reading, Reading RG1 5AQ, UK

11.1 INTRODUCTION

The landfill site is the traditional place for disposing of solid wastes. In the UK the practice of landfill disposal became established in the 1930s as a procedure to minimize the nuisance and danger from fires, vermin, birds, flies, litter and smell which characterized the organized collection and uncontrolled dumping of municipal refuse in locations away from the highly populated areas from which the refuse emanated. Current thought worldwide has developed a desire further to maintain and improve the quality of life which is threatened by the generation of increasing amounts of solid waste materials, and to consider also the need to mitigate the drain on the Earth's finite natural resources exacted by the world's ever increasing population. Legislative and economic pressures have brought about a clearly discernible change in attitude towards landfill technology. No longer does it provide only a method of waste disposal with potential problems of fire and explosion from methane generation and pollution from leachate production. Today a landfill site is, in addition, being considered as an anaerobic bioreactor with the potential for the controlled generation of methane for use as an energy source over a predictable time-scale, to be followed by safe and successful incorporation in a land reclamation programme.

11.2 THE NATURE OF MUNICIPAL REFUSE

The amounts and composition of municipal refuse and the favoured means of disposal vary with the size and life-style of the population from which it emanates. The use of specific areas for disposing of rubbish has been revealed by archaeological studies of sites used by communities in the Neolithic (New Stone) Age in Europe some 5000 years ago [1–3]. With the passage of time this sense of organization eventually gave way to indiscriminate littering of streets in towns and cities. This approach to refuse disposal is apparent from studies of the Middle Ages and continued to more recent times through the Industrial Revolution. Nuisance and dangers of this practice brought about by increases in volume and changes in composition dictated the return to an ordered system of removal of rubbish to designated areas.

Some idea of the changes in volume and composition that have occurred over the course of time may be gained by comparing contemporary data from various parts of the world—industrialized and developing countries—for municipal waste production (Table 11.1). Municipal refuse consists of domestic waste and material from

Table 11.1 — Composition (percentage by weight) of municipal refuse in various parts of the world [4, 28].

	EEC	USA	Japan (urban)	Middle East (urban)	Asia (urban)
Paper and cardboard	28.7	43.0	38.2	16.0	2.0
Putrescibles	25.4	12.0	36.7	50.0	75.0
Plastics	4.6	5.0	5.2	1.0	1.0
Textiles	3.1	1.5	3.0	3.0	3.0
Metals	6.0	9.5	2.3	5.0	0.1
Glass	8.3	9.0	2.7	2.0	0.2
Other	23.9	25.5	11.9	23.0	21.7
Annual production (kg/hd)	360	657	325	387	151

other sources, the nature of which influences the composition. Depending on the activities in the area there may be waste from offices, markets, public parks and industry. Thus, in the European Community for example, 80 per cent of municipal waste is domestic refuse but there are variations from country to country. In the Netherlands only 66 per cent is of domestic origin [4]. This gives rise to the range of proportions of various components of municipal refuse given in Table 11.2 for a selection of European countries. Other difficulties in arriving at accurate data include annual and seasonal variations. For example, in Japan there are annual fluctuations in the putrescible content of urban refuse of 23–39 per cent. In member states of the European Community there are seasonal variations of 38–54 per cent in the Netherlands, 10–20 per cent in Germany, and 10–25 per cent in France [4].

The refuse fraction which is of particular importance in the present context of methane generation is the biodegradable matter. This is commonly 60–70 per cent of the dry weight. Most of the biodegradable component, some 70 per cent in the UK, is cellulose from vegetables, paper and cardboard; there is also lignin, protein and hemicellulose, and small amounts of sugars, starch and lipids (Table 11.3).

Table 11.2 — Variation in composition (percentage by weight) of municipal refuse within the European Community [4].

	The Netherlands	Germany	France	UK
Paper and cardboard	23.0	27.5	35.0	30.0
Putrescibles	48.0	16.0	20.0	21.0
Plastics	6.0	4.0	5.0	3.0
Textiles	1.8	3.0	4.0	3.0
Metals	2.9	6.5	5.0	9.0
Glass	13.0	9.0	8.0	9.0
Other	5.3	34.0	23.0	25.0
Total annual production ($\times 10^6$ t)	5.3	25.0	16.0	25.0

Table 11.3 — Chemical composition (percentage dry weight) of municipal refuse and sewage sludge [29,30].

Municipal refuse	
Cellulose, sugar, starch	58.8
Lipid	5.7
Protein	2.6
Plastics	1.5
Ash, metals, glass	31.4
Sewage sludge	
Cellulose	34.5
Hemicellulose	6.2
Lipid	14.0
Protein	19.0
Ash	35.0

Decomposition of cellulosic material is a key aspect of polymer degradation. It occurs relatively slowly. Under optimal conditions in the laboratory the process may take several days, and is accomplished by a limited range of micro-organisms. Lignin is degraded only in the presence of oxygen and much more slowly than is cellulose, but the other components listed, including cellulose, are degraded both aerobically and anaerobically. Non-degradable and non-degraded materials in refuse are also indirectly important through their influence on the physical characteristics of the refuse which affect, for example, mobility of liquids, gases and micro-organisms. The wide variation in refuse composition may result in deficiencies in nitrogen and phosphorus which would limit the growth of micro-organisms and therefore polymer degradation. This is in contrast to sewage sludge, successfully used in industrialized countries for anaerobic digestion to yield methane, which contains more of the readily degradable protein and lipid components but less cellulose (Table 11.3).

11.3 MICROBIOLOGY OF REFUSE DEGRADATION AND METHANE GENERATION

The microbiological processes involved in the degradation of refuse polymers and the subsequent production of methane are poorly understood. This has remained largely so since studies on microbial activity in landfill were first reported in the Federal Republic of Germany in 1979 [5] and in the UK in 1980 [6]. The overall processes thought to be involved are outlined here; reviews should be consulted for more details of the current state of knowledge (Refs [7–9] and Ch. 6 of this volume). Much of what is written on methane generation is based on extrapolation from other more studied habitats such as water sediments, rumen and anaerobic digesters, but care has to be taken to have regard to the differences between the various systems.

The landfill ecosystem is a very difficult one to study because of the variations in refuse composition (Table 11.2), and also the differences in composition with position in a particular landfill, and fluctuations with time at any one position. In addition to the unpredictability of the numbers and types of micro-organisms present initially, those that flourish are governed by the chemical and physical characteristics in their immediate locality; for example, conditions and gradients of temperature, gas phase, moisture, Eh and pH. All are constantly subject to change. All of these factors may differ within distances of a few micrometres, notwithstanding the overall value recorded for the sample.

A heterogeneous mixture of micro-organisms is involved in a sequential series of biochemical steps, each brought about by a particular physiological group of organisms on whose activities the next step in the sequence depends. Overall, the carbohydrate, protein and lipid components are degraded [10,11] with the production of biogas (mainly CH_4+CO_2) and leachate (containing a wide range of elements, inorganic radicals, and aliphatic and aromatic compounds). There are three physiological stages: fermentation, acetogenesis and methanogenesis (Fig. 11.1). They take place in anaerobic conditions in the landfill, but initially oxidative processes also occur in the surface layers until the oxygen supply in air spaces and dissolved in films of moisture is depleted. Evidence of fungal activity in surface layers of a landfill has been reported on the basis of pH optima of cellulolytic enzymes extracted from the refuse [11].

Decomposition of cellulose is the dominant activity in the initial stages of degradation. Extracellular enzymes, i.e. cellulases, break the long chains of β1,4-linked glucose units which form the cellulose molecules. Cellulases are enzyme complexes which act in three ways: (1) endo-β1,4∞-glucanase randomly hydrolyses the bonds in the linear chain of glucose units, producing shorter chains. This exposes

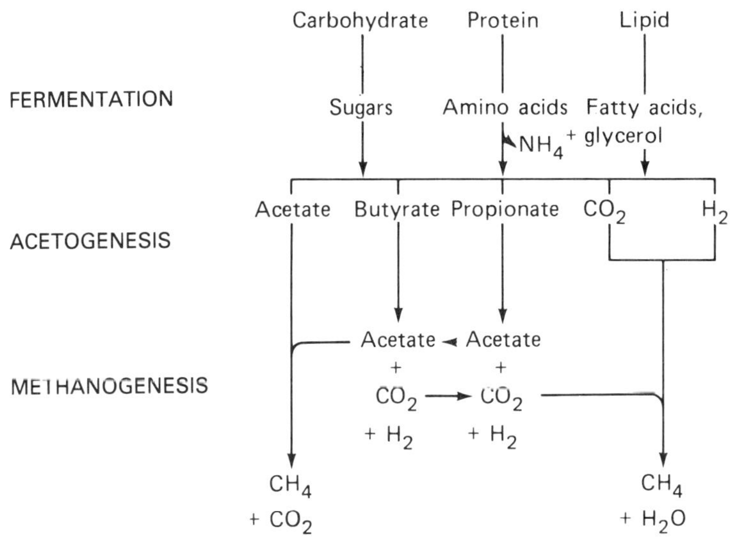

Fig. 11.1 — Stages in anaerobic digestion of municipal refuse polymers to methane.

more chain ends to the action of (2) exo-β1,4-glucanase (cellobiohydrolase), which removes cellobiose units from the non-reducing end of the polymer chain. Cellobiose units are hydrolysed to glucose by (3) β1,4-glucosidase (cellobiase). Degradation of cellulose is hampered by the presence of lignin, with which it is intimately associated in lignocellulosic materials; lignin limits the access of cellulases to their substrate. Enzymic degradation of cellulose and lignin is dealt with in many review articles ([12,13] and Ch. 10 of this volume).

Analysis of lignin:cellulose ratios shows that cellulose degradation occurs throughout the depths of a landfill [11], releasing glucose for fermentation to pyruvate and further transformation to acetate, butyrate, propionate, H_2 and CO_2. These products and others are also produced by fermentation of proteins and amino acids, lipids and long-chain fatty acids. In the acetogenic stage which follows fermentation, the fatty acids so produced, notably butyric and propionic acids, are converted to acetic acid, CO_2 and H_2. The bacteria responsible have been little studied, largely because they exist only in association with an anaerobic H_2-utilizing bacterium which acts as a scavenger, thereby removing H_2, the concentration of which would otherwise increase to levels inhibitory to the acetogenic bacteria. In consequence, fatty acids would accumulate and in their turn inhibit the final stage of methane generation. Another type of acetogenic bacteria converts carbohydrates, CO_2 and H_2 to acetic acid.

Methanogenic bacteria [14] grow slowly, with the consequence that methanogenesis is usually the rate-limiting step. Acetate is the source of most of the CH_4 produced, but other substrates utilized are CO_2+H_2 (thereby also affecting interspecies hydrogen transfer which relieves the inhibition of the acetogenic bacteria referred to above), formate, methanol, methylamines and carbon monoxide. Four of these pathways have been found to be operative in laboratory experiments with landfill material, i.e. from acetate, CO_2+H_2, methanol and trimethylamine [8]. In circumstances where more acetate is produced than the methanogenic bacteria can metabolize, acetate accumulates, the activities of the methanogens are inhibited and CH_4 production either declines or ceases. The inhibition is caused by the decrease in pH value [15]. Another example of the complexities of the interactions between various physiological groups of micro-organisms is provided by the role of sulphate as electron acceptor. The outcome depends upon sulphate concentration. At large concentrations the activities of sulphate-reducing bacteria predominate to the exclusion of those of the methanogens.

11.4 LANDFILL TECHNOLOGY AND MANAGEMENT

The unpredictability of rates of biogas production and migration from landfill sites present problems of equal importance whether the aim is to extract and flare the gas for environmental safety reasons or to collect it for use as a fuel. Although general points of procedure may be recommended, each landfill site has a unique combination of features to be taken into account, including geological characteristics of the site, daily waste input, availability of cover material, and proposed end-use of the site.

Landfills are made either by filling the large holes remaining from exhausted quarries, gravel and clay workings, or by constructing large mounds of refuse. Refuse is collected and either directly transported to a local landfill site or temporarily stored at a local collection point to await transport by road or rail to a distant landfill site. The refuse may be transported as collected or after processing. Processing includes milling, shredding, baling and compaction [16,17]. The resulting changes in physical nature and moisture content influence the biological activity in the landfill.

The area surrounding the site has to be protected from contamination by migrating leachate and biogas by lining with some form of impermeable barrier. Many materials have been proposed and tested for this, including plastic and bentonite walls and trenches of hardcore [8]. Placement of refuse may be over large areas, or confined to cells or terraces, and subjected to compaction by purpose-made vehicles [18]. The degree of compaction controls many factors, such as air and rainwater ingress, and temperature, which influence rates of methane formation. Initial aerobic degradation of the waste results in an increase in temperature to 35–45°C, which is desirable for high rates of gas production but may not be maintained in circumstances of cooling by excessive rainfall infiltration. Also, prolonged periods of aeration result in loss of potential CH_4 production by degradation of the waste to CO_2 only.

Each day's placement of compacted waste is required to be covered, the material used being dictated by local availability such as soil and pulverized fuel ash. Subsequent removal of cover material before placing more waste has the advantages of enabling better vertical movement of gas for abstraction, making a larger volume of the site available for waste deposition and permitting the reuse of cover material.

A programme of progressively restoring a landfill site to final levels, involving the use of small areas of the site at a time, reduces the size of areas not yet built up to final restoration levels which are vulnerable to excessive rainfall infiltration. After reaching restoration levels it is important that completed parts of the site are sealed with an adequate depth of final cover material, such as clay, to permit the retention of gas for controlled recovery. This procedure also prevents excessive rainfall infiltration, and thus leachate formation. Moisture content of the waste can be adjusted by the addition of controlled volumes of liquid beneath the capping material to maximize gas production.

Methane-rich gas is evolved within about 12 months from an adequately deep depostion of waste under appropriate conditions of moisture and temperature. At this stage collection systems must be in place to recover the gas, which will continue to be evolved for at least 5 years.

11.5 GAS ABSTRACTION

During deposition of waste, permeable horizontal trenches containing a perforated gas-collection pipe may be installed. However, in order to draw out the gas, the system depends on permeation in the vertical plane, which this method of waste emplacement does not encourage. More usually, vertical wells are inserted within 1–2 years of waste deposition. This system depends upon horizontal permeation of gas through the site and into the well. Good capping material is necessary to prevent air from being drawn in when a vacuum is applied to the wells (Fig. 11.2).

Yields of ~100 m^3 of biogas/tonne of refuse are achieved which, with a composition of 60 per cent CH_4 + 40 per cent CO_2, has a calorific value of $\sim 2 \times 10^6$ kJ. However, this is only about 25 per cent of the volume theoretically available and efforts to improve this yield are being made by controlling such factors as pH value and moisture, and increasing the microbial population by adding sewage sludge and cultures of micro-organisms, with or without genetic manipulation (Ch. 8, this volume). Also, there are moves towards increasing the area and depth of landfill sites to increase yield. The largest site in the USA on Staten Island, New York, generates ~140000 m^3/d of raw gas. In the UK the site at Aveley, Essex covers some 25 ha at a depth up to 37 m and produces ~70000 m^3/d. Traditionally designed and managed landfills generate gas over long periods of time, even up to 50 years. It is the aim of these new developments to increase the yield of gas and reduce the time over which it is generated [8,19].

11.6 PROSPECTS FOR LANDFILL GAS USE

Landfill is commonly chosen when sites are available within economical distances from the source of the refuse. Thus, in the USA and in the UK 90–95 per cent of municipal refuse is disposed of in landfill sites; the remainder is incinerated. Landfill offers the cheapest [4] and most reliable option in such circumstances. Elsewhere, suitable sites are becoming scarce. Consequently, the proportion of refuse dealt with in landfills is less, e.g. France 60–70 per cent, Japan 50 per cent and Denmark 30 per cent. Instead, incineration (sometimes with heat recovery) is used to a greater extent, with composting also being practised, e.g. in France 10 per cent of refuse is composted. As with landfill technology, however, the other options require more research and developmental effort to bring about necessary improvements. Not all

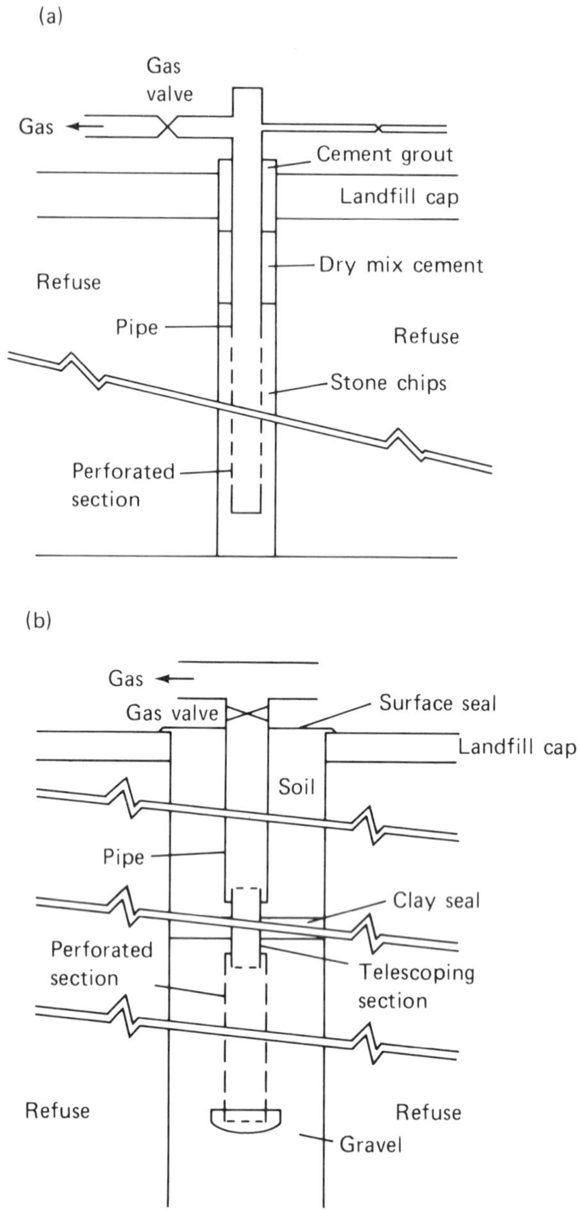

Fig. 11.2 — Landfill gas collection well designs in (a) the UK, and (b) the USA [21].

incineration plants yet incorporate provision for energy recovery, and neither is there adequate control over emissions which pollute air, water and soil, nuisance from noise and smell, and the safe disposal of fly ash.

Advances in optimizing gas production, extraction and handling [20] (Fig. 11.3)

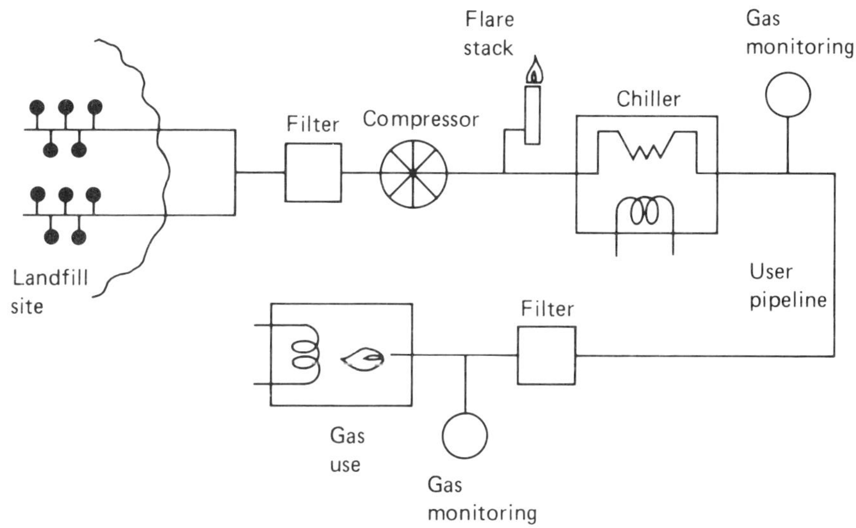

Fig. 11.3 — Plan of a landfill gas abstraction and user pipeline system [21].

indicate that landfill gas production is a commercial reality where continued production can be assured and customers for gas are located within 8 km or so. It is estimated that up to 1 per cent of the total energy needs of the USA could be met from the utilization of landfill gas, and more than 30 sites are in commercial use. In the UK about ten sites are in use and others are being developed. Major examples of use are in boilers, furnaces and kilns, for electricity generation, and for cleaning and upgrading to a higher fuel value [21,22]. Potentially 5 per cent of electricity used in the UK could be provided in this way. Moreover, gas extraction alleviates some of the environmental problems traditionally associated with landfill disposal, e.g. air pollution by hydrocarbon emissions, water pollution by leachate generation and hazards from gas migration. Also, gas extraction may enable quicker and more successful completion of land reclamation schemes for agriculture, recreation and building, over a predictable time-scale [23–27].

REFERENCES

[1] White-Hunt, K. (1980). Domestic refuse — a brief history (part 1). *Solid Wastes,* **70**, 609–615.

[2] White-Hunt, K. (1981a). Domestic refuse — a brief history (part 2). *Solid Wastes,* **71**, 159–166.

[3] White-Hunt, K. (1981b). Domestic refuse — a brief history (part 3). *Solid Wastes,* **71**, 284–292.

[4] Commission of the European Communities (1983). *Energy from Municipal Waste*: 1980/1981 Summary Report, Office for Official Publications of the European Communities, Luxembourg.

[5] Filip, Z. and Kuster, E. (1979). Microbial activity and the turnover of organic matter in municipal refuse disposed of to landfill. *European Journal of Applied Microbiology and Biotechnology,* **7**, 371–379.
[6] Jones, K. L. and Grainger, J. M. (1980). Estimation of cellulolytic, proteolytic and amylolytic activity in domestic refuse. *Journal of Applied Bacteriology,* **50**, viii.
[7] Rees, J. F. (1985). Landfills for treatment of solid wastes. In *Comprehensive Biotechnology*, (ed.) Moo-Young, M., Vol. 4, *The Practice of Biotechnology: Speciality Products and Service Activities*, eds Robinson, C. W. and Howell, J. A., Pergamon, Oxford.
[8] Senior, E. (1987). Design, control and exploitation of the landfill bioreactor. In *Environmental Biotechnology*, (eds) Forster, C. F. and Wase, D. A. Ellis Horwood, Chichester.
[9] Senior, E. and Balba, M. T. M. (1987). Landfill biotechnology. In *Biotechnology Applied to Environmental Problems*, (ed.) Wise, D. L., CRC Press, Cleveland.
[10] Jones, K. L. and Grainger, J. M. (1983). The application of enzyme activity measurement to a study of factors affecting protein, starch and cellulose fermentation in domestic refuse. *European Journal of Applied Microbiology and Biotechnology,* **18**, 181–185.
[11] Jones, K. L., Rees, J. F. and Grainger, J. M. (1983). Methane generation and microbial activity in a domestic refuse landfill site. *European Journal of Applied Microbiology and Biotechnology,* **18**, 242–245.
[12] Knapp, J. S. (1985). Biodegradation of celluloses and lignins. In *Comprehensive Biotechnology*, (ed.) Moo-Young, M., Vol. 4, *The Practice of Biotechnology: Speciality Products and Service Activities*, eds Robinson, C. W. and Howell, J. A., Pergamon, Oxford.
[13] Paterson, A., McCarthy, A. J. and Broda, P. (1984). The application of molecular biology to lignin degradation. In *Microbiological Methods for Environmental Biotechnology*, (eds) Grainger, J. M. and Lynch, J. M., Academic Press, London.
[14] Kirsop, B. H. (1984). Methanogenesis. *CRC Critical Reviews in Biotechology,* **1**, 109–159.
[15] Kirsop, B. H., Hilton, M. G., Powell, G. E. and Archer, D. B. (1984). Methanogenesis in the anaerobic treatment of food-processing wastes. In *Microbiological Methods for Environmental Biotechnology*, (eds) Grainger, J. M. and Lynch, J. M., Academic Press, London.
[16] Diaz, L. F., Savage, G. M. and Golueke, C. G. (1982). *Resource Recovery from Municipal Solid Wastes:* Vol. I, *Primary Processing*, CRC Press, Cleveland.
[17] Wilson, D. C. (1981). *Waste Management*, Oxford University Press, Oxford.
[18] Campbell, D. J. V. (1986). Landfill sites — design considerations. *Industrial Biotechnology,* **6**(1), article 6.1.85.
[19] Rees, J. F. and Grainger, J. M. (1982). Rubbish dump or fermenter? Prospects for the control of refuse fermentation to methane in landfills. *Process Biochemistry,* **17**, 41–44.

[20] Gill, E. (1985). Landfill gas—a fuel from waste for industry, *Industrial Biotechnology,* **5**.
[21] United States and United Kingdom Departments of Energy (1985). *Anaerobic Digestion and Biocatalysis*, United States and United Kingdom Departments of Energy, Washington and London.
[22] Richards, K. M. (1986). *Landfill Gas—A Rising Star*, Energy Efficiency Office, Energy Technology Support Unit, Harwell.
[23] EMCON Associates (1980). *Methane Generation and Recovery from Landfills*, Ann Arbor Science, Michigan.
[24] EMCON Associates (1981). State of the art of landfill gas recovery. Report No. ANL/CNSV-TM-85, Argonne National Laboratory, USA.
[25] EMCON Associates (1981). State of the art of methane gas enhancement in landfills. Report No. ANL/CNSV-23, Argonne National Laboratory, USA.
[26] Harwell Laboratory (1981). *Landfill Gas Symposium*, United Kingdom Atomic Energy Authority, Harwell.
[27] Roberts, R. D. and Gregson, S.K. (1986). *Landfill Restoration Workshop*, University of Essex. Colchester.
[28] Holmes, J. R. (1982). Waste management decisions in developing countries. *Chartered Municipal Engineer,* **109**, 11–16.
[29] Reese, E. T., Mandels, M. and Weiss, A. (1972). Cellulose as a novel energy source. *Advances in Biochemical Engineering,* **2**, 181.
[30] Hobson, P. N., Bousfield, S. and Summers, R. (1974). Anaerobic digestion of organic matter. *CRC Critical Reviews in Environmental Control,* **4**, 131–191.

12

Environmental biotechnology in developing countries

M. B. Pescod, Tyne & Wear Professor of Environmental Control Engineering, and Head, Department of Civil Engineering, University of Newcastle upon Tyne

12.1 INTRODUCTION

Environmental control generally has a low priority in developing countries and the public is not well informed on the health hazards of poor waste-disposal practices. Consequently, the biotechnical opportunities for contributing to waste treatment and reclamation herein described have not been widely implemented. This is not only due to public ignorance and apathy but also to the lack of awareness of professionals about the range of technology available. Most of the approaches suggested here are low-cost, simple in operation and maintenance and take advantage of natural environmental conditions which, in hot climates, provide unique and advantageous mechanisms to protect the environment and conserve resources.

Although a hot climate is beneficial for much of the biotechnology discussed in this chapter, and the systems described are particularly suited to conditions in developing countries, many of the processes have been adopted in developed countries under temperate climatic conditions. For example, the principles of biogas technology are the same as for the anaerobic digestion process, adopted throughout the world for the treatment of strong organic wastes, and wastewater lagoons are widely used in North America, West Germany and France. In most cases the biotechnology has been transferred from developed to developing countries and adapted to suit local conditions, which are often more conducive in developing regions. Factors which affect the appropriateness of these systems for application in any location are the cost and availability of land, the cost and skills of labour, the rates of reactions and biomass growth under ambient temperature conditions and the market for products. Simpler, labour-intensive, low-cost processes requiring a minimum of equipment, a description which could be applied to all the approaches discussed in the following sections, will generally be preferred in developing countries.

12.2 WASTEWATER LAGOON TECHNOLOGY

12.2.1 Terminology

The collective term 'stabilization ponds' has tended to supersede alternatives such as 'oxidation ponds' or 'treatment lagoons' to describe shallow, man-made lagoons which may be adopted to treat organic wastewaters. More specific terminology applies to differentiate between particular forms of pond. *Anaerobic ponds* are primarily used to treat strong organic wastewaters and are devoid of oxygen as a result of the high organic loading applied. *Facultative ponds* operate at lower organic loadings and dissolved oxygen persists in the water column throughout the day, mainly owing to the presence of algae. *Maturation ponds* are aerobic lagoons used as a polishing stage after facultative ponds in the treatment of wastewaters containing faecal material and their principal function is pathogen removal. *Aerated lagoons* are basically activated-sludge units without sludge recycle and operate at low mixed liquor suspended solids levels (MLSS 200–500 mg/l) and relatively long retention times. *Aerated ponds* are very shallow lagoons, usually incorporating mechanical aeration and are designed to optimize the growth of algae for harvesting and reuse.

The application of stabilization ponds for wastewater treatment depends on the availability of cheap land and investment in a collection system. Urban sewerage systems are not common in developing countries, nor are they necessarily the most appropriate sanitation technology, but where collection can be justified stabilization ponds will generally be the treatment system of first choice. Even where there is no sewerage system, nightsoil collection in tankers will allow treatment in stabilization ponds. In addition, organic industrial effluents, particularly from agro-industry, will be amenable to treatment in ponds, either separately or in combination with domestic sewage.

12.2.2 Pond combinations

Wastewater stabilization pond systems are designed to achieve different forms of treatment in up to three stages in series, depending on the organic strength of the input waste and the effluent quality objectives. For ease of maintenance and flexibility of operation, at least two trains of ponds in parallel are incorporated in any design. Strong wastewaters, with BOD_5 concentration in excess of about 300 mg/l, will frequently be introduced into first-stage anaerobic ponds which achieve a high volumetric rate of removal. Weaker wastes or, where anaerobic ponds are environmentally unacceptable, even stronger wastes (say up to 1000 mg/l BOD_5) may be discharged directly into primary facultative ponds. Effluent from first-stage anaerobic ponds will overflow into secondary facultative ponds, which comprise the second-stage of biological treatment. Following primary or secondary facultative ponds, if further pathogen reduction is necessary, maturation ponds will provide tertiary treatment. Typical pond-system configurations are given in Fig. 12.1.

12.2.3 Anaerobic ponds

Anaerobic ponds are very cost-effective for the removal of BOD when it is present in high concentration. Normally a single anaerobic pond in each treatment train is sufficient if the strength of the influent wastewater, L_i, is less than 1000 mg/l BOD_5. For high-strength industrial wastes, up to three anaerobic ponds in series might be

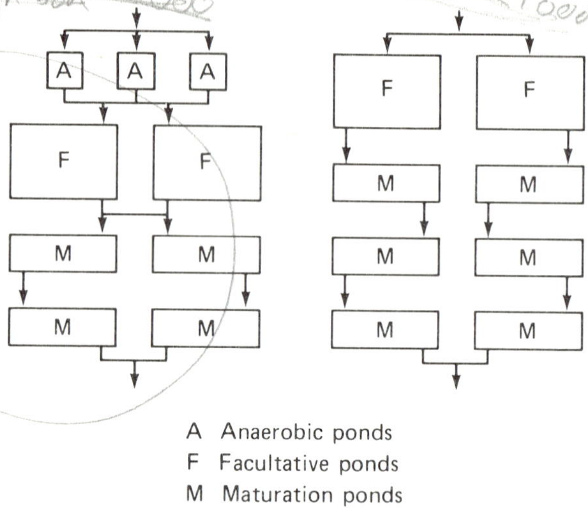

Fig. 12.1 — Typical stabilization-pond system configurations.

justifiable but the retention time, T_{an}, in any of these ponds should not be less than 1 day [1].

Anaerobic conditions in first-stage stabilization ponds are created by maintaining a high volumetric organic loading, certainly greater than 100 g BOD_5/m^3.d. Volumetric loading, λ_v, is given by:

$$\lambda_v = \frac{L_i Q}{V} \quad (1)$$

where L_i = influent BOD_5 (mg/l),
Q = influent flow rate (m^3/d) and
V = pond volume (m^3).

Or, since $V/Q = t_{an}$, the retention time:

$$\lambda_v = \frac{L_i}{t_{an}} \quad (2)$$

Very high loadings, up to 1000 g BOD_5/m^3.d, achieve efficient utilization of anaerobic pond volume [1] but with wastewater containing sulphate concentrations in excess of 100 mg/l the production of H_2S is likely to cause odour problems. In the case of typical municipal sewage, it is generally accepted that a maximum anaerobic pond loading of 400 g BOD_5/m^3.d will prevent odour nuisance.

Anaerobic ponds normally have a depth between 2 and 5 m and function as open septic tanks with gas release to the atmosphere. Ambient temperatures in hot-climate developing countries are conducive to the biochemical reactions which take place in anaerobic ponds, and expected BOD_5 removals for different retention times in treating sewage have been given by Mara [2], as shown in Table 12.1. Higher

Table 12.1 — BOD removals in anaerobic ponds loaded at 250 g $BOD_5/m^3.d$.

Retention (t_{an}, days)	BOD_5 removal (%)
1	50
2.5	60
5	70

removal rates are possible with industrial wastes, particularly those containing significant quantities of organic settleable solids. Of course, other environmental conditions, particularly pH, must be suitable for the anaerobic micro-organisms bringing about the breakdown of BOD.

The appearance of an algal bloom in an anaerobic pond indicates underloading, and oxygen produced by the algae can inhibit the methanogenic phase of digestion. Truly anoxic conditions must then be restored by increasing the volumetric loading to at least 100 g $BOD_5/m^3.d$. A very thin surface layer containing algae, usually the flagellate *Chlamydomonas*, is not generally harmful and no corrective action is required. Purple coloration of an anaerobic pond sometimes occurs owing to the proliferation of photosynthetic bacteria but this is likewise an acceptable condition. In certain instances, anaerobic ponds become covered with a thick scum layer which is thought to be beneficial but not essential. Solids in the raw wastewater, as well as biomass produced, will settle out in first-stage anaerobic ponds and it is common to remove sludge when it has reached half-depth in the pond. This usually occurs after two years of operation at design flow in the case of municipal sewage treatment.

12.2.4 Facultative ponds

The effluent from anaerobic ponds will require some form of aerobic treatment before discharge and facultative ponds will often be more appropriate than conventional forms of secondary treatment for application in developing countries. Primary facultative ponds will be designed for the treatment of weaker wastes and in sensitive locations where anaerobic pond odours would be unacceptable. Solids in the influent to a facultative pond and excess biomass produced in the pond will settle out, forming a sludge layer at the bottom. This benthic layer will be anaerobic and, as a result of anaerobic breakdown of organics, will release soluble organic products to the water column above.

Organic matter dissolved or suspended in the water column will be metabolized by heterotrophic bacteria with the uptake of oxygen, as in conventional aerobic biological wastewater-treatment processes. However, the dissolved oxygen utilized by the bacteria in facultative ponds is replaced through photosynthetic oxygen production by microalgae, rather than by aeration equipment. High temperature and ample sunlight create conditions which encourage algae to utilize the CO_2 released by bacteria in breaking down the organic components of the wastewater and take up nutrients (mainly nitrogen and phosphorus) contained in the wastewater. The symbolic relationship illustrated in Fig. 12.2 contributes to the overall removal

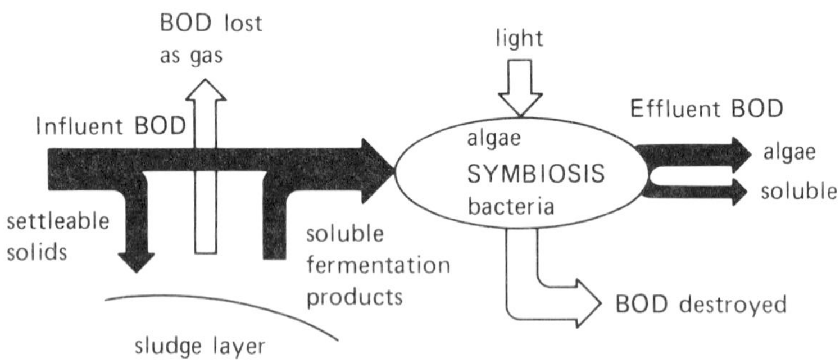

Fig. 12.2 — Pathways of BOD removal in primary facultative ponds [3].

of BOD in facultative ponds, described diagrammatically by Marais [3] as in Fig. 12.3.

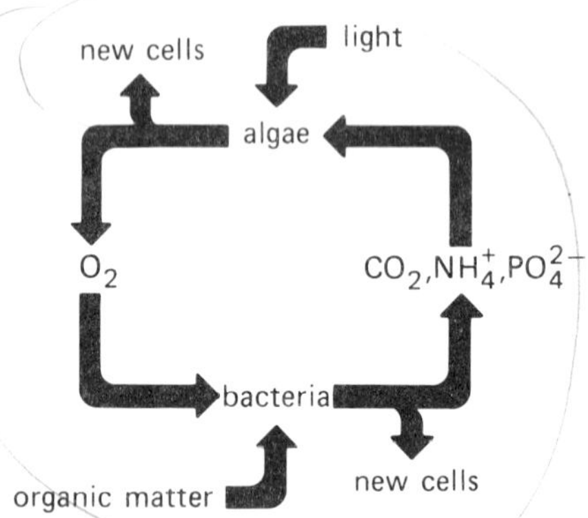

Fig. 12.3 — Symbiosis of algae and bacteria in stabilization ponds.

Even under satisfactory operating conditions, the dissolved oxygen concentration (DO) in a facultative pond will vary diurnally as well as over the depth. Maximum DO will occur at the surface of the pond and will usually reach supersaturation in tropical regions at the time of maximum radiation intensity, as shown in Fig.

12.4. From that time until sunrise, DO will decline and may well disappear completely for a short period. For a typical facultative pond depth, D_f, of 1.5 m the water column will be predominantly aerobic at the time of peak radiation and predominantly anaerobic at sunrise. As illustrated in Fig. 12.4, the pH of the pond contents will also vary diurnally as algae utilize CO_2 throughout daylight hours and respire, along with bacteria and other organisms, during the night.

Wind is considered important to the satisfactory operation of facultative ponds by mixing the contents and helping to prevent short-circuiting. Intimate mixing of organic substrate and the degrading organisms is important in any biological reactor, but in facultative ponds wind mixing is also essential to prevent thermal stratification causing anaerobiosis and failure. Facultative ponds are generally designed with length : breadth ratios of 3 : 10 and orientated with the longest dimension in the direction of the prevailing wind.

Although completely mixed reactor theory with the assumption of first-order kinetics for BOD removal can be adopted for facultative pond design, such a fundamental approach is rarely adopted in practice. Instead, an empirical procedure based on operational experience is more common. The most widely adopted design method currently being applied wherever local experience is limited is that introduced by McGarry and Pescod [1] in 1970. A regression analysis of operating data on ponds around the world relating maximum surface organic loading, λ_s in lb/acre.d, to the mean ambient air temperature, T in °F, of the coldest month resulted in the following equation:

$$\lambda_{s(max)} = 10(1.054)^T \tag{3}$$

Mara [2] adapted this formula and suggested a linear design equation, which Arthur [4] subsequently modified to fit with available operating data. Including a factor of safety of about 1.5, the recommended design equation is:

$$\lambda_s = 20T - 60 \tag{4}$$

with λ_s in kg/ha.d and T in °C.

This surface (or areal) BOD loading can be translated into a mid-depth facultative pond area (A_f in m^2) requirement using the formula:

$$A_f = \frac{10L_iQ}{\lambda_s} \tag{5}$$

Thus

$$A_f = \frac{L_iQ}{2T - 6} \tag{6}$$

and the mean hydraulic retention time in the facultative pond (t_f in days) is given by:

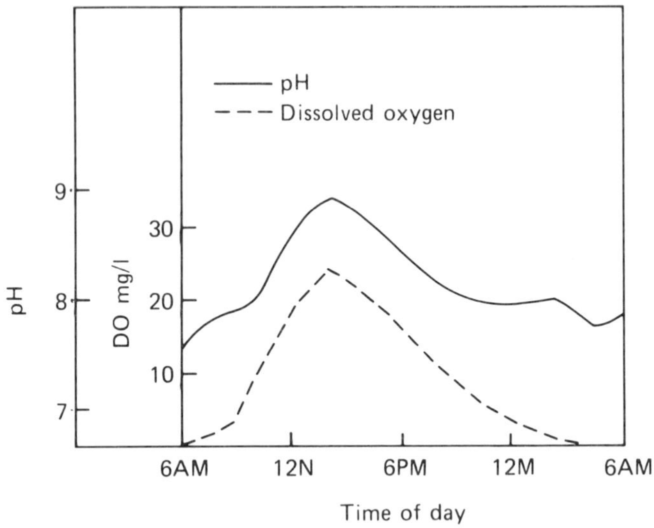

Fig. 12.4 — Diurnal variation of dissolved oxygen and pH in facultative pond effluent.

$$t_f = \frac{A_f D_f}{Q} \tag{7}$$

The removal of BOD in facultative ponds (λ_r in kg/ha.d) is related to BOD loading and usually averages 70–80 per cent of λ_s. Retention time in a properly designed facultative pond will normally be 20–40 days and, with a depth of about 1.5 m, the area required will be significantly greater than for an anaerobic pond. The effluent from a facultative pond treating municipal sewage in the tropics will normally have a BOD_5 between 50 and 70 mg/l as a result of the suspended algae. On discharge to a surface water this effluent will not cause problems downstream if the dilution is of the order of 8 : 1.

Efficiently operating facultative ponds treating wastewater will contain a mixed population of flora, but flagellate algal genera such as *Chlamydomonas*, *Euglena*, *Phacus* and *Pyrobotrys* will usually predominate. Non-motile forms such as *Chlorella*, *Scenedesmus* and various diatom species will be present in low concentrations unless the pond is underloaded. Algal stratification often occurs in facultative ponds, particularly in the absence of wind-induced mixing, as motile forms respond to changes in light intensity and move in a band up and down the water column. The relative numbers of different genera and their dominance in a facultative pond vary from season to season but species diversity generally decreases with increase in loading. Sometimes, mobile purple sulphur bacteria appear when facultative ponds are overloaded and sulphide concentration increases, with the danger of odour production. High ammonia concentrations also bring on the same problem and are toxic to algae, especially above pH 8.0.

12.2.5 Maturation ponds

The effluent from facultative ponds treating municipal sewage or equivalent wastewater will normally contain at least 50 mg/l BOD_5 and if an effluent with lower BOD_5 concentration is required it will be necessary to use maturation ponds. For sewage treatment, two maturation ponds in series, each with a retention time of 7 days, have been found necessary to produce a final effluent with $BOD_5 < 25$ mg/l when the facultative pond effluent had a $BOD_5 < 75$ mg/l.

A more important function of maturation ponds is the removal of excreted pathogens to achieve an effluent quality which is suitable for its downstream reuse. Although the longer retention in anaerobic and facultative pond systems will make them more efficient than conventional wastewater-treatment processes in removing pathogens, the effluent from a facultative pond treating sewage will generally require further treatment in maturation ponds to reach effluent standards imposed for reuse. Protozoan cysts and helminth ova are removed by sedimentation in stabilization ponds, and a series of ponds with overall retention of 20 days or more will produce an effluent totally free of cysts and ova [5].

Faecal coliform (FC) bacteria are commonly used as indicators of excreted pathogens and their reduction in any lagoon (anaerobic, facultative and maturation) has been found to follow first-order kinetics:

$$N_e = \frac{N_i}{1 + K_b t} \tag{8}$$

where N_e = number of faecal coliforms/100 ml of effluent,
N_i = number of faecal coliforms/100 ml of influent,
K_b = first-order rate constant for FC removal (d^{-1}), and
t = retention time in any pond (d).

For n ponds in series, Eqn. (8) becomes:

$$N_e = \frac{N_i}{(1 + K_b t_{an})(1 + K_b t_{fa}) \ldots (1 + K_b t_{m(n)})} \tag{9}$$

where $t_{m(n)}$ = retention time in the nth maturation pond (d).

The value of K_b is extremely sensitive to temperature [6]:

$$K_{b(T)} = 2.6(1.19)^{T-20} \tag{10}$$

where $K_{b(T)}$ = value of K_b at T°C.

A suitable design value of N_i in the case of sewage treatment is 4×10^7 faecal coliforms/100 ml, which is slightly higher than average practical levels. The value of N_e is obtained by substituting the appropriate levels of variables in Eqn. (9) and trial and error testing of maturation pond retention times.

Maturation ponds will be aerobic throughout the water column during daylight hours and the pH will rise above 9.0. The algal population of many species of non-flagellate unicellular and colonial forms will be distributed over the full depth. Very low concentrations of algae in a maturation pond will indicate excessive predation by zooplankton such as *Daphnia* sp. and this will have a deleterious effect on pathogen die-off, which is linked to algal activity.

12.2.6 Aerated lagoons

Aerators in a completely mixed aerated lagoon provide enough energy (about 20 W/m^3) to maintain the solids in suspension, and this is more than that required to satisfy the oxygen demand for aerobic oxidation at the low MLSS levels prevailing in aerated lagoons. In a partially mixed aerated lagoon, a power input of about 4 W/m^3 will transfer sufficient oxygen to meet the needs of the bacteria but will allow a sludge layer to form at the bottom of the lagoon in quiescent locations. Careful siting of many small aerators, rather than a few large ones, will minimize solids settlement and prevent the formation of troublesome sludge banks.

The design of aerated lagoons can be based on completely mixed reactor theory with the assumption of first-order kinetics for BOD removal. In practice, however, more empirical procedures are adopted and typically a 4-day retention time is taken to achieve 70–90 per cent BOD_5 removal, depending on operating temperature, in a 3–4 m deep partially mixed aerated lagoon. At tropical operating temperatures, BOD_5 removal can be expected to approach 90 per cent in treating sewage and faecal coliform reduction might reach 96 per cent [4]. Aerated lagoons should always be followed by settling ponds to remove effluent solids, and the effluent will require maturation pond treatment if faecal coliform reduction is important. By substituting for facultative ponds, aerated lagoons have a role to play in reducing the initial land requirements of new pond-treatment systems and in extending the capacity of exisiting ponds without increasing land requirements.

12.3 PLANT BIOMASS RECOVERY IN WASTE TREATMENT

12.3.1 Algae

Facultative ponds are designed to achieve BOD removal and algal growth is incidental, although necessary, to this process. Long retention time in 1.5 m deep ponds is optimal for wastewater treatment but not for algal culture. However, the high protein content of algae (40–50 per cent) and their potential for bioconversion to methane make their harvesting from wastewater ponds of possible commercial value. With this as the goal, the yield of algae from a pond becomes the primary design objective. Ponds which are optimized for algal biomass production are termed high-rate aerobic ponds. A reasonable estimate of productivity from such ponds is 12 g/m^2 per day (50 Mt/ha per year) of dry-weight, ash-free algae [7].

High-rate aerobic ponds are still at the experimental stage because of the difficulty of harvesting the algae economically from the relatively dilute suspension in pond effluent. The problems of marketing dried algae as a food supplement for animals (pigs, cattle and chickens) and methane fermentation costs also act as deterrants. Design of aerobic algal culture ponds can only be based on empirical procedures derived from experience, and research in Thailand [7] has indicated that the yield of algae, Y_c in kg/ha.d, can be estimated from:

$$Y_c = \frac{10 D_a C_c}{t_a} \tag{11}$$

where D_a = pond depth (m),
C_c = noon concentration of algae (mg/l), and
t_a = retention time (d).

For reuse as animal feed or bioconversion to methane, the algae must be separated from the pond liquid effluent and their size (predominantly less than 20 μm in diameter) makes this a considerable engineering problem. Research on techniques to control algal species so that larger varieties predominate in aerobic ponds is proceeding in the United States [8]. If larger algae (such as *Oscillatoria* or *Microactinum*) can be produced, then simpler types of solid/liquid separation techniques, such as micro-straining, sedimentation and filtration, will be feasible. However, under the normal conditions prevailing in aerobic ponds, more complex and costly processes, for example alum flocculation and flotation or centrifugation, are necessary to concentrate the algae. In addition, for reuse as livestock feed, vacuum filtration or heat drying of the algal concentrate will normally be required.

12.3.2 Macrophytes

Maturation ponds which incorporate floating, submerged or emergent aquatic weed species are termed macrophyte ponds and these have been used in recent years for upgrading effluents from stabilization ponds. Macrophytes take up large amounts of inorganic nutrients (especially N and P) and heavy metals (such as Cd, Cu, Hg and Zn) and decrease the concentration of algal cells through light shading by the leaf canopy and, possibly, adherence to gelatinous biomass which grows on the roots.

Emergent species such as *Phragmites communis* and *Scirpus lacstris* have been used in Europe in 0.5-m deep macrophyte ponds but require regular cutting and harvesting, attract animal and birds, and encourage fly and mosquito breeding. Floating species, with their larger root systems, are more efficient at nutrient stripping. Although several genera have been used in pilot schemes, including *Salvinia*, *Spirodella*, *Lemna* and *Eichornia* [9]; *Eichornia crassipes* (water hyacinth) has been studied in much greater detail. In tropical regions water hyacinth doubles in mass about every 6 days and a macrophyte pond can produce more than 250 kg/ha.d (dry weight). Nitrogen and phosphorus reductions up to 80 and 50 per cent have been achieved. In Tamil Nadu, India, studies have indicated that the coontail, *Ceratophyllum demersum*, a submerged macrophyte, is very efficient at removing ammonia (97 per cent) and phosphorus (96 per cent) from raw sewage, and also removes 95 per cent of the BOD_5. It has a lower growth rate than *Eichornia crassipes*, which allows less frequent harvesting.

Although fly and mosquito breeding is also a problem in floating macrophyte ponds they can serve a useful purpose in stripping pond effluents of nutrients and algae and at the same produce a harvestable biomass. The plants are fairly easily collected by floating harvesters and can be fed to cattle, used as a green manure in agriculture, composted aerobically to produce a fertlizer and soil conditioner, or can be converted into biogas in an anaerobic digester, in which case the residual sludge can then be applied as a fertilizer and soil conditioner.

12.4 AQUACULTURE IN WASTE DISPOSAL

To overcome the difficulty of harvesting algae from high-rate aerated ponds for algae reuse, fish can be used to harvest the algae and convert plant protein to animal protein. Species such as carp and *Tilapia* can be grown in maturation ponds or in fish-ponds fertilized with stabilization pond effluent or stored nightsoil. Yields up to 28000 kg/ha per year have been achieved in fertilized ponds where a broader polyculture of fish is adopted. With the long experience of fish farming in many developing countries, particularly in Asia, and the widespread need for animal protein, this form of wastewater reuse has the greatest potential for application throughout the world. A recent review of recycling organic wastes into fish in the tropics [10] emphasized the attraction of this form of treatment for nightsoil recovery in rural and urban areas. Raw poultry and pig manure has been fed to fish-ponds throughout Asia since ancient times.

Research in Thailand [11] has concentrated on fish-ponds stocked with *Tilapia nilotica*, subjecting them to a variety of waste fertilization conditions. In harvesting microalgae from the effluent from high-rate aerobic ponds, a stocking density of 10 *Tilapia*/m^3 in a fish-pond with phytoplankton concentration of 70 mg/l (to prevent deoxygenation) gave a yield of about 20000 kg/ha per year of small fish suitable for processing into fishmeal, to be used as animal feed. A lower stocking density will be necessary to produce larger fish for human consumption, or small fish could be fed to carnivorous fish such as the catfish (*Clarius* sp.) to obtain a marketable product for human consumption. The problem with direct human consumption of fish reared in sewage-fertilized ponds is the health hazard. Although more research on health aspects is necessary, residence in clean water for several weeks prior to harvesting seems to be an effective precaution.

12.5 BIOGAS PRODUCTION FROM WASTES

The potential for applying anaerobic digestion systems for wastewater treatment in developing countries is no different from that in developed countries. However, only in very few locations have conventional anaerobic processes been adopted for the centralized treatment of high-strength industrial wastes and sewage sludges. A more common approach, especially in Asia, has been the on-site treatment of wastes from farms and small communities in simple biogas plants.

Two main types of biogas plant have been developed in Asia, the Chinese fixed-dome digester and the Indian floating gas-holder digester, shown in Fig. 12.5. Other countries (Indonesia, Korea, Nepal, Pakistan, Philippines and Thailand) have adapted these two forms in their biogas programmes [12]. The main feedstock in most instances is animal manure, pig waste in China and cattle waste in India, although human and plant wastes are also fed to biogas digesters. None of these digesters is heated so problems arise in cold periods and gas production ceases during

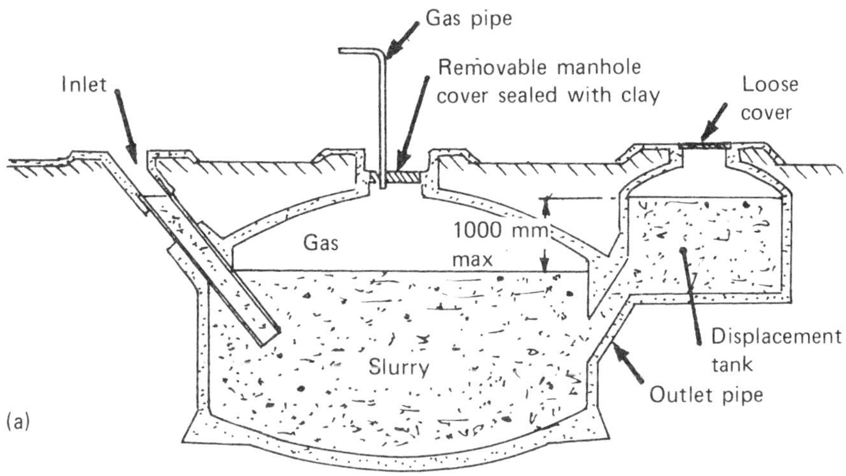

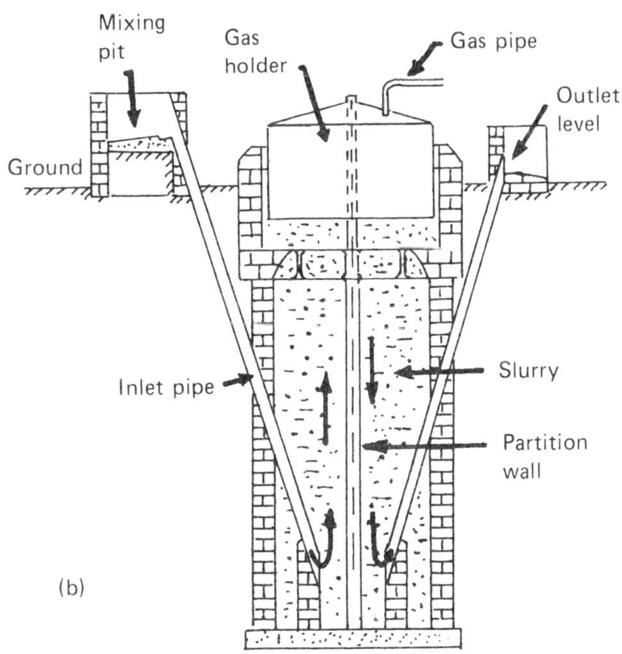

Fig. 12.5 — Biogas systems in China and India [10]. (a) Common circular fixed-dome digester (China). (b) Common circular digester with floating gas holder and no water seal (India).

winter in some countries. The variability of feedstock often leads to unsatisfactory operation. Conversion of macrophytes grown in wastewater ponds to biogas is also feasible. On a dry-weight basis, 1 kg of water hyacinth will yield about 370 l of biogas, with a methane content approaching 70 per cent and a calorific value of about 22 000 kJ/m^3.

Biogas digester loading rates vary between 0.5 and 2 kg total volatile solids (TVS/m^3.d), equivalent to about 10 kg of cattle dung/m^3.d, and gas production is generally of the order of 0.15 m^3/d per m^3 of tank volume in small plants, rising to 0.35 m^3/d per m^3 volume in larger, better-controlled plants. If nightsoil is disposed of in this way it must be only part of a mixed feed having a carbon : nitrogen ratio near 20 : 15 and a solids concentration of about 10 per cent.

In developing countries, more than 90 per cent of the biogas produced in small plants is used for cooking and lighting. It can be burnt like natural gas or LPG in a stove, but the air : biogas ratio should be in the range 1 : 1 to 4 : 1. Used in this way, 1 m^3 of biogas will cook three meals for a family of four people. Alternatively, 1 m^3 of biogas will ignite a mantle gas-lamp equivalent to a 60 W electric bulb for about 7 hours. Less common uses of the biogas in developing countries are to drive a petrol or diesel engine connected to a generator, when 1 m^3 of gas will produce 1.25 kW of electricity, or to run an absorption type refrigerator, in which case 1 m^3 of gas will drive a 300 l refrigerator for 3 hours. In addition to the gas product, a waste slurry remains and this can be used directly as a fertilizer or it can be composted before use in agriculture.

12.6 EFFLUENT REUSE IN AGRICULTURE

The value of wastewater for crop irrigation has been recognized in India and China for centuries and an increasing awareness of this resource is now apparent in the Middle East and North Africa. Although there is no doubt about the beneficial effects of wastewater nutrients on plant growth, the potential health hazards associated with reuse of effluent containing parasites and pathogens give rise to concern. In addition, the possible build-up of toxic materials within the soil, and subsequently within plant and animal tissues which might eventually reach the human food-chain, is a consideration with urban sewage. Groundwater pollution and soil salinization are two environmental risks which arise from dissolved substances in wastewater.

There is much evidence of the survival of excreted pathogens in the environment and some information on their removal in wastewater treatment processes [6]. Although much more data on the performance of developing-country wastewater-treatment plants are required, and particularly in respect of those quality parameters important to reuse, it would appear that stabilization-pond systems are the most effective means for preparing a municipal sewage for irrigation reuse. However, neither stabilization ponds nor conventional sewage-treatment processes remove inorganic salts which might build up in the soil irrigated with treated effluent, and it may be necessary in some locations to consider lime treatment in combination with ponds [13]. As a general approach for developing countries, the lowest quality effluent which the irrigation system, the soil and the crop can tolerate should be the treatment design objective.

The irrigation system will include balancing storage, distribution mains and pipe, sprinkler or trickle distributions. From the point of view of health and water conservation in arid areas, trickle irrigation is preferred. In this form of irrigation water is applied as required by the plant, either to the land surface or subsurface, by means of trickles from small-diameter pipes having ports or leaking seams at regular intervals, releasing flows of 2–15 l/h. Contact between the effluent and crops and workers is less than with other methods and this reduces the chance of contamination by pathogens.

The benefits of wastewater irrigation can only be realized when the total system is designed and managed properly. Since irrigation requires a controlled discharge of effluent, the application method selected should depend upon the soil, the type of crop, the climate and the topography. If only a single crop, or class of crops, is being grown, the reclaimed effluent will need to meet only one level of quality, as indicated in Table 12.2. Should several types of crop be envisaged, some method of devising

Table 12.2 — Recommended effluent reuse standards for irrigation [4].

Method of reuse	BOD_5 (mg/l)	Faecal coliforms (no./100 ml)[a]
Irrigation of trees, cotton and other non-edible crops	60	50 000
Irrigation of citrus fruit trees, fodder crops and nuts	45	10 000
Irrigation of deciduous fruit trees, sugar-cane, cooked vegetables and sports fields[b]	35	1 000
Unrestricted crop irrigation, including parks and lawns	25	100

[a] Not to be exceeded in 80 per cent of samples.
[b] Irrigation to stop 2 weeks before picking; no fruit taken from ground.

ways of satisfying variable quality requirements must be found. In many cases it will be necessary to restrict the choice of crop for effluent irrigation in the interests of economy of wastewater treatment and delivery. Because of the site-specific characteristics of effluent reuse in agriculture, system design features and quality guidelines should not be considered as absolute. Wastewater treatment, effluent storage and distribution and crop selection must be planned at the same time if an economic and conservative integrated system is to be achieved.

12.7 IMPLEMENTATION OF BIOTECHNOLOGICAL PROJECTS

Community motivation is essential if environmental biotechnology is to have a significant influence in developing countries. Public education is an important precurser of project implementation and, increasingly, community involvement is considered to be a critical factor at all stages of project development and operation. To be realistic, only the simplest forms of technology will be manageable by the ordinary citizen in developing countries but the complex biotechnological systems discussed here are entirely appropriate. They involve little sophisticated hardware and require only the most basic expertise for operation and maintenance. However, their implementation on a large scale will require a level of institutional organization and a political commitment which are uncommon in developing countries. It is to be hoped that politicians, planners and designers will become better informed on the biotechnological systems which are now available and which could improve the quality of life of poor people at little cost.

REFERENCES

[1] McGarry, M. G. and Pescod, M. B. (1970). Stabilization pond design criteria for tropical Asia. *Proc. 2nd Intl. Symp. Waste Treatment Lagoons, Kansas City*, 114–132.

[2] Mara, D. D. (1976). *Sewage Treatment in Hot Climates*, Wiley, Chichester.

[3] Marais, G. V. R. (1970). Dynamic behaviour of oxidation ponds. *Proc. 2nd Intl. Symp. Waste Treatment Lagoons, Kansas City*, 15–46.

[4] Arthur, J. P. (1983). Notes on the design and operation of waste stabilization ponds in warm climates of developing countries. *World Bank Technical Paper No. 7*, Washington, DC.

[5] Feachem, R. G., Bradley, D. J., Garelick, H. and Mara, D. D. (1983). *Sanitation and Disease: Health Aspects of Excreta and Wastewater Management*, Wiley, Chichester.

[6] Marais, G. V. R. (1974). Faecel bacterial kinetics in stabilization ponds, *J. Amer. Soc. Civ. Engrs., Env. Eng. Div.*, **100**, 119–139.

[7] McGarry, M. G., Lin, C. D. and Merto, J. L. (1973). Photosynthetic yields and byproduct recovery from sewage oxidation ponds. *Advances in Water Pollution Research*, **4**, 521–531.

[8] Benemann, J. R., Weissman, J. C., Koopman, B. L. and Oswald, W. J. (1977). Energy production by microbial photosynthesis. *Nature*, **268**, 19–23.

[9] O'Brien, W. J. (1981). Use of aquatic macrophytes for wastewater treatment. *J. Amer. Soc. Civ. Engrs., Env. Eng. Div.*, **107**, 681–698.

[10] Edwards, P. (1980). A review of recycling organic wastes into fish with emphasis on the tropics. *Aquaculture*, **21**, 261–279.

[11] Edwards, P., Sinchumpasak, O. A. and Tabucanon, M. (1981) The harvest of microalgae from the effluent of a sewage fed high rate stabilization pond by *Tilapia nilotica*, Part 2: Studies of the fish ponds. *Aquaculture*, **23**, 107–147.

[12] UN Economic and Social Commission for Asia and the Pacific (1981). *Renewable Sources of Energy*, Vol. II: Biogas, ECDC-TCDC Directory, Bangkok.

[13] Pescod, M. B. and Alka, U. (1984). Urban effluent reuse for agriculture in arid and semi-arid zones. *Proc. Int. Symp. Reuse of Sewage Effluent*, Institution of Civil Engineers, London, pp. 71–84.

13

Composting

J. G. Anderson and **J. E. Smith**
Division of Applied Microbiology, Department of Bioscience and Biotechnology, Strathclyde University, Glasgow G1 1XW

13.1 INTRODUCTION

Composting, which is essentially a traditional biological method of dealing with lignocellulosic waste materials, has seen a remarkable revival of interest in recent years. The early history of composting and its development as a systematized process has been described by Hughes [1]. Over the years a variety of definitions have been applied to the term 'composting' and in general these have encompassed the concepts of the decomposition or incomplete degradation of organic waste material by a mixed microbial population, usually under warm, moist, aerobic conditions, although anaerobic composting has also been referred to. A carefully worded definition proposed by Diaz *et al.* [2] describes composting as 'the biological stabilization of wastes of biological origin under controlled conditions'. Thus the 'biological' (essentially microbiological) process will produce a product from organic wastes which is 'stabilized' (without nuisance potential) using 'controlled' conditions (distinguishing the process from natural decomposition of organic materials). Because higher temperatures are attained and the nuisance potential is far less, aerobic composting is the preferred method in modern practice [2], although a new composting process involving both anaerobic and aerobic states has also been reported [3]. To form compost, the organic matter must have lost its original identity and be stabilized to a humus-like product with an earthy odour.

Many different composting systems have been developed to deal with various types of waste material. These systems, which will be described in Section 4 of this chapter, include various controlled 'open' static-pile processes and a wide variety of horizontally or vertically aligned 'enclosed' mechanical systems. Modern composting plants also have a wide range of machinery not directly involved with composting but with separation and size reduction of wastes prior to composting. The technology for efficient composting is aimed at providing optimum environmental conditions under which the process can proceed effectively and without adversely affecting the environment or causing public nuisance. Also composting must meet certain economic constraints and must be competitive with alternative waste-treatment strategies.

Increasingly in recent years composting has been perceived as a viable option and it now ranks as a major biotechnological method of solid waste disposal. Under appropriate circumstances composting can be viewed as a solution to two distinct but related problems, namely waste disposal and the need for recycling of organic matter in agriculture. In various countries composting is now being considered as a more acceptable means of solid-waste disposal than either dumping or incineration with their associated pollution problems. Also, growing unease about modern farming methods and over-reliance on chemical fertilizers, which can impoverish soil humus content, has led to an increasing demand for organic alternatives for some applications. In developing countries the appropriate application of composting can improve sanitation and public health as well as providing a valuable product for the improvement of impoverished soils, particularly in arid regions. Various examples of the application of composting in a number of countries are given in the following section to illustrtate the current worldwide interest in composting processes.

13.2 APPLICATIONS OF COMPOSTING IN DIFFERENT REGIONS

The upsurge of interest in composting in recent years has been nowhere more dramatic than in the USA. An appreciation of the pollution problems associated with incineration and dumping have led to the introduction of new legislative measures which have promoted composting as an environmentally acceptable means of disposing of sewage sludge and other solid wastes. Landfilling, which has previously been the method of choice for many cities, is now at crisis point for reasons of space and pollution, particularly pollution by leachate contamination of the groundwater table. Because of these problems there has been growing awareness in the USA that the relatively low tip fee for landfilling waste has never fully reflected the actual costs of burial of wastes to be borne by society and that this has curtailed a valid economic comparison between landfilling and composting. This situation has now radically changed. For example, in Minnesota legislation has been adopted which represents an innovative effort to shift into a post-landfill emphasis era. Full recognition has been given to the enormous long-term economic consequences of contending with polluted groundwater arising from landfill operations [4]. Interest in composting has been widespread throughout the USA, with more than 100 plants already in operation and many more constructed or being planned [5].

There has been a long-standing interest in composting in many European countries and in recent years the pace of research and development has intensified [6]. Within the EC, co-ordination of composting projects is being carried out by the Commission of the European Communities [7].

In the UK most interest over the years has been shown in the composting of domestic refuse, and although plants have been in existence since 1947 only three of those built remain operational. A major obstacle to the use of refuse composting in the UK is the very low cost of landfilling operations in many parts of the country. However, current problems associated with leachate and methane production from certain landfill sites, together with increasing transport costs associated with dumping, could enhance the prospects for composting in some regions [8]. There has also been little incentive in the past to develop composting processes for sewage-sludge disposal in the UK, since approximately half of the sludge produced is spread directly on agricultural land. However, the forthcoming EC Directive on the disposal of sewage sludge to land, together with problems associated with the field burning of cereal straw at harvest and smell complaints from disposal of animal slurries on land close to housing, are current major issues facing UK agriculture [9].

Some of the straw produced by agriculture has traditionally been composted with horse manure to produce a substrate suitable for the production of mushrooms. Each year the mushroom industry in the UK consumes about 2–300000 t of straw in producing mushroom compost, but this is only a small proportion of the straw from arable croppings (Table 13.1). Consequently the problems surrounding the disposal

Table 13.1 — Organic wastes in the UK (from Biddlestone and Gray [9]).

Waste	10^6 tonnes per year (fresh weight)
Wood shavings, sawdust and bark	>1
Food-processing wastes, brewers' grains	>1
Potato haulms, sugar-beet tops	1.6
Garden and nursery wastes	possibly 5
Cereal straws (surplus)	5–7
Municipal refuse (about 50% organic matter)	18
Sewage sludge (dry solids)	35 (1.2)
Farm manures	120

of straw in the UK and elsewhere provide a considerable incentive to devise low-cost technologies for the useful treatment of this substrate, the use of straw as a bulking agent in the composting of manure slurries and other wastes has been advocated by Biddlestone and Gray [9]. Another approach has been the development of a novel process based on the inoculation of straw with cultures of lignocellulolytic fungi and nitrogen-fixing bacteria to produce a material with fertilizer, soil-conditioning and plant-protection values [10].

Concern over a number of environmental pollution problems has provided a greater incentive for the development of composting processes in a number of other European countries and a large number of plants have been constructed, particularly to deal with domestic refuse. In the Salzburg region of Austria major environmental problems in the mid-1970s led to the construction of an advanced fully enclosed waste-treatment plant which included composting facilities [11]. Extensive biological, chemical and physical parameters have now been established in Austria to ensure that compost products meet satisfactory quality standards [12]. Lutz [6] reported that Austria composts some 21 per cent of the municipal solid waste generated. In Sweden the figure was 24 per cent and in Switzerland two compost plants were treating about 10 per cent of these wastes [6].

France has also acquired a great deal of experience in both the manufacture and utilization of compost from domestic refuse. Over 100 plants producing 800000 tons of compost per year were reported to be operating [13]. In 1980 Germany dealt with approximately one million metric tonnes of waste in 17 composting plants. New plants have also been set up to deal with bark and waste wood as well as sewage sludge [6]. The Birkenbach plant, described by Diaz and Golueke [14], co-composts approximately 12 m^3 of digested sludge with the paper fraction of municipal solid wastes. Italy has also taken a far-sighted approach to the management of some of its municipal wastes and a number of large plants have been set up for the co-disposal of urban solid wastes and sludges [15].

Composting mixtures of lignocellulosic residues and agro-industrial wastes is also receiving attention in a number of European countries. In France, for example, composting has been used to treat wool industry wastes. Pollution from the wool-skinning industry was effectively lowered by concentrating the effluents into sludges and then composting them with suitable agricultural wastes such as grape marcs, corn cobs, wood fibres and sawdust [16]. In Italy, studies have been conducted on composting mixtures of poplar bark and poultry manure [17]. Also in Italy, Vallini *et al.* [18] have studied the feasibility of composting wastes from several agricultural industries, including tomato-processing wastes, cork-processing residues, olive husks and vegetable tannery sludge. Satisfactory composts were obtained by co-composting various admixtures of these materials or by co-composting with sewage sludge or refuse. In Belgium tobacco waste has been successfully composted with bark to produce a horticultural substrate [19]. Researchers in Belgium have also developed a so-called high-rate anaerobic composting process for the treatment of municipal solid waste, with or without sewage sludge, which utilizes an initial 'dry' (high solids) anaerobic fermentation stage with biogas recovery, followed by an aerobic composting stage.

Japan has also seen a major revival of interest in composting and many facilities for the treatment of sewage sludge, refuse, manure, bark and food industry wastes have been constructed [20]. The main impetus has come from efforts to reduce the excessive reliance by Japanese farmers on chemical fertilizers.

There have also been recent reports on the value and applicability of composting in Brazil [21], Korea [22], South-East Asia [23] and certain other developing countries [24]. The particular value of composting in these countries centres on the restoration of soil fertility and productivity and, when dealing with sewage solids, the provision of a simple and efficient method of pathogen destruction. The latter is of particular importance when sewage is used as an organic fertilizer.

Economic appraisal of composting as an alternative waste-management strategy in different regions raises the problem of how to account for the cost of decisions made on political and environmental grounds. Changes in environmental control regulations, such as have occurred in the USA, can greatly alter the viability of composting compared with other forms of waste treatment. Economic appraisals of specific systems may only be relevant for particular types of waste material in particular locations, and caution must be used in extrapolating conclusions about the viability of similar systems where conditions differ [25]. In the composting of domestic refuse, for example, the waste available may differ considerably in different regions, as illustrated in Table 13.2 [26], and a compost system must be chosen to suit.

Table 13.2 — Comparison of British, Indian and Middle Eastern refuse wastes. (From Ambrose [26]).

Constituents	Percentage by weight		
	India	Middle East	Britain
Essential to compost			
Vegetable, putrescible	75	50	28
Acceptable for compost			
Paper	2	20	37
Inert below 10 mm	12	14	9
Compostable total	89	84	74
Salvageable constitutents			
Paper (also included above)	2	20	37
Metals	0	9	9
Glass	0	4	9
Textiles	3	4	3
Plastics	1	3	3
Total of potential salvage	6	40	61

13.3 THE MICROBIOLOGY OF COMPOSTING

Composting is basically a biodegradative process in which organic wastes are transformed and stabilized by the metabolic activities of a succession of mixed microbial populations, each suited to the environment produced by the previous population. The microbiological and biochemical changes which take place during composting have been extensively studied (see Ref. [27] for a review) and will not be detailed here except in brief outline. The essential features are the initiation of the process in the organic mass by a heterogeneous population of mesophilic bacteria, fungi and actinomycetes which are responsible for degrading a large proportion of the low molecular weight compounds present. The exothermic reactions associated with this metabolic activity cause the temperature to increase. At about 40°C the mesophiles become inactivated and are replaced by various thermophilic micro-organisms, including certain thermophilic fungi which are particularly active in decomposing the cellulose fraction. If the temperature is allowed to reach 70°C or higher almost all microbial activity is inhibited and does not restart until the temperature falls and re-invasion can occur.

Experience has shown that the various agricultural and domestic wastes, by virtue of natural contamination, contain the necessary heterogeneous microflora required to carry out the composting process. Although various compost 'starters' are commercially available studies with, for example, bark composting [28] and sewage-sludge composting [29] have shown no beneficial effect of seeding. Inoculum technology, however, may be appropriate for some novel processes such as the production of organic fertilizers by the controlled microbial degradation of straw [10].

The precise microbial populations and biochemical changes involved in composting are influenced by the substrate and composting process in use. Although a good deal of data are available regarding the different microbial groups involved in the composting of various substrates, the quality of the information is limited by the methods available for the analysis of complex mixed microbial populations. Even with the production of mushroom composts, the most extensively studied composting system, much remains to be learned about aspects of the process such as the role of micro-organisms in establishing conditions which allow the selective growth of the desired mushroom *Agaricus bisporus* [30].

General microbial activity during composting can be assessed by measuring oxygen consumption or carbon dioxide production and by monitoring certain chemical and physical changes in the composting mass. Also specific biochemical analyses have been applied, such as the measurement of hydrolytic enzyme activities [31] and ATP levels [32]. The evolution of CO_2 from the composting waste is a particularly convenient parameter to monitor, and graphs of CO_2 production rates with temperature change typically show two peaks. This is well illustrated by the data of Plat *et al.* [16] for the co-composting of wool industry wastes (Fig. 13.1). The two peaks in CO_2 evolution correspond to the peak activities of the mesophilic and the thermophilic populations. The fall after the first peak is due to the time lapse between the inactivation of the mesophiles and the succession of the thermophiles. The slopes of the linear ascending parts of the plot reflect the metabolic activity which decreases during the thermophilic stage as a result of the change in microflora [16]. At this stage the substrate has been depleted of the more easily available constitutents and microbial activity becomes less intense as the thermophilic micro-organisms attack the larger insoluble molecules.

An important aspect of compost microbiology concerns the destruction of pathogens during the waste-conversion process. This is particularly true when sewage sludge is composted, pathogen destruction being one of the main aims of process optimization with this substrate. The human pathogens potentially present in sewage wastes include bacterial, viral, protozoan and helminthic representatives, and a good deal of research has been carried out to determine the fate of these pathogens during composting [33–35]. The major factor influencing the death of pathogens is the temperature–time function during composting. Accordingly, temperature–time standards have been proposed and for static-pile systems pathogen elimination is considered to have occurred if a temperature of 55°C has been achieved and maintained over a three-day period [36].

Monitoring of pathogen destruction can be carried out using an indicator

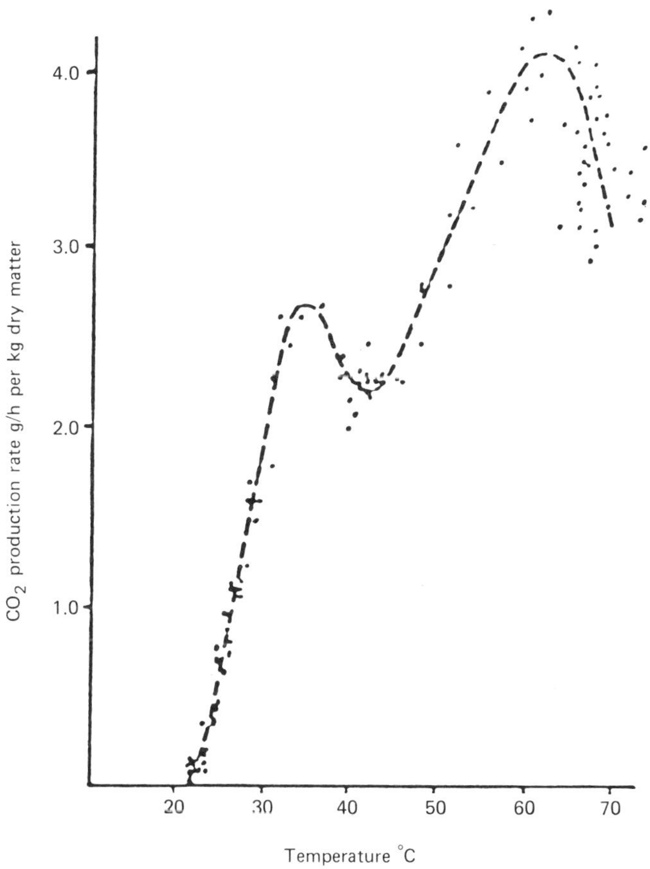

Fig. 13.1 — CO_2 production rates v. temperature during the composting of a wool industry sludge–sawdust mixture. Plat *et al.* [16].

organism, and the f2 bacteriophage has proved useful for this purpose. The f2 phage has heat-resistant properties equivalent to or higher than that of enteric pathogens. The suggested standard is the temperature–time relationship required to inactivate 15 logs of this phage [37].

After compost has cooled some recolonization by certain enteric pathogens is possible if these have not been entirely eliminated during the high-temperature stage. *Salmonellae* are the main enteric pathogens that can repopulate sewage-sludge compost but these should be inhibited by competition from other organisms. The conditions reported to be most conducive to *Salmonellae* repopulation are temperatures between 20 and 40°C, a moisture content of 20 per cent and a carbon : nitrogen ratio higher than 15 : 1 [38].

Whereas criteria have been established for the monitoring and control of human pathogens during sewage-sludge composting, equivalent standards have not yet been developed for the control of plant pathogens during the composting of agricultural wastes, although some work in this area has been done [39–41]. Because of the obvious possibility of the rapid reinfection of crops by the recycling of infected residues, evaluation and determination of minimum operating standards for plant pathogen removal will be required, at least for certain applications of agricultural-waste composting.

Returning to considerations of human pathogens in composting processes, although the major concern has been the possible survival of enteric organisms in some circumstances, there would appear also to be a potential health problem caused by the growth and aerial dissemination of the opportunistic fungal pathogen *Aspergillus fumigatus*. Hypersensitivity pneumonitis due to *A. fumigatus* in compost has been described [42].

A recent epidemiological survey of sewage-sludge composting personnel in the US also gives rise to some concern [43,44]. Tests indicated an increased incidence of skin, nose and ear conditions relative to unexposed control groups. This suggested a low-grade inflammatory response. *A. fumigatus* was frequently detected in nose and throat swabs of the exposed individuals. If these findings are substantiated then greater emphasis will have to be given to minimizing the growth and dissemination of such undesirable organisms during composting processes.

13.4 THE TECHNOLOGY OF COMPOSTING

'Natural' decomposition of organic wastes requires excessive time and is unsuitable for industrial use. Positive intervention is required to optimize the process and produce conditions that will lead to high rates of microbial activity. To make composting an efficient waste-disposal process three fundamental points require to be met [45]: brevity of the process and low energy consumption; guarantee of a standard end product which is not only safe for agricultural use but also has satisfactory fertilizer value; and finally hygienic safety of plant operation and compost end-product.

For industrial composting of organic residues the composting process must be controlled to obtain optimum efficiency and this can be achieved by maximizing microbial growth and activity. During the initial mixing stage of the process the main factors which can be optimized to some extent, C:N ratio, moisture content and materials size and structure, which influence the porosity of the mass. The range of equipment available for the handling, sorting and size reduction of waste materials prior to composting has been described by Martegani and Zoglia [46].

The external controls exerted during the composting process either take the form of mechanical agitation with or without forced aeration, or alternatively forced aeration of a static mass. A wide range of composting systems have been developed which can be classified according to the degree of containment, system configuration and method of aeration and/or agitation. Some of the more common 'open' non-reactor-based systems and 'enclosed' mechanical reactor-based systems are summarized in Table 13.3.

13.4.1 Open (non-reactor-based) composting systems

Windrowing, a traditional method, is still widely practised and has been the method of choice in some of the most recently built or planned composting facilities in the US [47]. The process is fairly simple and requires relatively low capital costs. However, a

Table 13.3 — Types of composting system.

Example	Process features
	Open systems
Windrow	Waste piled in long rows, generally outdoors. Aeration by periodic turning using machines, although forced aeration may also be used
Static pile: Beltsville process	Elongated pile aerated by timer-controlled suction system
Static pile: Rutgers process	Pile aerated by forced pressure with temperature feedback actuation of blower
Static pile: Other processes	Pile aerated by alternate blowing and suction, with or without temperature control
	Closed systems
Dano system	Sloping plug-flow system with mixing by rotation of an inclined cylinder
Tunnel system	Horizontal plug-flow system with waste moved by a hydraulic ram in rectangular enclosed concrete reactors
Metro system	Horizontal agitated solids bed system with aeration through perforated bottoms of rectangular tanks and with travelling endless conveyor-belt mounted on wheels as the agitator-unloader
Fairfield–Hardy digester system	Horizontal agitated-solids bed system with mixing in circular digesters using augers
Silo or tower systems:	Vertical plug-flow reactors which may be cylindrical, square or rectangular in cross-section.
Continuous systems	Material composted in one large mass using forced ventilation. Waste loaded at top and compost withdrawn from bottom by an extraction screw
Discontinuous systems	Digesters divided into a series of levels or floors onto which the waste is sequentially transferred, from top to bottom

large land area is required and labour and operating costs are generally higher than for static-pile composting. In the windrow process the waste is piled in long rows (of the order of 2–4 m wide at the base and 1–2 m high) on a hard surface and usually in the open, although a roofed area may be necessary in areas of high rainfall. Aeration of the windrow is by periodic turning using equipment such as a front end loader or more efficiently by specially designed machinery such as described by Diaz *et al.* [2]. Occasionally forced aeration in conjunction with turning has been applied to the windrow process.

Although windrowing solid wastes can provide high rates of organics' breakdown, it is less effective in terms of pathogen inactivation than aerated static piles [48,49]. It has also been reported [50] that pile turning can release dust containing large numbers of *Aspergillus fumigatus* spores.

With aerated static-pile composting the solid waste is heaped in a large pile or an extended multi-pile and aeration is achieved by forced ventilation through perforated pipes situated in the base of the pile. This method of composting, initiated in the US some 15 years ago [51], has seen extensive improvements in process control and is now widely regarded as a highly efficient composting process.

In the so-called Beltsville process [52], which has been widely adopted in the US for composting sewage sludge, vacuum-induced ventilation (sucking air through the pile) was favoured so that odorous exit gas could be passed through a scrubber pile. A claimed disadvantage of suction ventilation is that excessively high temperatures (over 60°C) are reached in the pile, causing inhibition of essential microbial activity. In the so-called Rutger's process, developed as an alternative to the Beltsville process, the strategy is to manage ventilation as a means of heat removal to prevent excessive accumulation [53]. The strategy is implemented via a temperature feedback control system which communicates demand for heat removal from the composting mass to a blower which forces air upwards and outwards from the base of the pile (Fig. 13.2). This constitutes a time-variable interactive control system which

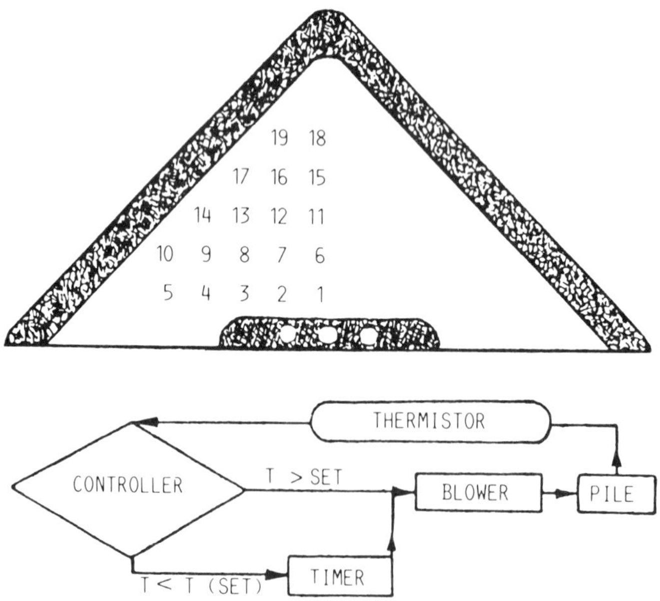

Fig. 13.2 — Rutger's process for static-pile composting. The forced pressure ventilation is controlled by a temperature-control feedback system. Finstein *et al.* [54].

provides good temperature control and ensures continuity of the decomposition process at an efficient and predictable rate [54].

In the UK considerable research has been carried out to adapt the static-pile process for the co-composting of mixtures of domestic refuse and sewage sludge [8,49,55]. The layout of a suitable pile structure for refuse/sewage-sludge mixtures is shown in Fig. 13.3. During development of the process vacuum-induced and forced

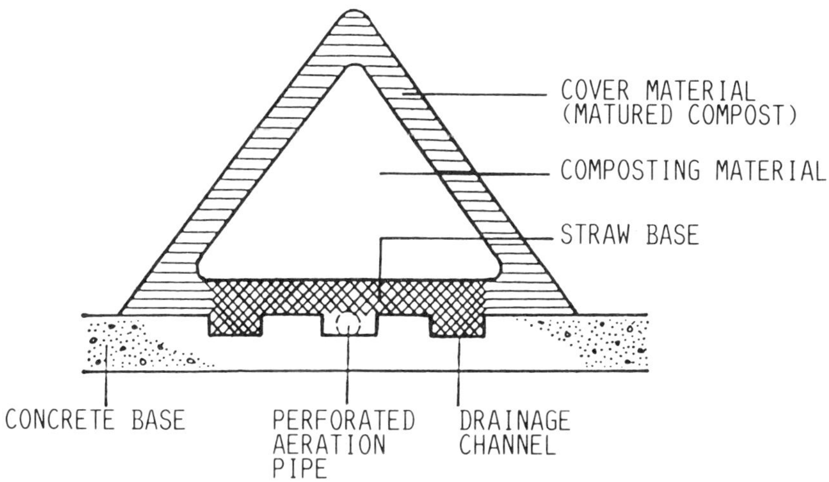

Fig. 13.3 — Cross-section of an aerated static-pile structure suitable for the co-composting of domestic refuse and sewage sludge. Pereira-Neto *et al.* [49].

ventilation methods of pile aeration were compared. The former was found to be unsatisfactory, partly because of pile collapse and consolidation but mainly because of inadequate facility for temperature control [8]. Monitoring temperature distribution in piles which were run on fixed aeration cycles demonstrated that with suction aeration the highest temperatures occurred in the core of the pile near the aeration pipes, whereas with forced aeration the highest temperatures were near the pile apex (Fig. 13.4). Although forced ventilation was chosen as the method of pile aeration it was suggested that the best system for pathogen inactivation might be a process which utilized both modes of ventilation. An initial phase of suction aeration would allow core temperatures to reach 55–60°C. The air flow could then be reversed, driving heat out to the peripheral regions, and thereafter the process would proceed most efficiently using forced aeration in conjunction with temperature feedback control [8].

Aerated static-pile composting is generally carried out in the open but it may be under roof or even totally enclosed within a building, although the latter results in greatly increased capital costs. For the enclosed static-pile composting of sewage sludge the building should have special lighting, be insulated to minimize condensation problems and have a ventilation and odour-control system with the capacity to deal with the exhaust air from the entire structure [56].

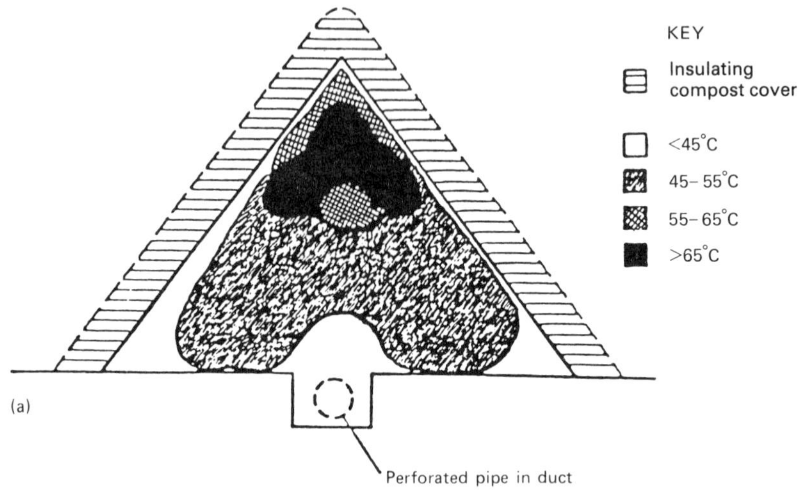

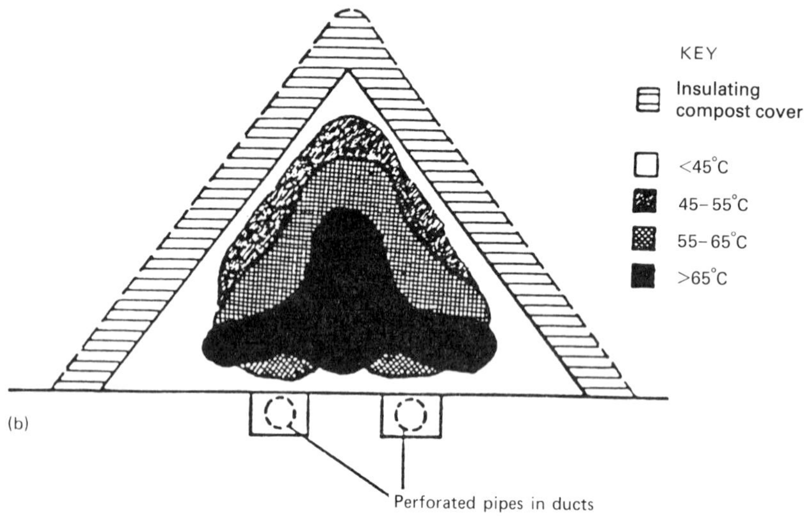

Fig. 13.4 — Typical temperature cross-sectional distributions in a pile with (a) positive pressure (blowing) aeration; and (b) negative pressure (sucking) acration. Stentiford *et al.* [8].

13.4.2 Enclosed (reactor-based) composting systems

With the enclosed mechanical composting systems the process takes place within a vessel or bioreactor, of which there are many types available (Table 13.3). Advantages claimed for these systems are that external environmental factors do not affect the process, less land is required and that better odour and operational control are possible. Disadvantages are that these systems have high equipment, maintenance and energy costs.

Aeration in composting bioreactors is accomplished by tumbling or stirring the material with or without forced aeration. Horizontal plug-flow systems include the Dano biostabiliser and the Tunnel bioreactor. In the Dano system (Fig. 13.5) the

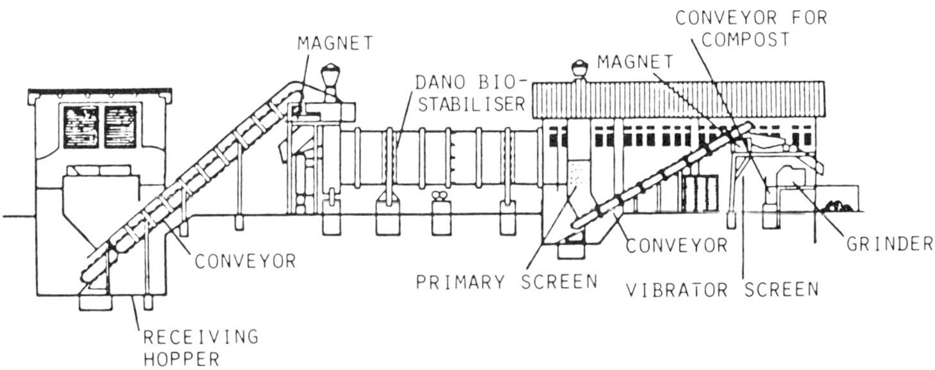

Fig. 13.5 — Typical layout of a Dano biostabiliser plant. Moo-Young *et al.* [60].

solid wastes are treated initially for 1–5 days in a slowly rotating inclined cylinder, and the discharged material is then cured in windrows for up to 6 weeks to obtain a mature compost [1,2].

The Tunnel reactor (Fig. 13.6(a)) is a rectangular enclosed concrete container divided into aeration zones containing aeration headers which discharge air perpendicular to the direction of compost travel [56]. A hydraulically activated ram pushes new material into the composting mass and this simultaneously results in the discharge of composted sludge, from the opposite end, which is then conveyed to the curing and storage facilities.

Agitated-solids bed composting systems, as described by Anderson *et al.* [56], are shallow, horizontal flow-reactor systems which intermittently mix the composting material. These reactors may be rectangular or circular and the various types differ mainly in the equipment used for compost mixing and removal. In the Metro system the waste is dumped into long bins. Along the bottom there is a set of rails over which a small conveyor-belt mixer travels from one end of the bin to the other. The floor is also perforated and air is forced through the material to provide for aeration.

An example of the circular agitated-beds design is the Fairfield–Hardy digester, which has been used successfully for many years [57]. A totally enclosed version of the reactor, which was recently chosen [56] for a new sewage-sludge composting facility in the US, is shown in Fig. 13.6(b). With this system mixed waste-feed material is introduced to the outer areas of the reactor. A series of augers agitate the compost to enhance aeration and gradually move the material from the outer wall to a central discharge area. Aeration is achieved by blowing air upwards through the agitated mass. The augers and much of the other machinery for operating the reactor are fixed at the top of the vessel to a radial bridge, which pivots about the centre while riding on a track around the top of the outer circular wall.

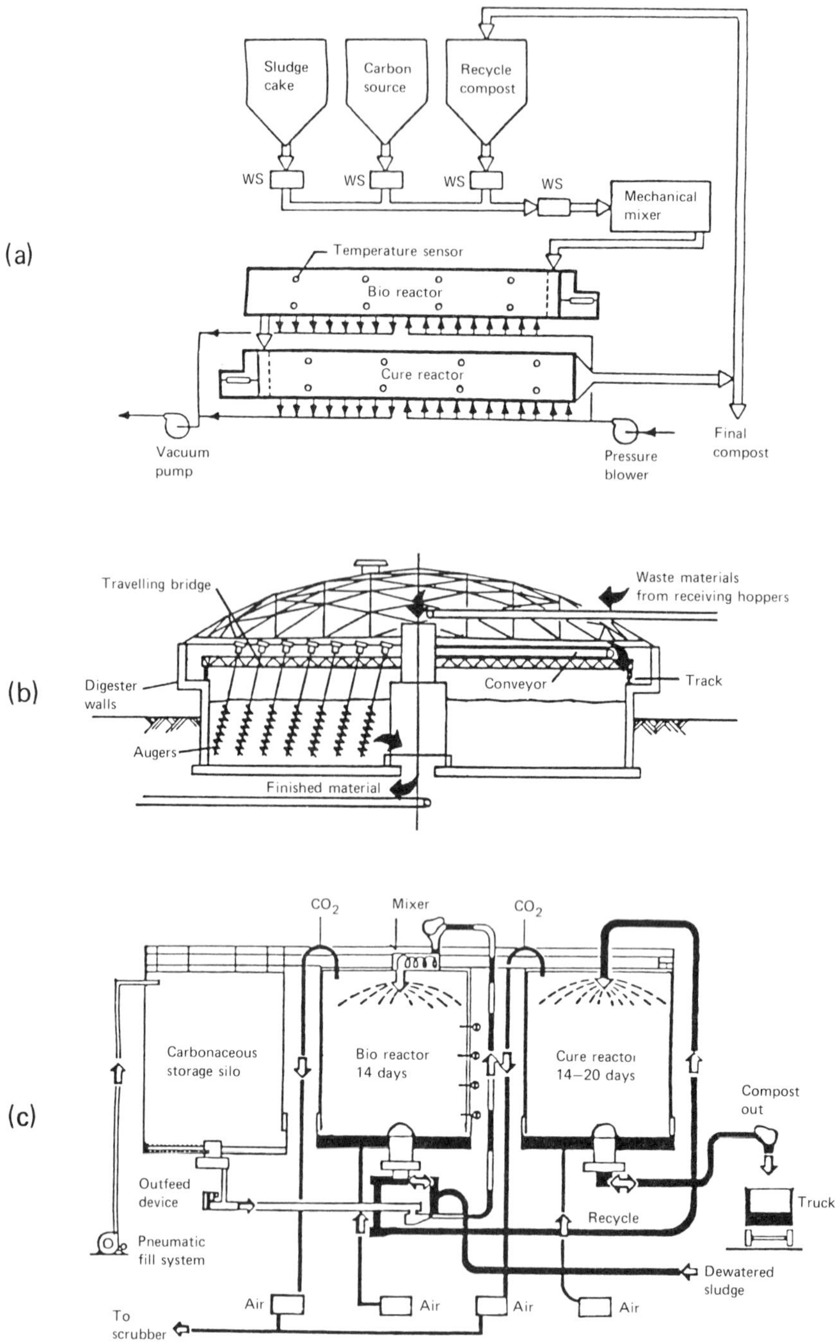

Fig. 13.6 — Several enclosed composting systems. Anderson *et al.* [56]. (a) Tunnel reactor system. (b) Circular agitated-solids bed system. (c) Silo-type composting system.

Silo or tower composting systems are vertical plug-flow reactors which can be cylindrical, square or rectangular in cross-section. In 'continuous' systems there is one single mass of material in the vessel, with fresh material added at the top and composted material withdrawn from the bottom. Excessive height (over 3 m) which is used in some reactors has been criticized because of inadequate aeration [45] and inhibitively high temperatures [58] in the upper regions of the mass.

There are at least five types of composting silo which have been successfully operated in European countries and the operational features of these systems have been described by Easter [59]. With rectangular silo units the length can be extended to meet increased demand, whereas the round silos are effectively limited in radius to the practical length of the discharge screw. The two designs are quite similar in operation. Compost material is withdrawn evenly from the bottom of the silo in a clean cut. The entire contents sink down smoothly as the screw passes down the length of the silo. A new layer is added across the top to replace what has been withdrawn from the bottom. The rectangular design employs a special discharge screw which traverses on parallel rails under the storage silo, whereas the round silo units employ a central screw for compost retrieval.

A silo-type composting system which is in use at the Birkenbach co-composting facility in Germany is shown in Fig. 13.6(c). This plant, described by Diaz and Golueke [14], uses the Taulman–Weiss system to co-compost approximately 12 m^3 of digested sludge with the paper fraction of municipal solid waste. The compost remains in the bioreactor for about 14 days before being transferred to the cure reactor, where stabilization occurs. After 14–20 days about one-quarter of the material is removed, bagged and sold. This material is replaced by an equivalent amount of material from the bioreactor.

In 'discontinuous' vertical composting systems the reactor is divided into a series of levels or floors, as in the Earp–Thomas tower digester (Fig. 13.7). With such systems the material is transferred downwards from one floor to the next, usually at daily intervals, until the composted material is withdrawn from the bottom floor. A variety of designs have evolved, which essentially differ from each other according to the technique of transferring the solids from one level to the next.

13.4.3 Choice of composting system

There is no simple answer as to which of the various competing technologies offers the best solution to the conversion of solid wastes to a useful stabilized compost material. Regardless of configuration the same ecosystem dynamics are at play and so the control strategies to maximize decomposition rate can be implemented in many of the composting systems available. It has been pointed out [58] that the additional capital expenditure for a bioreactor or enclosure-based system might be justified only if superior performance is demonstrable, based on objective criteria, relative to rationally controlled, unenclosed composting. Undoubtedly the advances in process control made over the last ten years with static-pile composting have made this method particularly attractive as an efficient and low-cost option. Aerated static-pile methods are now well proven, having been used extensively with sewage sludge, and are now being considered for full-scale refuse composting or co-composting operations.

On the other hand reactor-based systems, which are certainly much more

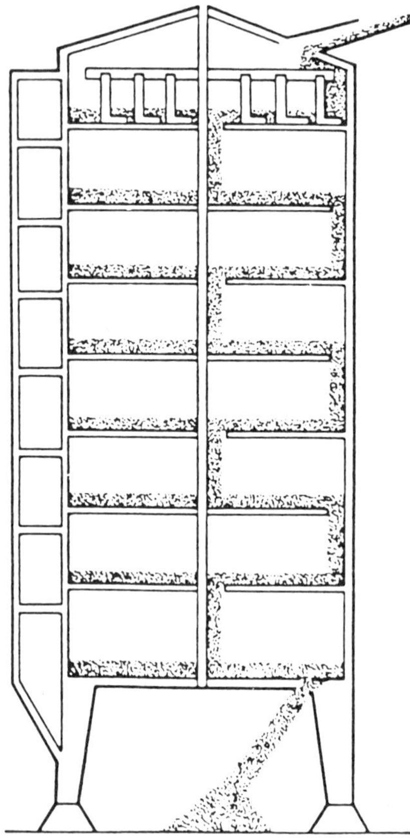

Fig. 13.7 — Diagrammatic sketch of the Earp–Thomas tower digester. Moo-Young *et al.* [60].

expensive to install, nevertheless continue to offer certain facilities which are seen as necessary by many operators. The complex of factors which can lead to the choice of an enclosed composting system for a particular waste in a particular location have been well illustrated in the report by Anderson *et al.* [56]. In this study of various options for composting sewage sludge, the open aerated static-pile method was initially chosen as the most cost-effective solution, but pressure from local residents who were worried about odours and dust resulted in an eventual choice of a totally enclosed composting method. In order to decide on the precise techology to be employed a functional analysis was carried out which addressed various cost, process control and environmental impact factors. It was considered that in-vessel mixing was particularly important since this would allow for correction of any inadequate initial mixing; it would also prevent compaction and promote more even air distribution and provide more flexibility over pathogen control. The eventual choice made in this particular case was the totally enclosed circular agitated-solids bed system based on the type of reactor shown in Fig. 13.6(b).

It must be emphasized that this example has been chosen from the literature because the various factors influencing the decisions were clearly identified and described, and is not meant to imply any 'universal' superiority of the composting option chosen. Similar exercises have been carried out at different locations where a different set of criteria has applied and quite different choices of composting technology have been made for apparently equally valid reasons.

It should also be remembered that many claims have been made for the relatively short composting times which are possible in reactor-type systems but it is unlikely, even under the most beneficial conditions, that the rapid bio-oxidative stage can be completed in less than 7–10 days. Also there is a need for a maturation period outside the reactor which, for example, may be up to 4 months with domestic refuse. Further months of storage time may also be required before the compost is sold, so that the saving of one or two weeks in the initial stage can become relatively insignificant when viewed in the context of the subsequent storage requirements.

13.5 THE COMPOST PRODUCT—TYPES AND QUALITY

Many different kinds of compost can be produced, depending on the type of waste used, the nature and efficiency of the composting process employed and on the intended application of the finished product. An extreme case where the process is most product (compost) oriented is the production of mushroom compost. In this process waste management is only marginally involved. An intermediate situation is the production of compost from certain agricultural wastes, such as bark, which can be practised as an economically viable process *per se*, although an undoubted incentive has been the accumulation and availability of the material. The other end of the applications' spectrum has been the production of compost from the unwanted end-products of human society, particularly domestic refuse and sewage sludge. With these materials waste management is the key objective and compost production is viewed as a bonus and not a process which could be operated economically in the absence of a waste-disposal problem. Given these various scenarios it follows that the term 'compost' covers a range of products which differ in their properties, uses, acceptability and consequently in their monetary value.

Good-quality composts should have a rich brown colour, be visually homogeneous and emanate a pleasant, earthy odour. However, more specific criteria are required to define compost quality and by general opinion, the following are considered the most important:

(1) The compost should contain low levels of toxic components (such as pesticides and heavy metals) and non-biodegradable materials (such as glass and plastics).
(2) There should be an absence or 'acceptably low' levels of human and plant pathogens in the finished product.
(3) The compost should represent an organically stabilized (mature) product with chemical and physical properties beneficial to soil and growing crops.

For the achievement of these objectives domestic refuse and sewage sludge represent difficult starting materials. With refuse composting the waste must first undergo an initial physical treatment to produce a suitable particle size and to remove non-compostable items such as glass, plastics and rags. Source-separation of wastes for composting, as practised in, for example, some parts of Japan [61], is certainly advantageous. Sources of heavy metals in particular should be eliminated whenever possible, in view of concern about the relatively high local concentrations of metal which can accumulate when large quantities of 'contaminated' compost are applied to limited ground areas.

Composted municipal refuse has a rather low fertilizer value since its combined nitrogen, phosphorus and potassium (NPK) content is usually less than 3 per cent. A combined composting of refuse and sewage sludge (co-composting) is beneficial for several reasons, including the fact that the fertilizer value of the compost is increased. Also in the co-composting process the refuse acts as a bulking agent for the sludge, absorbing excess moisture and increasing the interstitial volume. The addition of bulking agents is necessary for sludge composting and examples of such materials (other than refuse) are woodchips, sawdust, ground bark, straw, leaves, rice hulls, as well as the dry compost itself [2]. When the composting process involves the treatment of sewage sludge then a key factor in evaluating the compost product is the requirement for pathogen reduction, as discussed in Section 13.3.

Composts prepared from plant materials and animal manures are more readily acceptable by a variety of users than products prepared from refuse and sewage sludge. Composting mixtures of lignocellulosic residues and agro-industrial waste is receiving attention in a number of countries (see Section 13.2). Of the various materials used, tree bark has proved particularly valuable as a compost substrate. Large amounts of bark are available from pulp and sawmills but the fresh material cannot be used for many applications because of the immobilization of nitrogenous matter and phytotoxic properties of such material. Co-composting bark with nitrogen-rich substrates or simply composting bark with added chemical nitrogen has produced excellent quality composts. In co-composting operations bark has been successfully composted with a variety of substrates, including sewage sludge [62], pulp- and papermill sludges [63], poultry manure [17] and tobacco waste [19].

Good-quality composts can now be produced from a wide variety of solid wastes provided that efficient processing and quality-control measures are adopted. There has also been much wider acceptance and use of the compost products but at the same time there has been growing pressure for legislation on quality requirements both in the USA [64] and in Europe [25]. Ohio has been the first State in the USA to adopt a policy on composted sludge with requirements that relate to the level of contaminants, certain physical properties, adequate labelling and regular testing [65]. Within Europe, Austria has set extensive quality requirements for solid-waste compost [12]. Parameters have been established for organic substances, nutrients, physical properties, plant tolerance, impurities and heavy metals.

An important aspect of compost quality relates to the degree of stabilization or maturity of the product. In this respect products can vary greatly, with some essentially being organic matter in a state of decomposition rather than a mature compost. When stabilization is not achieved, decomposition continues during storage or after it has been applied to the soil, foul odours develop and metabolites are produced which are toxic to plants [66]. Increasing the time of processing guarantees stabilization but it becomes incompatible with industrial programmes owing to the additional requirements for space, handling and equipment. Rapid, efficient processes are necessary which in turn require definitions of standard quality and of suitable methods to monitor process performance [66].

Various methods have been proposed for evaluation of process efficiency and maturity of the compost product (Table 13.4). Although the problem has been investigated extensively, unequivocal standards for maturity are yet to be established. It is generally agreed that no single analytical method may be expected to satisfy all the specified requirements and that a number of parameters require assessment. A distinction should also be made between the need for relatively simple

Table 13.4 — Summary of methods which have been used for the evaluation of compost maturity

	Principle of test
Chemical tests	
Various carbon : nitrogen ratios: totC : totN, orgC : orgN, orgC : totN, totC : orgN (final C : N)/(initial C : N)	Ratios change (usually decrease) during composting to values 'characteristic' of mature compost. Takes special account of C : N ratio of initial material
Form of nitrogen present	Appearance of NO_2^- and/or NO_3^- caused by nitrification during the composting of some wastes
Polysaccharide content	Patterns of polysaccharide degradation and synthesis during composting
Humic substances	Increase in humic components is associated with stabilization of organic matter
Conductivity measurements	High salinity wastes show conductivity decrease during composting
Biochemical (microbiological) tests	
Respirometric analyses ATP content Hydrolytic enzyme activities	Related to changes in microbial biomass/activities which can be correlated with the rate of decomposition during composting
Plant growth (phytotoxicity) tests	
General phytotoxicity tests	Growth of test plants on compost compared with growth on control substrate
Cress bioassay	Compost extracts tested for toxicity by assessment of germination and root growth of cress seed

methods necessary for farm use or at an industrial composting plant and, on the other hand, the usually more sophisticated techniques required for research and development projects [25].

13.6 UTILIZATION OF COMPOST

Potentially the highest volume market for compost would be on land used for crop production. Compost, with its high humus content, can be used to break up heavy clay soils or to bind the larger particles of sandy soil together. Compost can be added particularly to reverse the damage caused by over-farming and soil erosion. Improvement of soil structure upon amendment with compost has been shown by measuring various physicochemical parameters such as porosity, aggregation, retentivity, etc. [67].

Although there are potential advantages in the use of compost in large-scale agriculture the demand in most countries remains low. The major factors responsible for this are bulkiness of the product and the disparity between the cost of chemical fertilizer elements and the cost of the equivalent amounts of these elements in the form of compost [2]. Nevertheless, Japan in particular is making special efforts to promote compost as an alternative to chemical fertilizers (see Section 13.2). Also, the application of compost in many developing countries where soil erosion is a severe problem will be especially beneficial.

Of the various potential outlets for compost products it is the horticultural industry that is most promising. Compost has been successfully marketed for orchard and vineyard applications in many countries. In Europe an estimated three-quarters of the compost product is being used in vineyards to combat erosion and as a soil amendment [68]. The compost is also valued for its moisture-retention qualities and because it imparts a higher grape-sugar content to the crop [59]. The remainder of the compost produced in Europe is used primarily in gardening and landscaping, as a substrate for ornamental plants, in tree nurseries and as digging earth for piglets (a prophylactic against piglet anaemia due to the compost's high iron content).

Among the wholesale customers, producers of flowers and woody ornamentals might attach the highest value to compost. Tests have shown [69] that compost is satisfactory for use as one-third by volume of root media in combination with several other materials (peat, perlite or bark) commonly used in a soil-based or a soil-less medium for cultivation of greenhouse ornamental plants. Growers of containerized plants are also particularly interested in obtaining compost because it contains microorganisms antagonistic to fungi and other plant pathogens found in other potting media [70].

Landscaping is another important outlet for compost products and successful compost-marketing efforts targeted on landscape contractors have been mounted. Compost is easier to apply than are some organic materials (such as topsoil) when lawns are installed. Land reclamation also constitutes a potentially large source of demand for compost and indeed may prove to be the principal use for municipal compost [2]. This application has the advantage of not requiring a top-quality compost and so a low-cost production process such as the windrow method can be used.

It follows from what has already been discussed that the price that can be realized for compost products depends upon their quality, on consumer demand and on the type of application. The importance of the latter factor is well illustrated by reference to a study of potential markets in the USA for a sewage sludge/hardwood bark compost [62]. The maximum prices (per dry metric tonne) which might be realized from different user groups were: horticultural industry \$75; landscape contractors \$45; stripmine reclamation \$15 and crop farmers \$5. Clearly the relative monetary values of compost for these various applications will differ considerbly from country to country and even within different regions of the same country. The precise values placed on compost products by different potential user groups are strongly influenced by the costs of more conventional materials (peat, topsoil, chemical fertilizers, etc.) as well as by any perceived advantages or disadvantages associated with the use of the compost alternative. It is, however, generally recognized that the operation of waste-recycling programmes, such as composting, produce benefits to society and the ecosystem in general, which are difficult if not impossible to quantify in monetary terms.

REFERENCES

[1] Hughes, E. G. (1980). The composting of municipal wastes. In: Berwick, M. M. (ed.) *Handbook of Organic Waste Conversion*, New York and London: Van Nostrand Reinhold, New York, pp. 108–134.

[2] Diaz, L. F., Savage, G. M. and Golueke, C. G. (1982). *Resource Recovery from Municipal Solid Wastes*, Vol. 11, CRC Press, Boca Raton.

[3] De Baere, L. and Verstraete, W. (1984). High rate anaerobic composting with biogas recovery. *Biocycle,* **25**, 30–31.

[4] Nelson, D. (1984). What public officials can do about landfills. *Biocycle,* **25**, 31–32.

[5] Willson, G. B. and Dalmat, D. (1983). Sewage sludge composting in the U.S.A. *Biocycle,* **24**, 20–23.

[6] Lutz, W. (1984). International perspective on composting. *Biocycle,* **25**, 22–25.

[7] Ferrero, G. L. and L'Hermite, J. (1985). Composting–progress to date in the European Economic Community and prospects for the future. In: Gasser, J. K. R. (ed.) *Composting of Agricultural and Other Wastes*, Elsevier, London, pp. 3–10.

[8] Stentiford, E. I., Mara, D. D. and Taylor, P. L. (1985). Forced aeration co-composting of domestic refuse and sewage sludge in static piles. In: Gasser, J. K. R. (ed.) *Composting of Agricultural and Other Wastes*, Elsevier, London, pp. 42–55.

[9] Biddlestone, A. J. and Gray, K. R. (1985). Practical experience with farm scale systems. In: Gasser, J. K. R. (ed.) *Composting of Agricultural and Other Wastes*, Elsevier, London, pp. 111–131.

[10] Lynch, J. M. and Wood, D. A. (1985). Controlled microbial degradation of lignocellulose: the basis for existing and novel approaches to composting. In: Gasser, J. K. R. (ed.) *Composting of Agricultural and Other Wastes*, Elsevier, London, pp. 183–193.

[11] Lutz, W. (1982). Full-spectrum waste management, European style. *Biocycle,* **23**, 22–24.

[12] Lutz, W. (1984). Austria's quality requirements for solid waste compost. *Biocycle,* **25**, 42–44.
[13] Mousty, P. A. and Reneaume, M. (1984). Household refuse composting in France. *Biocycle,* **25**, 26–29.
[14] Diaz, L. F. and Golueke, C. G. (1984). Co-composting refuse and sludge. *Biocycle,* **25**, 21–25.
[15] Bosco, B., Vastola, F. and Donato, F. A. (1982). The solid waste disposal problem in Southern Italy: the Lecce, Cosenza and Lamezia Terme plants. In: *Proceedings of the 1982 National Waste Processing Conference, 10th Biennial Conference*, American Society of Mechanical Engineers, New York, pp. 231–254.
[16] Plat, J. Y., Sayag, D. and Andre, L. (1984). High-rate composting of wool industry wastes. *Biocycle,* **25**, 39–42.
[17] Jodice, R., Barberis, R., Consiglio, M. and Roletto, E. (1984). Composting bark and agro-industrial sludges. *Biocycle,* **25**, 36–38.
[18] Vallini, G., Bianchin, M. L., Pera, A. and De Bertoldi, M. (1984). Composting agro-industrial by-products. *Biocycle,* **25**, 43–46, 51.
[19] Verdonck, O., De Boodt, M., Stradiot, P. and Penninck, R. (1985). The use of tree bark and tobacco waste in agriculture and horticulture. In: Gasser, J. K. R. (ed.) *Composting of Agricultural and Other Wastes*, Elsevier, London, pp. 203–215.
[20] Kubota, J., Matsuda, S. and Sasaki, M. (1984). Composting has promising future in Japan. *Biocycle,* **25**, 28–31.
[21] COMLURB report summary—Composting in Brazil. *Biocycle,* **25**, 36–37.
[22] Hyung, J. I., Matsuda, J. and Ikeuchi, Y. (1984). Survey of rural composting practices in Korea. *Biocycle,* **25**, 52–53.
[23] Gaur, A. C. (1984). Rural composting in South East Asia. *Biocycle,* **25**, 45.
[24] Dalmat, D. S., Parr, J. F., Von Lignau, A. and Laquerre, P. A. (1982). Co-compostings potential for developing nations. *Biocycle,* **23**, 43–47.
[25] Gasser, J. K. R. (1985). Conclusions and recommendations. In: Gasser, J. K. R. (ed.) *Composting of Agricultural and Other Wastes*, Elsevier, London, pp. 310–312.
[26] Ambrose, J. A. (1982). Composting. In: *Reuse of Solid Waste*, Thomas Telford Ltd, London, pp. 87–90.
[27] De Bertoldi, M., Vallini, G. and Pera, A. (1983). The biology of composting: a review. *Waste Manag. Res.,* **1**, 157–176.
[28] Solbraa, K. (1984). An analysis of composting starters used on spruce bark. *Biocycle,* **25**, 46–47.
[29] Nakasaki, K., Sasaki, M., Shoda, M. and Kubota, H. (1985). Effect of seeding during thermophilic composting of sewage sludge. *Appl. Environ. Microbiol.,* **49**, 724–726.
[30] Flegg, P. B. (1985). Research on mushroom composts in Europe. In: Gasser, J. K. R. (ed.) *Composting of Agricultural and Other Wastes*, Elsevier, London, pp. 194–201.
[31] Godden, B., Pennickx, N., Pierard, A. and Lannover, R. (1983). Evolution of enzyme activities and microbial groups during composting of cattle manure. *Eur. J. Appl. Microbiol. Biotechnol.,* **17**, 306–310.

[32] Lehtokari, M., Nikkola, P. and Paatero, J. (1983). Determination of ATP from compost using the firefly bioluminescence technique. *Eur. J. Appl. Microbiol. Biotechnol.,* **17**, 187–190.
[33] Wiley, J., S. and Westerberg, S. C. (1969). Survival of human pathogens in composted sewage. *Appl. Environ. Microbiol.,* **18**, 994.
[34] Golueke, C. G. (1983). Epidemiological aspects of sludge handling and management. *Biocycle,* **24**, 50–59.
[35] Finstein, M. S., Wei-Ru Lin, K. and Fischler, G. E. (1978). Sludge composting and utilisation: review of the literature on temperature inactivation of pathogens. *Report New Jersey Agric. Exp. Stn. Project 03543.*
[36] USEPA (1981). *Technical Bulletin: Composting processes to stabilize and disinfect municipal sewage sludges.* Office of Water Program Operations, Washington, DC. EPA 430/9-81-011.
[37] Burge, W. D. (1983). Monitoring pathogen destruction. *Biocycle,* **24**, 48–50.
[38] Russ, C. F. and Yanko. W. A. (1981). Factors affecting *Salmonellae* repopulation in composted sludge. *Appl. Environ. Microbiol.,* **41**, 597–602.
[39] Hoitink, H. A. J. (1980). Composted bark, a light weight growth medium with fungicidal properties. *Pl. Disease,* **64**, 142–147.
[40] Bollen, G. J. (1985). The fate of plant pathogens during composting of crop residues. In: Gasser, J. K. R. (ed.) *Composting of Agricultural and Other Wastes*, Elsevier, London, pp. 282–290.
[41] Lopez-Real, J. and Foster, M. (1985). Plant pathogen survival during the composting of agricultural organic wastes. In: Gasser, J. K. R. (ed.) *Composting of Agricultural and Other Wastes*, Elsevier, London, pp. 291–299.
[42] Vincken, W. and Roels, P. (1984). Hypersensitivity pneumonitis due to *Aspergillus fumigatus* in compost. *Thorax,* **39**, 74–75.
[43] Clark, C. S., Bjornson, H. S., Linnemann, C. C. and Gartside, P. S. (1984). Evaluation of health risks associated with wastewater treatment and sludge composting. Part 1. *US Nat. Tech. Infor. Ser.,* Springfield, Va. Rep. No. PB85-115639.
[44] Clark, C. S., Bjornson, H. S., Linnemann, C. C. and Gartside, P. S. (1984). Evaluation of health risks associated with wastewater treatment and sludge composting. Part 2. *US Nat. Tech. Infor. Ser.,* Springfield, Va. Rep. No. PB85-115889.
[45] De Bertoldi, M., Vallini, G., Para, A. and Zucconi, F. (1985). Technological aspects of composting including modelling and microbiology. In: Gasser, J. K. R. (ed.) *Composting of Agricultural and Other Wastes*, Elsevier, London, pp. 27–41.
[46] Martegani, A. D. and Zoglia, M. (1985). Machinery aspects of compost making. In: Gasser, J. K. R. (ed.) *Composting of Agricultural and Other Wastes*, Elsevier, London, pp. 89–109.
[47] Kuchenrither, R. D., Martin, W. J., Smith, D. G. and Psaris, P. J. (1984). An economic comparison of composting and dual utilisation. *Biocycle,* **25**, 33–37.
[48] De Bertoldi, M., Vallini, G., Para, A. and Zucconi, F. (1982). Comparison of three windrow compost systems *Biocycle,* **23**, 45–50.
[49] Pereira-Neto, J. T., Stentiford, E. I. and Mara, D. D. (1986). Comparison of windrows and aerated static piles for refuse/sludge composting. Paper pre-

sented at *International Symposium on Compost Production, Quality and Use*, Udine, Italy.
[50] Millner, P. D., Bassett, D. A. and Marsh, P. B. (1980). Dispersal of *Aspergillus fumigatus* from sewage sludge compost piles subjected to mechanical agitation in open air. *Appl. Environ. Microbiol.*, **39**, 1000–1009.
[51] Epstein, E., Willson, G. B., Burge, W. D., Mullen, D. C. and Enkiri, N. K. (1976). A forced aeration system for composting wastewater sludge. *J. Wat. Pollut. Con. Fed.*, **48**, 688–694.
[52] Willson, G. B., Parr, J. F., Epstein, E., Marsh, P. B., Chaney, R. L., Colacicco, D., Burge, W. D., Sikora, L. J., Tester, C. F., and Hornick, S. (1980). *Manual for composting sewage sludge by the Beltsville aerated-pile method*, USEPA Report No. EPA-600/880-022.
[53] Finstein, M. S., Cirello, J., MacGregor, S. T., Miller F. C. and Psarianos, K. M. (1980). *Sludge composting and utilization: Rational approach to process control*. USEPA Report No. C-340-678-01-1.
[54] Finstein, M. S., Miller, F. C., Strom, P. F., MacGregor, S. T. and Psarianos, K. M. (1983). Composting ecosystem management for waste treatment. *Biotechnology,* **1**, 347–353.
[55] Stentiford, E. I., Pereira/Neto, J. J., Taylor, P. L., Mara, D. D., Lopez-Real, J. and Witter, E. (1985). Sanitisation potential of composting for sewage sludge and refuse in a static pile system. In: Tebbutt, T. H. Y. (ed.) *Advances in Water Engineering*, Elsevier, London.
[56] Anderson, J., Ponte, M., Biuso, S., Brailey, D., Kantorek, J. and Schink, T. (1984). Evaluating enclosed composting systems. *Biocycle,* **25**, 20–25.
[57] Shultze, K. L. (1965). The Fairfield–Hardy composting pilot plant at Altoona, Pa. *Compost Science,* **5**, 5–10.
[58] Finstein, M. S. and Miller, F. C. (1985). Principles of composting leading to maximization of decomposition rate, odour control, and cost-effectiveness. In: Gasser, J. K. R. (ed.) *Composting of Agricultural and Other Wastes*, Elsevier, London, pp. 13–26.
[59] Easter, J. M. (1982). Composting silos in Europe. *Biocycle,* **23**, 18–21.
[60] Moo-Young, M., Moreira, A. R. and Tengerdy, R. P. (1983). Principles of solid–substrate fermentation. In: Smith, J. E., Berry, D. R. and Kristiansen, B. (eds) *The Filamentous Fungi*, Vol. 4, Edward Arnold, London. pp. 117–144.
[61] Chanyasak, V. and Kubota, H. (1983). Source separation of garbage for composting. *Biocycle,* **24**, 56–58.
[62] Southgate, D. D. (1984). Potential markets for Akron sludge-derived compost. *Biocycle,* **25**, 42–43.
[63] Carter, C. N. (1983). Composting disposes of sludge, yields by-product at Glatfelter. *Pulp and Paper,* **57**, 102–104.
[64] Higgins, A. J., Goldshore, L. and Wolf, M. (1982). Risk asessment involving sewage sludge and compost. *Biocycle,* **23**, 32–33.
[65] Reported in *Biocycle,* **25**, 45 (1984).
[66] Zucconi, F., Monaco, A., Forte, M. and De Bertoldi, M. (1985). Phytotoxins during the stabilisation of organic matter. In: Gasser, J. K. R. (ed.) *Composting of Agricultural and Other Wastes*, Elsevier, London, pp. 73–86.

[67] Jacobowitz, L. A. and Steenhuis, T. S. (1984). Compost impact on soil moisture and temperature. *Biocycle,* **25**, 56–60.

[68] Weber, H. and Meyer, M. (1982). Utilization of compost in agriculture—experiences in Europe and especially in the Middle East. In: *Reuse of Solid Waste*, Thomas Telford Ltd, London, pp. 71–79.

[69] Shanks, J. B. and Gouin, F. R. (1984). Compost suitability for greenhouse ornamental plants. *Biocycle,* **25**, 42–45.

[70] Hoitink, H. A. J. and Kuter, G. A. (1984). Role of composts in suppression of soilborne plant pathogens of ornamental plants. *Biocycle,* **25**, 40–42.

Index